EVOLUTION AND THE

CHRISTIAN DOCTRINE OF CREATION

Evolution and the Christian Doctrine of Creation

A Whiteheadian Interpretation

by

Richard H. Overman

The Westminster Press
Philadelphia

LIBRARY OF CONGRESS CATALOG CARD No. 67–15089

PUBLISHED BY THE WESTMINSTER PRESS®
PHILADELPHIA, PENNSYLVANIA

PRINTED IN THE UNITED STATES OF AMERICA

CONTENTS

PREFACE

" In the beginning God created the heavens and the earth."
" If any one is in Christ, he is a new creation." These sentences
from the Old and New Testaments seem to express faith in a real
God, one who is creator both of our ordered universe and of
saving novelty within it. But men in our time find it increasingly
difficult to rest easy with these sentences, to understand what they
meant to the people who wrote them, or to explain just what they
may mean to us. Why is this? Why do we find it so hard to speak
now of God as Creator?

Every human society develops some deep-lying and pervasive
style of feeling and responding to its world, and this style expresses
itself in typical modes of thought that dominate the action and
outlook of people, setting both the limits for what they can hope to
achieve and the bounds for what they find credible. If the modes
of thought typical of a society change so that they no longer express the depths of those experiences on which the society was
built, we see the birth of a new society — a greater society if it is
founded on a renewed plumbing of the depths, a decline if its new
modes of thought betray a constricted vision. In particular, modes
of thought that do not express a lively apprehension of the reality
of God may, over a period of time and by shaping the common
sense of large numbers of people, gradually dampen the very
vividness of that apprehension, so that the reality of God is felt
only vaguely or fails entirely to become part of conscious experience.

In our own time, the vision of reality that is uppermost — or

more accurately, most deeply engraven — in the minds of people
is that provided by the enterprise we call " science," and it is beyond doubt that the scientific world view fails to nourish a lively
apprehension of God. There is no a priori reason why science
should condition our common sense, for there have been ages
when religion was the dominant force in providing ideas for civilization, and the Greeks were shaped by artistic and mathematical
intuitions. But for historical reasons it is so, and the unresolved
conflict between scientific and religious assumptions lies somewhere near the center of modern society, troubling much of our
life together.

Some have been content with this uneasy division of thought.
Some have abandoned the quest for greater vision and deeper
understanding by regarding the conflict as inevitable and permanent, perhaps even grounded in the nature of things. Some believe
that human language is unable to relate itself to the world except
by a split within itself. And perhaps most hopelessly, there are
those who have so lost their zest for understanding that they believe themselves to be doing nothing more than playing games
when they think. But we are past the time when we can indulge
ourselves by splitting reality or language to mask our ignorance,
and civilization is balanced too precariously for us to pretend that
thinking is but a game. A very great deal depends on our thinking, and every grain of understanding is priceless.

In the nineteenth century a number of scientific and philosophic
ways of thinking joined to produce a change of the greatest magnitude, deposing intuitions of permanence that had provided the
basis of cultured thought in Christendom for a thousand years,
and substituting for them intuitions of change, movement, and
growth. All of this came into clear focus in the notion of biological
evolution, a notion that was developed scientifically without attention to the reality and purposes of God and that has had the widest kind of implications. It is because theories of evolution have
been so important as barometers of modern thought that they provide a path to follow when we ask how ideas have contributed to a
decline in our understanding and apprehension of God. Conversely, if it can be shown that a modern understanding of our

evolving world may include belief in the reality and effectiveness of divine purpose, may we not hope that a recovery of *belief* in God can be followed by a recovery of man's ability to find God in conscious *experience?*

This book is written as a contribution to the task of providing such an understanding, and it rests on the belief that efforts to understand nature in the past have been handicapped by over-stressing some one mode of explanation — the Old Testament writers attributed too much to the causal efficacy of God, Aristotle overemphasized the inherent purposiveness of nature, and modern neo-Darwinians tend to attribute too much to efficient causation. Instead, we must try to understand biological evolution, using both the objective categories of modern scientific thought and the subjective, personal categories of Biblical thought. In what follows I shall try to show that nature itself includes final causation as well as the efficient causation which scientists have studied so fruitfully for centuries; also I shall try to show that the purposes of a real God are partially determinative of every event, so that the search for understanding nature becomes a search for the content and relative importance of these three modes of causation. To do this I shall describe the decline of a medieval Aristotelian outlook that overstressed the role of purpose in nature, and its gradual replacement by the modern scientific view, which recognizes neither natural nor divine purposes. Finally, I shall propose an understanding of evolution that tries to express the fullness of both scientific and Biblical experience, and that allows us to believe that God is literally the Creator and Sustainer of an evolving world. Here the philosophy of Whitehead has proved to be an indispensable tool, and I am persuaded that, as a vehicle for allowing the depths of human experience to reach expression in the form of ideas, it surpasses any rival.

Anyone who writes a book knows how much he owes to other people, and I feel very keenly this debt, unpayable partly because of its immensity and partly because I can never really hope to know all who are my creditors. Partly this is true, I confess, because I find it difficult to recall the source of an idea once it has become part of my thinking; but partly it is true because this book so explicitly depends on the reflections of all those who have preceded me. Most immediately, I am grateful for the help of my wife, whose sensitively nonphilosophical ear has helped me eliminate many awkwardnesses of exposition, and who has typed most of the manuscript without losing heart. The extent to which my efforts to seek a larger vision have been kindled and encouraged by John B. Cobb, Jr., far surpasses my ability to express it. And I am grateful to my children, who will recognize in the writing of these lines the time when we can resume our play.

This book is dedicated to Phyllis, who does not forget what it means to go on to perfection.

R. H. O.

University of Puget Sound
Tacoma, Washington

I

THE COMING OF EVOLUTIONARY THEORY

Viewed in the sweeping perspective of human history, modern evolutionary science is a quivering new creature that has burst on the scene, still flicking pieces of moist shell from its feathers and casting a quizzical glance backward to see what astonishing maze of events has led up to its awkward peckings. It is this maze we seek to understand, or at least to glimpse in broad outline, but from our more limited usual perspective, it seems intricate indeed. How are we to begin?

The most obvious clue is that we must try to see evolutionary thought as part of science as a whole. Science, we recall, began as a kind of reverent attention to what reality was saying to men, so the respect of scientists for their craft is not misplaced; the technological successes of modern science are indeed awe-inspiring, and we stand in amazement at the genius and penetrating vision of the men who have built the tower of scientific thought. But science has become for many people in our time a new personal deity, and they are chary of questioning its birthright and the legitimacy of its concepts. In this light, we must listen carefully to scientists, but we must examine what they have left for us, remembering that among other things the history of science is a story of modest theories grown proud with success. There is a sense, then, in which we need to take the claims of scientists with a grain of salt — recalling that a grain of salt adds flavor to the best of bread!

A second clue is that the edifice of evolutionary science was built on intuitions which jostled one another over the centuries before a series of brilliant men saw how to fit them together and think new ideas with them. Although the beginnings of evolutionary thought are lost in antiquity, and it is easy to find " anticipations " of our modern theory scattered in the writings of such men as Heraclitus, Empedocles, and Plato, we must not suppose that our modern ideas were snoozing in the sun of ancient Greece, merely waiting for the pen of Charles Darwin to rouse them. There is far too much novelty of thought in modern science for us to believe that! Indeed, epochal advances in science always take place in response to *new ways of thinking about old facts and old concpts*. Therefore, if we seek to understand evolutionary thought, we must pay primary attention to the ways ideas finally come together and only secondary attention to their ultimate origins.

The recent Darwin Centennial celebrations only serve to emphasize what we all know, that publication of *The Origin of Species* in 1859 marked a turning point in the history of science and that the book became a text for far-reaching changes in man's understanding of himself and his world. These facts suggest that we may begin our study of evolutionary thought appropriately by studying that epochal event. Here, although many avenues might lead to a fruitful analysis of Darwin's impact, there is one that promises to be especially fruitful for our purposes: we shall try to illuminate the relationships between evolutionary theory and theological thought by viewing Darwin's work as the point where two major movements in Western thought came to a clear and decisive meeting. These were (*a*) the gradual exclusion of concepts of final causation from the purview of scientific thought, and (*b*) the gradual accumulation of evidence for and the philosophical inclination toward an evolutionary view of nature. During the remainder of this chapter, we shall examine these two movements, paying attention also to the relationship between religious and scientific intuitions in the thought of some principal figures involved.

1. THE DECLINE OF ARISTOTELIAN SCIENCE

As far back as the Ionian philosophers of the seventh and sixth centuries B.C., Greek thinkers saw the cosmos as something " ensouled," a rational living organism within which there were lesser organisms, each with its own directive soul. The earth struck them as a single coordinated drama in which every creature played its appropriate part, and the word " nature " in their writings referred to an *internal principle of movement* that enabled creatures to play their proper roles. It was a vision of the world profoundly concerned with the ends of things, their " why," or purpose, in the overall rational scheme of the universe, and we still imitate their style of thought whenever we content ourselves in explaining a river by saying that it is the " nature " of water to run downhill to the sea. Later, giving further expression to this vision of a world whose creatures were achieving their ends, Plato wrote that things in the world tend to change in certain definite ways in the process of realizing their " natures." What he called " forms " were the final causes (ideal possibilities) of " nature," and he could discuss God as the source of the world's self-moving tendency to realize its " nature." [1]

In the great systematic work of Aristotle, this Greek vision of purpose in nature received its classical expression, and Aristotle believed that four kinds of causes must be sought whenever we try to explain events in nature. There is, first, the material cause, " that out of which a thing comes to be and which is present as a constituent in the product." Second, there is the formal cause, " the form or the pattern, i.e., the formula of what it is to be the thing in question." Third, there is the efficient cause, " that from which comes the immediate origin of the movement or rest." And fourth, there is the final cause, " the end or aim." [2] Although Aristotle believed that everything is a complex result of all these causes, he laid his stress on the formal and final causes, convinced that the aim to realize its eternally fixed possibility was the defining characteristic of any natural being. In this way, the " formal cause " and the " final cause " could act together as the " efficient cause " of motion, for what we call " motion " in a natural object reflects its inward tendency to reach its end, and what we call " rest " is the state of an object that has reached its end or goal. Aristotle realized that it was possible to analyze something

---

[1] Plato, *Timaeus* 28c.
[2] Aristotle, *Physics* 2. 3 (194b 16–195a 3).

solely in terms of its " matter," i.e., to consider its constituent elements in abstraction from its " form " and " end," the purposeful
way its " matter " was organized in a particular way. But since
" nature operates for a purpose," [3] the proper study is one that
seeks to discover the ways matter receives form. Thus, although
" matter " and " end " both must be considered in explaining anything, we should look " especially [for] the end, for that is the
cause of the matter, and not *vice versa*." [4]

In A.D. 529, epitomizing the decline of learning in the West,
Justinian closed the philosophical schools in Athens, but during
the ensuing Dark Ages in Europe, the Aristotelian vision of nature was kept alive in the East by Syrian and Arab scholars. Finally, during the height of Arab learning (ca. A.D. 900–1100),
Aristotle's works were reintroduced to Europe by Muslim scientists and philosophers; during this period, Arabic had become the
classical language of culture, so that European scholars first acquired their taste for Aristotle in twelfth-century Latin translations from the prevailing Arabic versions. But Aristotle's great scientific and metaphysical system had reappeared in Europe at a
time when men were hungry for a cosmology able to express their
Christian faith in a purposeful creation, and it is not hard to see
why Aristotelian philosophy became the framework on which the
culture of Western Christendom was rebuilt after the Dark Ages.
His metaphysics thus helped make sense of the world during the
Middle Ages when men were busy creating a rational synthesis of
Christian faith and secular knowledge.

Judged by any standard, the medieval synthesis was a brilliant
achievement. Aristotle's doctrine of " form " allowed men to understand the events of nature and human history as movement
toward ends that were entertained eternally in the mind of God,
and much of medieval culture expressed the conviction that human
institutions were a limited earthly realization of an eternal divine
plan. But at this point in our story, it is most important to note
that scientific thought reappeared in the West as an effort to understand the " natures " of things in the world by apprehending

---

[3] Aristotle, *De Anima* 2. 8 (199b 33).
[4] Aristotle, *De Anima* 2. 9 (200a 33).

their ends or purposes with the human mind. During the high
Middle Ages, study of nature began with the intuitions of purpose
that men knew consciously from their own inwardness, moving
out to interpret nature in terms of an analogous purposiveness,
and the keenest minds of the age agreed that such a method was
truly " scientific." [5] Here there is no better example than Roger
Bacon (ca. 1214–1294), probably the greatest scientific thinker
of the medieval period and first to use the term *scientia experi-
mentalis* in pointing to the importance of experiment and sense
perception as avenues to knowledge. Bacon wrote in true Aristotelian style that all natural beings are characterized by a desire to realize new forms.[6] " Nature," he wrote in a treatise
on alchemy, " tries ceaselessly to reach perfection — that is,
gold." [7]

Aristotle's vision of rationality and purpose at the heart of nature thus served as the keystone of scientific advance between the
Middle Ages and the Renaissance, but his belief in unchanging
forms also helped fix men's minds during these centuries on the
static elements in their experience. Among other things, this led
them finally to the erroneous scientific belief that animal species
were fixed and unchanging. Also, as we shall see, when men expressed their Biblical faith in creation through Aristotle's doctrine of forms, they raised some theological problems that remained to plague later generations. In particular, when the notion
of fixed species was combined with belief in divine creation, there
grew up the popular doctrine that God had created every species
complete " in the beginning." As a result of this fusion of Aristotelian and Christian ideas, when Darwin finally published his
hypothesis of evolution, he brought down nearly as much theological fire for having abandoned the Aristotelian notion of unchang-

---

[5] In this sense, it may be said that Aristotelian science was fundamentally " subjective," but we must not confuse the word with one of its modern synonyms, " illusory." Medieval scientists were confident that this subjective category of purposiveness or final causation was truly explanatory
of what scientists now recognize as objective nature.

[6] Roger Bacon, *Opus Majus* 2. 65.

[7] Sir William Cecil Dampier, *A History of Science and Its Relations
with Philosophy & Religion* (4th ed.; Cambridge: At the University Press,
1961), p. 92.

ing forms as for having abandoned the Christian notion of divine purpose!

During the lifetime of Copernicus (1473–1543), Aristotelian modes of thought were still the basis for reflection about nature, providing scientists with rational justification for their intuitions of purposeful order in the world around them. But Copernicus' theory expressed his faith that the world was fundamentally *mathematical*, and in this it sounded a death knell for the Aristotelian method, according to which the *qualitative* aspects of things were part of the " form " that scientists strove to recognize. There followed a profound cosmological upheaval that lasted well into the seventeenth century, nearly two hundred years during which scientists increasingly abandoned the Aristotelian belief that events in nature can be understood teleologically by reason, in favor of the doctrine that mathematics and sense perception alone are the tools of scientific progress. No longer was the model of scientific explanation to be a rational demonstration of " formal cause " and " final cause," and scientific research became instead a search for " efficient causes," now meaning the already existing entities or brute facts that could account for change and motion in nature. Francis Bacon (1561–1626) summed up the new attitude concisely by comparing notions of final causation in science with a virgin consecrated to God: neither of them, he said, bore any fruit.[8] Modern scientists echo his view whenever they reject the idea of purpose, because it cannot be verified experimentally.

In Galileo (1564–1642), the new vision of nature reached a maturity that later years only served to ripen, for he set the mood of modern science when he based his scientific thought self-consciously on sense perception, neglecting intuitions of purpose. His method involved resolving sense experience into simple elements that could then be expressed in mathematical form, and this attention to the mathematical aspects of everyday objects gradually made their nonmathematical qualities seem less real. Finally, Galileo was led toward a doctrine of primary and secondary qualities, in which the secondary qualities — attributes such as warmth and color — were conceived of as being merely subjective, contributed

[8] Francis Bacon, *De Aug. Sci.* 3. 5.

by the human mind. In this way, he developed the classical mathematical conception of nature in terms of measurable forces and bodies, visualized most easily as a universe of material atoms moving through time and space.

Whitehead observes that in devising formulae to describe his ideal atoms, Galileo made the assumption of " simple location." [9] This was his belief that he could describe an atom completely by stipulating *where* it was in space and *when* it was in time, so that the ultimate particles of nature could be described fully at any moment without reference to events at other times and in other places. It is the famous notion, accepted by every physicist after Galileo, of an atom as only accidentally related to other atoms, describable by indicating merely how it follows a path imposed by its external relations with other atoms. Galileo modestly sought only to describe this motion of atoms, still assuming that the motion itself was caused by internal forces which the atoms somehow communicated to one another. But clearly the notion of purpose was not required for his explanation, and even the idea of God could be introduced only arbitrarily by supposing that God had created the lifeless swarm of atoms in the first place.

Galileo's work was a triumph of scientific abstraction, providing concepts necessary for the scientific tasks of the next three centuries, but it was achieved at the price of abstracting from nature all the subjective categories known to us in human experience. Nature was left empty of value, purpose, and life, and the mind itself became a spectator at the game of nature.

The stage was set for Cartesian dualism. Descartes (1596–1650) accepted Galileo's scientific abstractions as the basis for metaphysics, elaborating a philosophy in which minds formed a class of entities outside of material nature and posing the problem which has belabored all later philosophers: how are minds related to matter? Descartes himself required the idea of God to explain their relationship, while Spinoza (1632–1677) and Leibniz (1646–1716) also attacked the problem in slightly differing ways. But in any case, by the end of the seventeenth century the

[9] Alfred North Whitehead, *Science and the Modern World* (Mentor Books, New American Library of World Literature, Inc., 1948), p. 49.

problem was taken for granted; the fundamental cleavage between mind and the physical world was already an almost unquestioned axiom of scientific and philosophical thought.

In the genius of Isaac Newton (1642–1727), the revolt against Aristotelian science finally reached full flower. His *Mathematical Principles of Natural Philosophy* (1687) was the crowning statement of the new scientific cosmology, bringing heaven and earth together in a single system of natural law. Newton was the first great positivist, avoiding speculation because of his persuasion that science could become a body of certain truth if all the nonmathematical aspects of reality were rigidly excluded from its purview. Thus he wrote of a universe composed of tiny impenetrable corpuscles, attracting each other in some unspecified way, but utterly empty of purpose and feeling. Like Galileo, Newton was quite aware that the tiny bodies disclosed no reasons for their orderly behavior; but as a pious Christian, he felt it only natural to suppose that God supported the physical order that he described.[10] In this naïve belief, we may note, he was typical of the men who laid the foundations of modern science, for their faith in the very possibility of science was linked closely to faith in a God who was the Creator of a real world and the Sustainer of its order. Even in our own time, when many scientists reject faith in God, faith in an intelligible order of nature remains as the keystone of scientific research.[11]

Many scientists after Newton shared his faith, but regardless of the personal religious views of scientists, the science of biology was destined to grow from infancy to maturity in the intellectual climate of this Newtonian world, from which the notion of final causation had been removed. Modern biologists thus faced from the outset the immense problem of thinking about living creatures with the conceptual tools of a science that already had ruled life out of nature, but not until the nineteenth century did biology fi-

[10] Even Newton's doctrines of absolute time and space reflected his faith in the eternity and omnipresence of God.

[11] Some scientists will, of course, challenge the use of "faith" in this sentence, preferring to describe their activities as a search for whatever order there *may* be. See, e.g., Peter Caws, *The Philosophy of Science* (D. Van Nostrand Co., Inc., 1965), pp. 254 f.

nally follow physics by explicitly denying purpose in living organisms. It was this step, nearly inevitable in the light of what had
gone before, that was dramatized by Darwin and that came as
such a profound shock to people whose outlook was yet steeped in
the Biblical faith in God's purposes.

2. THE FULLNESS OF GOD'S CREATION

Having taken this brief look at the changing fortunes of notions of final causation in science, we must turn now to see how
ground gradually was laid for belief in evolution.

People of every age have recognized some rough hierarchy of
creatures in nature, beginning perhaps with the simplest sea life
and ending in man, but Aristotle is our chief source for the belief
that all creatures are to be classified along a single graded scale
according to their degree of " perfection." He proposed a hierarchy in terms of " powers of soul," i.e., the degree of inward ac-
tiveness possessed by animals,[12] and this idea turns up again and
again in later speculations about man's place in an evolving world.
But besides the notion of a hierarchy of creatures, Aristotle also
introduced into science the principle of continuity, speaking of the
indistinguishable boundaries that separate inanimate from animate nature and plants from animals.[13] Thus we find already in
Aristotle the roots of a recurrent and perplexing problem: are we
to think of nature in terms of sharply defined individual entities
and class concepts, or in terms of insensible continuity? In Aristotle's writings we find support for each view, but because Renaissance scientists were so impressed with the elements of discreteness in their experience, Aristotle's notions of continuity in nature
were destined to play a minor note in scientific thought until the
twentieth century.

During the seventeenth and eighteenth centuries, however, Aristotle's notion of a hierarchy in nature reigned in Europe as the

[12] Aristotle, *De Anima* 2. 3–4 (414a 29–415a 13).
[13] " Nature proceeds little by little from things lifeless to animal life
in such a way that it is impossible to determine the exact line of demarca-
tion, nor on which side thereof an intermediate form should lie." Aristotle, *Historia Animalium* 8. 1 (588b 4–6).

extremely popular theological doctrine of a " chain of being," powerfully projecting the image of a permanently structured world, ordered by God.[14] This doctrine first arose during the Middle Ages, when men fused their faith in God's creative power and goodness with the notion of continuity, moving on to believe that God had created a world containing samples of every possible kind of creature. Because of its wide acceptance by 1600, this " principle of plenitude " [15] was of immense practical value as a stimulus to research in biology. For one thing, it served as a *conceptual* link between man and the great apes, stimulating the first efforts to find a " missing link " between man and the anthropoids that so clearly resembled him. This shows, by the way, that people had been content for centuries to *resemble* animals; it is only in the limited sense of suggesting a common *ancestry* that evolutionary thought may be said to have " erased the gap " between man and the rest of animate nature.

Darwin's work would have been impossible without the admirable work of naming, classifying, and arranging that was done during those centuries by naturalists eager to explore God's chain of being. One of the greatest was John Ray (1627–1705), a keen observer whose interest in nature was kindled by his deep faith that God had created a finished world according to a grand design in which the lower forms of life existed to serve the higher forms.[16] Just two years after Ray died there was born Carolus Linnaeus (1707–1778), the man who founded our present system of classifying and naming animals and plants. He became the most famous biologist in Europe, and so great was his popularity that at his death he was borne to his tomb like a king.[17] This was a tribute befitting the majesty of his work, for Linnaeus had tried to bring order to our knowledge of the earth as Newton had brought order

[14] See the discussion by Arthur O. Lovejoy in *The Great Chain of Being: A Study of the History of an Idea* (Harper Torchbooks, Harper & Brothers, 1960).

[15] *Ibid.*, p. 52.

[16] For a comprehensive study of Ray's wide-ranging scientific interests, see Charles E. Raven, *John Ray, Naturalist: His Life and Works* (Cambridge: At the University Press, 1942). Ray's most famous work was *The Wisdom of God Manifested in the Works of Creation* (1691).

[17] Loren Eiseley, *Darwin's Century: Evolution and the Men Who Discovered It* (Anchor Books, Doubleday & Company, Inc., 1961), p. 18.

to our knowledge of the heavens. Linnaeus' work testified to his belief that man should study nature in order to glorify God in his works, so that there arose a saying, " God created, Linnaeus arranged." [18] His great system helped confirm the church in its belief that all species of animals and plants were created directly by God in the beginning, and his influence in this direction was barely diminished by the fact that in later years he came to doubt that all species were quite fixed.[19]

During these centuries of confidence in the fullness of creation, there always lurked in the background a perplexing theological and philosophical question: was this fullness a necessary fact? That is, was God *bound* to create just such a world? Did believing in God as the source of all forms of *possibility* require one to believe also that each of these eternal possibilities was *realized in fact?* Thomas Aquinas had, at one point, used Aristotle's principle of continuity to suggest that God willed the actual existence of everything which is possible,[20] but he knew only too well that such a complete correspondence between the realms of the possible and the actual threatened belief in divine freedom, and he tried to hold back from such an awkward conclusion. Four hundred years later, Spinoza was still puzzling over the question, arguing from the fact of God's timeless fullness to a belief that the world contained all possible beings and that nothing which existed could have been different. No real novelty, said Spinoza, *could* have appeared in the world since God created it in its eternal and pristine fullness. This amounted to belief in a kind of cosmic determinism that very closely paralleled one implication of the new scientific cosmology, and in a way reminiscent of Francis Bacon, Spinoza could conclude that " final causes are nothing but human fictions." [21]

Whether they sprang from science, philosophy, or theology, all

---

[18] John C. Greene, *The Death of Adam: Evolution and Its Impact on Western Thought* (Iowa State University Press, 1959), p. 131.

[19] In the last edition of his famous *Systema Naturae* (1776), he admitted hesitantly that new species might be formed by hybridization, or even by chance, from the originally created forms.

[20] Thomas Aquinas, *Summa Contra Gentiles* I. 75; II. 68.

[21] Spinoza, *Ethics*, Pt. I, Appendix, in *Spinoza: Selections*, ed. by John Wild (Charles Scribner's Sons, 1930), p. 139.

such doctrines as Spinoza's seemed to leave God a prisoner of human logic, and during the seventeenth century, the rise of determinism was accompanied by a wave of theological reaction against the idea that God *had* to create this world or any world.[22] This was mainly a way of emphasizing that nothing we may discover about the actual state of the world can account for the fact that there *is* a world in the first place. But at a time in history when " creation " was taken popularly to refer to a single divine act, placing the *fact* of creation beyond the grasp of human reason was about the same as claiming also that divine agency fully accounted for the actual state of nature as a hierarchy of creatures. It was no wonder, then, that many Christians later felt their faith in creation to be threatened the moment evolutionists began to invoke some natural causes in explaining the hierarchy of creatures.

3. TEMPORALIZING THE CHAIN OF BEING

All of us have seen the great skeletons of extinct reptiles in museums of natural history, and we have grown up taking for granted that such fossils are the primary evidence for evolution and the antiquity of life. But not a single skeleton could have been reconstructed for us before the eighteenth century, when some men began to realize that the well-known chain of being might function not only as a sign of divine plenitude but also as a clue to the past. We cannot recount in detail the fascinating process by which these men ceased to regard the hierarchy of creatures as a still photograph and began to see it as an exciting motion picture of earth's history, but some salient points must be noted.

For a long while, Christian scholars had agreed that the earth was something over six thousand years old, but after 1650, there was widespread acceptance of Archbishop James Ussher's calculation that Creation had occurred in 4004 B.C., and his chronology

---

[22] Bishop Pearson's *Exposition of the Creed* (1659) declared that " God is in respect of all external actions absolutely free without the least necessity. . . . Indeed, if God were a necessary agent in the works of creation, the creatures would be of as necessary being as he is; whereas the necessity of being is the undoubted prerogative of the First Cause." Cited in **Lovejoy,** *op. cit.*, p. 158.

was even added to the Authorized Version of the Bible in such a way that many people took it to be part of the original Mosaic account of Creation. Charles Darwin, for one, was surprised to discover that the date 4004 B.C. was not part of the text! [23] By 1700, however, many men recognized that the earth might be a good deal older than the Archbishop supposed, and the major scientific challenge to his dating had come in the form of fossil studies. These were already quite advanced by the time his date had passed into common usage, for men had been gathering fossil shells and musing over their meaning since the time of Leonardo da Vinci. During the sixteenth century, however, it was still commonly agreed that fossils had been laid down by the Great Flood, even though the presence of fossil shells in high mountains was an obvious embarrassment for this theory. The only really feasible alternative seemed to be that the mountaintops were not always so elevated, and during the seventeenth century, when scientists had begun their great adventure of reconciling every observation with the Newtonian vision of matter in motion, such ideas finally became fashionable.

Robert Hooke (1635–1703) was typical of the Newtonians who were fascinated by fossils. He was persuaded that they were the remains of living organisms, and their presence in the mountains forced him to conclude that the earth's surface had been subject to some great disruptions, perhaps including among them the great catastrophe that had destroyed Atlantis! Even such a pious observer as John Ray mused in 1671, " If the mountains were not from the beginning, either the world is a great deal older than is imagined, there being an incredible space of time required to work such changes . . . or, in the primitive times, the creation of the earth suffered far more concussions and mutations in its superficial part than afterwards." [24] Ray saw the alternatives clearly, and the notion of recurring catastrophes has continued to be the main weapon of those who on religious grounds seek to combat

[23] Francis C. Haber, " Fossils and Early Cosmology," in *Forerunners of Darwin: 1745–1859*, ed. by Bentley Glass, Owsei Temkin, and William L. Straus, Jr. (The Johns Hopkins Press, 1959), p. 4.

[24] John Ray, *Observations* (1673), cited in Raven, *op. cit.*, p. 425.

the belief that the world is older than the traditional six thousand years.

During the seventeenth century, several men ventured to explain the origin of the earth in terms of Newton's cosmology, and Descartes even tried to present a theory of the creation of the universe using only mechanical principles but taking the Genesis story as his framework. Thomas Burnet (1635?–1715) was fascinated with Newtonian science, and his *Sacred Theory of the Earth* (1681) was an effort to show how events in the Biblical narrative might be understood in terms of the new cosmology, much of which he knew from Descartes. His work was the first of a host of books in the tradition of " Scriptural geology," a tradition that continues even into the twentieth century. A few years later, William Whiston (1667–1752), who succeeded Newton to the Lucasian chair at Cambridge, published a book dedicated to Newton and using Newton's laws of matter in motion to explain the earth. Its prodigious title needs no comment: *A New Theory of the Earth, from its Original to the Consummation of all Things, Wherein the Creation of the World in Six Days, the Universal Deluge, and the General Conflagration, as Laid Down in the Holy Scriptures, are Shown to be Perfectly Agreeable to Reason and Philosophy* (1696). The book was praised both by John Locke and by Newton, who, by that time, was trying to unravel the puzzles of *Revelation* and *Daniel.*[25]

The eighteenth century thus could begin with some important steps toward a theory of evolution already taken. (*a*) There was increasing agreement that the earth and its creatures had changed since the time of creation, even though this meant to most people a process of degeneration. (*b*) There was a recognition that fossils were organic remains, and that they occurred in strata which must have been laid down over a long period of time. (*c*) There was a general agreement that Newton's vision of matter in motion would prove adequate to explain natural events, although most people still believed that the explanation by Newtonian science would agree with " Biblical " chronology.

After 1700 the advance of science was stimulated by the same

[25] Haber, in Glass, Temkin, and Straus, Jr., eds., *op. cit.*, p. 29.

mood that produced two great revolutions, a mood on which the image of a static order was losing its grip. The century was unfolding into a great wave of confidence in social progress, coupled with a deep respect for nature, and it was becoming more and more obvious that nature did not stand still. Partly, this enthusiasm for nature reflected a lingering desire to return to " natural " classical standards of culture, but in the main it was stimulated by the brilliant successes of Newtonian science. In England, this love of nature produced a breed of " parson-naturalists," men who like Ray and Linnaeus still saw in scientific research an expression of their faith in God. But as soon as men could identify the " laws of nature " with nature's own behavior instead of with the mind of God, a wedge was set between Biblical faith and nature study. Consequently, the eighteenth-century disciples of Newton very often either abandoned religion explicitly or transferred their real allegiance from God to nature.[26] These men investigated nature for its own sake, not because they sought to uncover the mind of God by understanding his handiwork, and they became more and more persuaded that God's laws *were* written in nature, not in the Bible. To the extent that they retained belief in God, they revised their doctrines of God to harmonize with what they found in nature, which meant viewing God as the designer of the Newtonian world machine.

Part of the eighteenth-century concern for progress was focused in an effort to temporalize the old " chain of being " by visualizing the hierarchy of creatures now as a chain that had been forged one link at a time. In the main, however, men who had this vision still clung to their belief in the Creation as a single act of God, and they merely stretched out the creative act by introducing the notion of temporal change in nature. In a very perplexing way,

[26] Colin Maclaurin, professor of mathematics in the University of Edinburgh, wrote in 1775: " Nature . . . is the supreme object of the speculations of a philosopher; who, while he contemplates and admires so excellent a system, cannot but be himself excited and animated to correspond with the general harmony of nature." *An Account of Sir Isaac Newton's Philosophical Discoveries*, p. 95, cited in Carl L. Becker, *The Heavenly City of the Eighteenth-Century Philosophers* (Yale Paperbound, Yale University Press, 1959), p. 62.

they seemed to say that what appears to us as a multitude of events in earth's long history somehow appears from God's point of view as a single event without any temporal succession. Kant, for example, was quite familiar with the French evolutionary thought of his time, and he realized that nature was characterized by some sort of continuous development and diversification. But his theory of cosmic evolution was really only a temporalized version of the single chain of being, its fullness and continued development guaranteed by the eternal omnipotence of God.[27] The idea of a single eternal divine plan of creation was still in his mind, shaping his speculations about the past so that they turned out to be a combination of the old static chain of being, eighteenth-century confidence in progress, and Newtonian cosmology. He was still some distance from a truly evolutionary system in the modern sense.

It was really not until the philosophy of Schelling (1775–1854) that the work of temporalizing the chain of being came to its ultimate logical conclusion. Schelling introduced into metaphysics and theology a kind of radically evolutionistic thought that both ensured the notion of evolution a place in the future and raised perplexing problems for its interpretation. In his writing not only was the chain of being temporalized, but God himself was temporalized so that in *every* respect the lower forms preceded the higher forms in time. God, as the highest form, could not fully exist as God until the whole evolutionary process had reached concrete realization. Thus Schelling concluded that God never *is*, but is only coming-to-be through nature and history. He wrote: "I posit God as the first and the last, as the Alpha and the Omega; but as Alpha he is not what he is as Omega, and insofar as he is only the one — God ' in an eminent sense ' — he cannot be the other God. For in that case, let it be expressly said, the unevolved (*unentfaltete*) God, *Deus implicitus*, would already be what, as Omega, the *Deus explicitus* is." [28]

---

[27] See his *Allgemeine Naturgeschichte und Theorie des Himmels* (1755) and the discussion in Lovejoy, *op. cit.*, p. 265.

[28] Translated from F. W. J. Schelling, *Denkmal der Schriften von den göttlichen Dingen*, in *Schellings Werke*, hrsg. Manfred Schröter (Munich: C. H. Beck'sche Verlagsbuchhandlung, 1958), Vierter Hauptband, p. 457.

4. THE WINDS FROM FRANCE

The discipline of biology was not yet far enough advanced in the mid-eighteenth century to provide a factual basis for a theory of evolution, and the first modern evolutionists were not primarily biologists but philosopher-scientists, intent on building Newton's physics into a complete philosophy of nature. These men appeared in France during the years before the French Revolution, and their evolutionary speculations had, from the very beginning, that decidedly materialistic flavor which became a hallmark of enlightened French thought as the Revolution drew near.

The first man on the Continent to grasp the Newtonian vision of nature and propagate it there was Pierre Louis Moreau de Maupertuis (1698–1759). As a young man, he visited London, where he became a member of the Royal Society and a disciple of Newton. Later he became the perpetual President of Frederick the Great's Academy of Sciences in Berlin, and his consistently mechanistic views did much to establish the French style in evolutionary thought. Applying the Newtonian vision of matter in motion to biology, he gave exact expression to the idea that horrified multitudes a hundred years later in Darwin's work: not only stars and planets, but living things must be explained scientifically without introducing the concept of final causation.

Somewhere in his work, Maupertuis touched on every basic idea essential for the type of evolutionary theory devised by Darwin. He exactly anticipated the idea of " survival of the fittest," attributing the appearance of Design in nature to chance variations,[29]

---

[29] " May we not say that, in the fortuitous combination of the productions of Nature, since only those creatures *could* survive in whose organization a certain degree of adaptation was present, there is nothing extraordinary in the fact that such adaptation is actually found in all those species which now exist? Chance, one might say, turned out a vast number of individuals; a small proportion of these were organized in such a manner that the animals' organs could satisfy their needs. A much greater number showed neither adaptation nor order; these last have all perished. . . . Thus the species which we see today are but a small part of all those that a blind destiny has produced." Quoted from the translation in Bentley Glass, " Maupertuis, Pioneer of Genetics and Evolution," in *Forerunners of Darwin*, p. 58.

and in an age when others still held the preformationist theory of individual growth, he proposed a theory of heredity strikingly similar to the modern theory of genes.[30] Starting with his belief in Newtonian forces of attraction and bodies in motion, he suggested that heredity is governed by particles derived from the mother and the father, drawn together by "attractive forces." Occasionally there may be accidents in this procedure, he said, allowing new anomalies and varieties to appear, and it seemed possible that whole new species might appear in this fashion.

Maupertuis' writings were not known to the English evolutionists of the nineteenth century, partly because of Voltaire's hostility, but it is evident now that he preceded them in seeing the necessary biological implications of the Newtonian vision. Still, he was no atheist, and he did not wish to deny that there was any ultimate purpose in the universe. Realizing that an atoms-plus-chance materialism did not seem to explain intelligence, he tried to resolve the problem by introducing the divine intelligence as the ultimate source of purpose in nature.[31] Accordingly, he redefined Newton's "matter" to include some psychical aspects, saying that God had created each material particle with some mentality. Thus his genetic particles had a low form of intelligence, a property "akin to what in us we term desire, aversion, memory."[32] Of course, this was an impossible position for a strict Newtonian; a point-mass in motion could not be granted any mentality, because it had been defined in the first place precisely by abstracting *away* from all aspects of intelligence in nature. Maupertuis really was presenting a rather incompatible mixture of Newtonian materialism, eighteenth-century Deism, and panpsychism.

Denis Diderot (1713–1784) developed ideas of evolution in which he sought to be even more consistently materialistic than Maupertuis. He began his first work (*Pensées philosophiques*,

---

[30] *Vénus Physique, contenant deux dissertations, l'une sur l'origine des hommes et des animaux; et l'autre sur l'origine des noirs* (1745).

[31] Maupertuis, *Système de la nature* (1751, 1754).

[32] Maupertuis, *Système de la nature*, II, pp. 157 f., cited in Lester G. Crocker, "Diderot and Eighteenth Century French Transformism," *Forerunners of Darwin*, p. 126.

1746) as a Deist,[33] but by 1749 he was persuaded that nature was
completely independent of any external agency. Thus where Maupertuis had felt able to attribute some mentality to his genetic
particles by bringing in the notion of God, Diderot felt himself
obliged to sever nature from God entirely. How, then, could he
explain the complexly organized structures of living creatures,
heretofore attributed to divine purpose? Diderot took what seemed
the only possible step — he proposed the existence of material organizing forces resident within creatures themselves. Finally in
1769 he published his great system of materialism in *Rêve de
d'Alembert*, writing of an immense universe composed of a single
substance variously organized, evolving from a primeval chaos by
means of a kind of internal teleology that produced adaptations
to conditions and even allowed for transformations of species. In
a way typical of his age, he assumed that acquired characteristics
are inheritable: " The original conformation is altered or per-
fected by necessity and habitual function. We walk so little, work
so little and think so much, that I should not think it strange if
man ended up by being only a head." [34] Diderot looked on his
notion of internal organizing forces as a reasonable extension into
biology of Newton's doctrine that all motion can be traced to
forces immanent in nature, and this proposal did help him to explain evolution without God, as a purely *natural* process. But no
" internal organizing force " would be found in a strictly Newtonian world, and it is clear that Diderot's materialism was
blended with a large measure of the old Aristotelian belief that
creatures enjoy an inward tendency toward their ends.

While these Frenchmen were at work, the philosopher Jean Baptiste Robinet (1735–1820) made yet another suggestion.[35] A be-
liever in fixed species, he proposed that all species of creatures
had originated from a single prototype, merely appearing at different times without being descended from each other. Assuming
that man was the goal of the whole process, he wrote, " I think we

[33] Crocker, *loc. cit.*, p. 115.
[34] Diderot, *Rêve de d'Alembert*, p. 69, cited in Crocker, *loc. cit.*, p. 139.
[35] *De la nature* (1761) and *Considerations philosophiques sur la grada-
tion naturelle des formes de l'être, ou les essais de la nature, qui apprend
à former l'homme* (1768).

may call the collection of the preliminary studies the apprenticeship of Nature in learning to make a man." [36] Robinet was well aware of the problem posed by trying to explain mentality in terms of the Newtonian abstractions, but he was anxious to maintain both the principle of continuity in nature and some degree of intellectual coherence, so he proposed finally that all psychical factors have a basis in matter. In this vein he wrote: " All things . . . have some degree or measure of any quality which is possessed by anything. Thus to the lowest orders of being must be ascribed some rudiments of the attributes conspicuous in the highest, and to the highest some vestiges of the characteristics of the lowest." [37] Like Maupertuis, he was attributing to the Newtonian atoms a character that they did not have.

The work of Charles Bonnet (1720–1793) was a curious blend of philosophical biology and theology, worth recounting as an example of how a pious biologist could temporalize the old static chain of being in terms of a naïve " Biblical " cosmology. Bonnet recognized the evidence for a temporal sequence between the lowest and highest forms of life, but also he was persuaded that every creature had developed from a " germ " preformed at the moment of creation. Everything that appears to us as evolutionary development, then, really must be the unfolding of a divine plan, eternally complete in the mind of God. He therefore explained the sequence of animal forms in nature by suggesting that God repeatedly introduces new epochs, endowing each epoch with " germs " of increasingly complex developmental potential. In a future epoch, he believed, every present form of life will experience a palingenesis, i.e., a rebirth. [38] There God will provide a better condition for all his creatures, and the orangutan may well hope to acquire the characteristics of a man! Bonnet's Biblical piety was only too evident in the interpretation he gave to his discovery of parthenogenesis in plant lice; he took it to be the scientific support for his belief in the virgin birth. This argument continues to be used by some people, even though parthenogene-

---

[36] *De la nature*, V, cited in Lovejoy, *op. cit.*, p. 280.

[37] *De la nature*, IV, cited in Lovejoy, *op. cit.*, p. 276.

[38] Charles Bonnet, *Palingénésie philosophique, ou Idées sur l'état passé et sur l'état futur des êtres vivans* (1769). See the discussion of Bonnet in Arthur O. Lovejoy, " Kant and Evolution," *Forerunners of Darwin*, p. 201.

sis does not occur naturally in vertebrates.

This may be a good place to pause for a look at the word " evolution " itself. The Latin *evolvere* meant to unroll or roll forth, and in classical usage it acquired the special meaning of unrolling a scroll. But during the Middle Ages, when scrolls had been replaced by books with leaves, the word found little usage. Finally, the word " evolution " was introduced into modern literature by a group of seventeenth-century philosophers known as the Cambridge Neoplatonists, to describe the unrolling of vast periods of time that are represented to God all at once.[39] It is this meaning of " evolution " that we find in the thought of Kant and Schelling, and in this they are typical of German idealism, visualizing the entire evolutionary sequence as though it were somehow a single event without real temporal sequence.

Bonnet's notion that each creature developed from a preformed miniature implied that the process of individual growth was an " unfolding," i.e., an " evolution " in this classical sense, and it was this meaning of " evolution " that entered the French language during the eighteenth century. Until recently, French writers have preferred to use the word *transformisme* for Darwinian evolution.

Probably the most important name from eighteenth-century France in terms of his ultimate impact on evolutionary thought is that of Georges Louis Leclerc, Comte de Buffon (1707–1788). During his lifetime, he rivalled Linnaeus in popular affection, and his works reached an immense audience. He too was a great admirer of Newton's writings, even translating the treatise on calculus into French, and in 1739 he began to write the first of forty-four quarto volumes of *Natural History, General and Particular,* as a commentary applying Newton's principles to living nature. During the decades in which this long series of books appeared, Buffon's thought grew and changed; almost inevitably he contradicted himself here and there, but he managed to mention somewhere every significant ingredient that Darwin used in his great recipe of 1859.

Buffon attempted in 1749 to explain the solar system and the

[39] Charles Singer, *A Short History of Scientific Ideas to 1900* (Oxford: At the Clarendon Press, Oxford Paperbacks, 1959), p. 501.

earth on Newtonian principles, and like Burnet he interpreted changes in the earth as decline from an original pristine state.[40] But he put aside Scripture, rejecting Burnet's assumption that the Bible could be used as a source book for scientific data. Refusing to explain everything by the Deluge, he was persuaded that only by delving into the *present* workings of nature could he hope to uncover the past history of the earth. The earth might have originated in the cataclysmic collision of a comet with the sun, he said, but everything since then must have taken place by the uniform working of natural forces. This important insight later became attached to the name of James Hutton as the doctrine of " uniformitarianism."

His essay was condemned by the Sorbonne in 1751, but Buffon smoothed over the situation by retracting his theory as a mere " supposition of philosophy." [41] However, in 1778 he took up the same theme again in a subdivision called " Epochs of Nature," where he divided the history of the earth into seven epochs that bore a certain resemblance to the seven days of Genesis; evidently Buffon was not quite so far removed from Burnet's kind of " Scriptural geology " as he supposed! In this later essay, which was the first really comprehensive effort to write a history of the earth, including discussion of fossils, Buffon proposed that the earth had evolved from a lump of molten metal. By experimenting on the refrigeration of various metals, he estimated that the earth's crust would have required more than seventy thousand years to cool,[42] a clear departure from the " Biblical " chronology.

By drawing attention to the underlying unity of form that characterized vertebrates, Buffon made a major contribution to biology, and his writings on this topic provided information for many other notables of his time, including Kant, Herder, and Goethe.[43] He was still persuaded that the homologies of animal form pointed to a single plan used by God at the Creation, but in true Newtonian fashion he resolved to seek only the mechanical laws that

[40] Buffon, *Histoire naturelle*, I (1749).

[41] *Op. cit.*, IV, cited in Greene, *op. cit.*, p. 58.

[42] Greene, *op. cit.*, p. 74.

[43] Arthur O. Lovejoy, " Buffon and the Problem of Species," *Forerunners of Darwin*, p. 112.

regulated homologies, not to consider their purposes. Here he toyed with the idea of descent. We might be led to suppose, he wrote, " that all animals are descended from a single animal, from which have sprung in the course of time, as a result of progress or of degeneration, all the other races of animals. . . . But no! It is certain from revelation that all animals have participated equally in the grace of direct creation, and that the first pair of every species issued fully formed from the hands of the Creator." [44]

Actually, Buffon had what seemed fairly good scientific reasons for rejecting the idea of descent at that time. First of all, considering the fact that no one had described any new species since the time of Aristotle, the proposed seventy thousand years seemed much too short a time for the gross changes in species that would be required for evolution by descent. But Buffon's second reason was more important — he believed (erroneously) that hybrid forms were sterile, which implied that no new species could evolve by becoming infertile with its parent species. In spite of the fact that the famous hybrid shorthorn breed of cattle already had been developed in England,[45] Buffon's view, which he called " the most fixed point that we possess in natural history," [46] dominated biology for a century, hindering the advance of evolutionary thought clear into the twentieth century. In spite of his views that animal species had not changed,[47] however, he was fascinated by the great variability of animals, and in one essay he tried to resolve this question by tracing the present two hundred species of quadrupeds back to thirty-eight original families. This he did by a verbal sleight of hand, suggesting that the modern species really were very long-lasting " varieties " of primordial " species." [48]

Buffon was always an enthusiastic Newtonian, but he believed it was an error to explain life solely on principles that had been

[44] Buffon, *Histoire naturelle*, IV (1753), p. 383.
[45] Sir William Cecil Dampier, *A Shorter History of Science* (Meridian Books, Inc., The World Publishing Company, 1957), p. 88.
[46] Cited in Lovejoy, " Buffon and the Problem of Species," p. 98.
[47] Buffon, *Histoire naturelle*, XIV, p. 358.
[48] In his " Second View of Nature," *Histoire naturelle*, XIII (1765), he wrote: " Species are the only entities of nature (*les seuls êtres de la nature*) — perduring entities, as ancient, as permanent, as Nature herself." Cited in Lovejoy, " Buffon and the Problem of Species," p. 101.

derived from observing the uniformities in the behavior of inanimate bodies. Why should there not be quite different laws for living things? [49] To explain this he ascribed an "internal mold" (*moule interieur*) to organic molecules, giving them a tendency to organize. Of course, this was nothing more than endowing the Newtonian atoms with the very property they were to account for, and in doing this Buffon echoed the logical errors of Maupertuis and Diderot. All three men were seeking a way to safeguard thought about the world of living creatures from the logical consequences of the Newtonian vision, but in terms of their own thoroughly Newtonian orientation their proposals came to little more than an admission that there must be *some* explanation for the complexity of living organisms. Buffon's own suggestion, therefore, became only one of many unsuccessful efforts to impress biological notions on the materialism of the seventeenth century.

5. THE SEARCH FOR CAUSES: ERASMUS DARWIN AND LAMARCK

We turn now to the work of Erasmus Darwin (1731–1802) and Jean Baptiste Pierre Antoine de Monet, Chevalier de Lamarck (1744–1829), the men who first directed attention to the *causes* of evolution in addition to affirming it as a fact. We must begin, however, by taking another dip into the theological currents of the time. We recall that the seventeenth century saw God effectively removed from nature and raised to a place of honor (or so they thought then!) as a master craftsman who had designed a magnificent mechanical world to dazzle man and call forth his admiration. During those years, the great book of nature became a textbook for understanding the mind of God, and confidence in man's "natural reason" as the only tool necessary to read the book sparked the Deist controversy in England, beginning with the publication of John Toland's *Christianity Not Mysterious* in 1696. Natural theologians turned again and again during that period to evidences of God's design in nature, and this mood in theology dominated the eighteenth century.

[49] Greene, *op. cit.*, p. 142.

The works of William Paley (1743–1805) reveal at its best this rationalistic tone in late eighteenth-century theology. Clearly written and widely circulated during the early nineteenth century, Paley's books [50] climaxed the hundred years after John Ray, during which clergymen immersed themselves in the study of nature, and we still remember them by the phrase "Paley's watchmaker." Briefly, Paley's argument went like this: from a watch we infer a watchmaker, and from the marvelous adaptations of the human body we ought to infer an almighty designer. The frontispiece of *Natural Theology* showed a pious man standing on a promontory, Bible in hand, gazing adoringly at the spectacle of nature; underneath were the words, "The World thenceforth becomes a Temple and Life itself one continued act of adoration." Throughout, observations of the world of nature served Paley as proof for the activity of God, and he could write, "The hinges in the wings of an earwig and the joints of its antennae, are as highly wrought, as if the Creator had had nothing else to finish." [51]

By 1800 the notion of Design in nature was the reigning doctrine in both theology and biology; some notion of its hold on the popular mind can be gained by realizing that Hume's attack on Design in *Dialogues Concerning Natural Religion* was withheld by its author from publication during his lifetime, in order that he might avoid the inevitable storm of protest. Erasmus Darwin grew up in this world, as did Lamarck, and both men began their work in biology with an almost unquestioned belief in design. Later, Charles Darwin memorized Paley's "evidences" at Cambridge, and he was an admirer of *Natural Theology* before he sailed on the *Beagle*.[52] The Newtonian revolution in philosophy and science had been followed by a theological world of Design, a world where Christians were encouraged to believe that the grounds for their faith in God could be *demonstrated* by the methods of sci-

[50] *View of the Evidences of Christianity* (1794) and *Natural Theology: or, Evidences of the Existence and Attributes of the Deity, Collected from the Appearances of Nature* (1802).

[51] Paley, *Natural Theology* (London ed., 1826), II, p. 201, cited in Eiseley, *op. cit.*, p. 176.

[52] Francis Darwin, ed., *The Life and Letters of Charles Darwin: Including an Autobiographical Chapter* (D. Appleton & Company, 1896), I, p. 41.

ence, even that their faith in God *depended* on the facts which scientists could read in the great book of nature.

Biology grew up in Britain partly as the hobby of genteel families, and we can find no better illustration than the Darwins. Erasmus Darwin was Charles Darwin's grandfather, but there can be no doubt that he was also his grandson's precursor in British evolutionary science, for he was the first man to present a reasoned and convincing argument for the fact of biological evolution in the modern sense. Darwin was a leading physician of his day, even receiving an invitation to attend George III,[53] but for him the study of medicine was also an avenue to the understanding of natural history. His great work was a two-volume treatise entitled *Zoonomia, or the Laws of Organic Life,* published in 1794–1796, but he also wrote two long philosophical poems, *The Botanic Garden* (1791) and *The Temple of Nature* (1803). These works were well known in Britain during the early nineteenth century, and it seems fairly certain that Charles Darwin's early exposure to the notion of evolution came through these writings of his grandfather, read while he was a medical student in Edinburgh. Curiously, however, he seemed to have almost no awareness of the intellectual debt that he owed to his grandfather.[54] Apparently, his grandfather's ideas became a part of him, and he forgot their source.

Erasmus Darwin held the Deist view that human affairs and nature are not subject to the intervention of a personal God,[55] and he wanted to show that natural law accounted for the present state of living nature, independently of God. His scientific works, therefore, were designed to show how geological and biological events could be explained in terms of a system of matter in motion, and in *The Botanic Garden* he put forth a theory much like Buffon's,

---

[53] C. D. Darlington, *Darwin's Place in History* (The Macmillan Company, 1961), p. 8.

[54] In a rather tardy and perhaps misleading " Historical Sketch " prefaced to the third edition of *The Origin of Species,* Darwin wrote, " It is curious how largely my grandfather, Dr. Erasmus Darwin, anticipated the views and erroneous grounds of opinion of Lamarck."

[55] Norton Garfinkle, " Science and Religion in England, 1790–1800: The Critical Response to the Work of Erasmus Darwin," *Journal of the History of Ideas,* 16 (1955), p. 377.

wherein the earth began as a molten offshoot of the sun. This was such a success that Darwin quickly became one of England's most widely read poets. Encouraged, he brought forward a prose work begun many years earlier, and in 1794 he published the first volume of *Zoonomia*. It was basically an effort to systematize the facts about animal life in order to arrive at a theory of disease, and it, too, was acclaimed for its medical ideas. The work reached a wide international audience within a decade,[56] and in a manner reflecting the tolerance toward heterodox opinion that was typical of eighteenth-century Britain, critics passed over the obviously unbiblical notions of evolution which the book contained.

By the time Darwin wrote, a welter of facts had been gathered — fertilization and the process of embryological development had been studied under the microscope; plants and animals had been bred extensively; the great plenitude of animals and plants had been classified into an intelligible system; chimpanzees had been dissected and compared with man and with monkeys. Reflecting over all this, Darwin concluded that all living things had descended from a common ancestor.[57] But what did this mean? Darwin concluded that " all nature exists in a state of perpetual improvement by laws impressed on the atoms of matter by the great CAUSE OF CAUSES; and that the world may still be in its infancy, and continue to improve FOR EVER AND EVER." [58] This view allowed his works to serve popularly for a time as a kind of scientific underwriting for the belief in human progress that was held by so many, but in his own mind the question of *causes* for this " perpetual improvement " was more important.

Accordingly, Darwin devoted himself to unraveling this part of the riddle, and in *Zoonomia* we find his answer: the " great first cause " had endowed living matter with an inherent power to improve. Each organism, he wrote, was endued with " the power of

[56] There were four British and two American editions, plus translations into German, French, Spanish, and Italian. Garfinkle, *loc. cit.*, p. 380.

[57] He wrote, " Would it be too bold to imagine, that all warm-blooded animals have arisen from one living filament, which THE GREAT FIRST CAUSE endued with animality . . . ? " *Zoonomia; or the Laws of Organic Life* (2d American from the 3d London ed.; Thomas and Andrews, 1803), I, p. 397.

[58] Erasmus Darwin, *Zoonomia*, I, p. 437.

acquiring new parts attended with new propensities, directed by irritations, sensations, volitions, and associations; and thus possessing the faculty of continuing to improve by its own inherent
activity, and of delivering down those improvements by generation
to its posterity, world without end." [59] We note that Darwin believed in the inheritance of acquired characteristics, and that he
believed variations were produced as a result of both *external
forces* (" irritations ") and *internal purposes* (" volitions "). Environment had a definite effect in altering heredity, and so did the
organism's internal response; here Darwin's thought resembled
that of his contemporary, Lamarck.

Darwin also called attention to the importance of competition
as an agency of change in nature, noting that overpopulation produced by abundant fertility leads to competition for the resources
of life. Here, it is of some interest to note that he was acquainted
with Benjamin Franklin, who in 1755 had published an essay entitled *Observations concerning the Increase of Mankind and the
Peopling of Countries.*[60] Also Malthus' famous *Essay on the Principle of Population* appeared in 1798, only four years after Darwin's *Zoonomia* — evidently the idea of competition was well circulated long before Charles Darwin made it a central feature of
his evolutionary theory.

Darwin's genuine interest in delineating the *causes* of evolutionary change was an immense step forward in finding purely
natural causes for evolution. But his notion of an organism im-
proving " by its own inherent activity " was an impossible proposal within the Newtonian conceptual scheme that he avowed. In
this sense, it really was not an advance beyond Buffon, and Darwin's work remains as a vivid testimony to the ambiguities of a
century whose writers tried to affirm faith in God and divine Design within the Newtonian vision.

Like Darwin, Lamarck was a late eighteenth-century Deist
whose belief in design deeply colored his evolutionary thought. He
thus viewed evolution as the gradual accomplishment of an immanent purpose to perfect the creation, a process in which the old
ladder of being now represented a moving stair up which life

---

[59] *Ibid.*, p. 397.   [60] Darlington, *op. cit.*, p. 12.

ascended to its climax in man.[61] His belief in purpose was expressed particularly, as we shall see, in a part of his theory for
which he became famous (or infamous, depending on one's
view!), the part where he proposed that variations in organisms
arise partly as an expression of creaturely habits.

Modern critics of Lamarck sometimes forget, however, that he
was also a thoroughgoing Newtonian. He had studied Buffon's
thought, and like Buffon he was intent on deriving organic phenomena from the operations of Newtonian systems of matter in
motion.[62] But unlike Buffon, he would not grant to organisms any
" principle of organization " in addition to the purely material
atoms of which they were made; life, he claimed, was really a
phenomenon that accompanied certain states of matter.[63] Obviously, he faced the ever-present problem: how could the Newtonian vision be reconciled with belief that there was Design in
nature? How could an " inner perfecting principle " be reconciled with materialism?

Lamarck began his scientific work late in life as a botanist, but
during the French Revolution he was appointed to a chair in zoology, lecturing on the invertebrates. Very significantly, as he reflected on the intricate relationships between organisms and their
environments, the basic style of his thought remained biological
and not mechanical. He was well aware that the physical environment changes continually, and he reasoned that if the condition of
organic forms depends partly on their environment, they, too,
must change if the environment changes. By 1797 he had abandoned the traditional belief in fixed species, and he was busily engaged in a search for the physical laws that he was sure must
govern change in animal species. His research was based on belief
in a sharp cleavage, even a struggle, between matter and life,[64] and
this assumption shaped his belief that the key to organic change

[61] Charles C. Gillispie, " The Formation of Lamarck's Evolutionary
Theory," *Archives Internationales d'Histoire des Sciences*, 9 (1957), pp.
323-338.

[62] Greene, *op. cit.*, p. 155.

[63] *Ibid.*, p. 158.

[64] Charles C. Gillispie, " Lamarck and Darwin in the History of Science," *Forerunners of Darwin*, p. 273.

lay somewhere in the relationship between living organisms and their physical environments.

Lamarck presented his evolutionary ideas first in *Système des animaux sans vertèbres* (1801) and finally in systematic form in *Histoire naturelle des animaux sans vertèbres* (1815–1822). Throughout, he continued to emphasize the great gap between the living and nonliving parts of nature, although he believed that life continually emerged in simple forms from physical nature. This continual emergence of life explained for him the existence of simple forms of life in his own time — they had begun traveling more recently on the moving stair by which life strove to rise toward man. The many irregularities and blind alleys in evolutionary history stemmed from frustrations to this immanent thrust of life, frustrations traceable to the physical world. Design, we might say, was somehow thwarted by the swarming, purposeless Newtonian atoms.

In *Histoire naturelle,* Lamarck gave the results of his quest for the physical basis of evolutionary change, in the form of four laws:

" 1. Life, by its own forces, tends continually to increase the volume of every body possessing it, and to extend the dimensions of its parts, up to a limit which it brings about itself.

" 2. The production of a new organ in an animal body results from the arisal and continuance of a new need (*besoin*) and from the new movement which this need brings into being and sustains.

" 3. The degree of development of organs and their force of action are always proportionate to the use made of these organs.

" 4. All that has been acquired, imprinted or changed in the organization of the individual during the course of its life is preserved by generation and transmitted to the new individuals that descend from the individual so modified." [65]

Here we see a specific effort to spell out laws for the process relating an organism's inward drive to perfection and the retarding

<hr />

[65] Quoted from the translation by E. S. Russell in *Form and Function: A Contribution to the History of Animal Morphology* (London: J. Murray, 1916), pp. 221 f.

effect of the inorganic world. A changed physical environment produces new needs in an organism, and it responds inwardly by changes in its own behavior. These become new habits, and the new habits may lead to alterations in organs and finally even in the whole plan of organization, as small habit-induced changes then accumulate generation by generation through heredity. In this way, organs that lose their usefulness because of a newly adopted way of life can disappear gradually as the generations pass; likewise, organs helpful for the new mode of behavior slowly make their appearance. The whole process, we note, assumes that each organism passes on to its young whatever small changes are acquired during its own lifetime of coping with a changing environment.

To this day, Lamarck's doctrines are misunderstood in the English-speaking world because his French word *besoin* was mistranslated by Charles Lyell and others as " desire " instead of " need." [66] This error has perpetuated the belief that Lamarck attributed change in bodily form to the *conscious desires* of animals, which is something he never meant to suggest; as a Newtonian, he used the word " need " only to indicate the mechanical necessity that animals modify their habits in accordance with changing physical conditions in their environment. More than once, he emphasized that changes in the physical environment only cause changes in animal habits, and it was these *changes in habit* which ultimately were so important in bringing about evolutionary change. [67] However, biologists have grown so accustomed to this erroneous view of Lamarck's theory that in most modern discussions " Lamarckian " or " neo-Lamarckian " theories of evolution

[66] See H. Graham Cannon, "What Lamarck Really Said," *Proc. Linnaean Soc.*, 168 (January, 1957), p. 71, and *Lamarck and Modern Genetics* (Manchester: Manchester University Press, 1959).

[67] For example, in Chapter 7 of *Philosophie Zoologique* (Paris: 1873 ed.), I, p. 223: " *Car quelles que puissent être les circonstances, elle n'opèrent directement sur la forme et sur l'organisation des animaux aucune modification quelconque.*" Cited in Sir Alister Hardy, *The Living Stream* (London: William Collins Sons & Co., Ltd., 1965), p. 160. Hardy summarizes the context as follows: " Circumstances influence the form of animals, but I must not be taken literally, for the environment can effect no direct changes whatever upon the organisation of animals."

are discredited on the assumption that such theories trace evolutionary change directly to the subjective purposes of creatures.

Frequently the phrase " Lamarckian inheritance " is used to refer to the doctrine of inheritance of acquired characteristics, as though Lamarck had originated the idea. However, as we have seen, this notion of inheritance was used by such men as Diderot and Erasmus Darwin, and it was, in fact, merely a widespread folk belief that these men accepted in their theories.[68] We shall comment in a later chapter about this idea, accepting the phrase " Lamarckian inheritance " as a working definition, but it is important to note here that this doctrine was not central to Lamarck's theory. In terms of his own day, the real ambiguity in his thought seems to lie in his assumption that changes in animal habits can be explained physically, i.e., that what seem to be purposeful creaturely responses to a changing environment are merely the effects of Newtonian forces at work. At this point, his belief in Design and purpose was fused arbitrarily to his Newtonian assumptions, so it is at least symbolically impressive that the originator of the word " biology " [69] is remembered as the father of all those who rest uneasily with Newtonian interpretations of evolution and who see purpose as a causal agency in the process.

The work of Erasmus Darwin climaxed eighteenth-century evolutionary thought in England, but between his *Zoonomia* (1794) and the publication of Robert Chambers' *Vestiges of the Natural History of Creation* (1844), no single major work devoted to the topic of evolution appeared in Britain. Even Lamarck's theory, which was well known on the Continent as *transformisme* or " the development hypothesis," remained unknown in England until Charles Lyell introduced it as a foil in his nonevolutionary *Principles of Geology* (1830–1833). Thus a gap of fifty years appears in the British evolutionary movement. What had happened? The best clue to this hiatus is found by a look at the changing relations

[68] See Conway Zirkle, " The Early History of the Idea of Acquired Characters and of Pangenesis," *Proceedings of the American Philosophical Society*, n.s., Vol. 35 (1946), p. 111; and the discussion in Eiseley, *op. cit.*, p. 50.

[69] He coined the term in 1802 to emphasize the continuity of the animal and plant series, over against the whole inorganic realm.

of science and religion during the last decade of the eighteenth century.[70] The impact of the French Revolution, with its atheistic and materialistic overtones, was added to that of the Evangelical Revival, effecting a return toward religious orthodoxy and a revived emphasis on the authority of the Bible. People feared the social implications of unrestrained and atheistic scientific speculations, and a look at France only confirmed their fears: the entire French school of evolutionists had given up the Bible as their norm. No longer was it possible to assume naïvely that scientific research would only confirm the Biblical stories of Creation, and some of the defenders of orthodoxy reacted in a concerted effort to spike the guns of those scientists who openly professed non-Scriptural doctrines.

This movement did not get seriously under way until the 1790's, so that Darwin's *Zoonomia* was well received. But *The Temple of Nature* (which merely elaborated on the evolutionary ideas of *Zoonomia*) fell virtually without an audience, condemned by some of the same journals that had praised his earlier works.[71] A principal objection to Darwin's doctrines was that he overemphasized the role played by the volition of individual animals in evolution, a view which struck his critics as dangerously analogous to the ominous Revolutionary belief that human institutions can be remodeled by the exercise of human reason. This hostility to " non-Scriptural " scientific ideas and French rationalism became a powerful current in British culture, extending well into Charles Darwin's lifetime and greatly slowing the progress of evolutionary thought.[72]

6. THE STRUGGLE FOR TIME: HUTTON AND CUVIER

At the end of the eighteenth century, both Erasmus Darwin and Lamarck were restrained from a genuinely Newtonian explanation

[70] See the discussion by Garfinkle.

[71] Garfinkle, *loc. cit.*, p. 386.

[72] The impact of this intellectual current in America was measured in Timothy Dwight's well-known sermon of 1797, " On the Nature and Danger of Infidel Philosophy." For a short summary, see Winthrop S. Hudson, *Religion in America* (Charles Scribner's Sons, 1965), Ch. VI.

of evolution partly because geologists had not yet granted them the immense stretches of time required. They were agreed that there was an evolutionary sequence of animal forms, but in order to account for the fact that evolution seemingly had arrived so quickly at its climax (man) they retained belief in a supernatural designer. Time, time in nearly infinite quantities, was the missing ingredient at 1800.

It was a Scottish farmer and landowner who first looked at the history of the earth and saw " no vestige of a beginning, no prospect of an end." [73] James Hutton (1726–1797) was absorbed with a passion for bringing to geology the vision of mathematical order that Newton had brought to physics, and he saw the earth as a machine governed by perpetual and unswerving laws of geological change. Assuming nature to be a strict Newtonian system, he wrote that in explaining it " no powers are to be employed, that are not natural to the globe, no actions to be admitted except those of which we know the principle." [74] This belief, foreshadowed in Buffon, became known as Hutton's doctrine of " uniformitarianism," and he presented it first to the Royal Society of Edinburgh in 1785. In 1795 Hutton expanded his views into a two-volume work, *Theory of the Earth*. He said there never had been a universal deluge. Agencies such as wind, frost, and running water had, over countless millennia, gradually worn down the continents, and geological strata had been formed not by Noah's Flood but by an incredibly slow and persistent process of sedimentation in the oceans. Subterranean heat and pressure first consolidated the layers of sediment, then elevated them in a compensating uplift of new continents and mountains.

In Hutton's scheme, time was no longer a short one-way street, the scene of God's drama of creation and the redemption of man. Indeed, his vision of nearly unlimited time during which cyclical forces repeatedly tore down and rebuilt the earth's surface harked back to the cyclical world view of ancient Greece. Yet Hutton was able to combine his Newtonian principles with belief in Design,

[73] These were Hutton's final words to the Royal Society in 1785, cited in Milton Millhauser, *Just Before Darwin: Robert Chambers and Vestiges* (Wesleyan University Press, 1959), p. 44.

[74] Dampier, *A Shorter History of Science*, p. 90.

claiming that the perfect geological equilibrium was the work of a divine hand that maintained the surface of the planet in a state fit for human habitation.[75] He wrote, " Thus . . . from the top of the mountain to the shore of the sea . . . everything is in a state of change; the rock and solid strata slowly dissolving, breaking and decomposing, *for the purpose of becoming soil;* the soil traveling along the surfaces of the earth on its way to the shore; and the shore itself wearing and wasting by the agitation of the sea, an agitation which is essential *to the purposes of a living world.*" [76]

Hutton's doctrine of uniformitarianism held one of the keys that would help unlock the secrets of evolution, but it suffered at the hands of religious conservatives after 1795. Also, it was conceived at an awkward time, when a completely different doctrine was orthodox in geological circles. This was the doctrine of " catastrophism," which explained the present features of the earth's surface in terms of one or more catastrophes in the past. During Hutton's lifetime, this very ancient idea was expressed in the " Neptunist " school of geology, according to which all rocks are of aqueous origin; it was fundamentally an effort to read the geological strata in terms of the book of Genesis. Then after Hutton's death, a second version of catastrophism gained wide acceptance, further delaying the day when his ideas would find their proper place in geological theory. This was the theory proposed by Cuvier, in which Noah's Flood was but the most recent in a series of tremendous cataclysms that had devastated the earth and separated one world of prehistoric creatures from the next.

Georges Cuvier (1769–1832) was born in the Jura, son of a Swiss army officer and a member of the Swiss Reformed faith. He studied in Stuttgart, where he was exposed to German *Naturphilosophie,* and in 1795 he was called to Paris when the new French scientific institutions were being formed. There he entered on a spectacular career at the Jardin des Plantes, becoming a favorite of Napoleon and finally holding important civic positions. His work in biology determined the direction of thought in zoology during the early nineteenth century, and as a great antievolution-

[75] Greene, *op. cit.,* p. 78.
[76] Cited in Eiseley, *op. cit.,* p. 73, italics mine.

ist he was primarily responsible for the disrepute into which La-marck's evolutionary hypothesis fell. As was so common, Cuvier's work expressed a rather uneasy blending of Newtonian principles and Biblical faith. From Buffon he took over the concept of an organism as a system of matter in motion, but he likened a living body to a furnace in which inert substances are subject to a self-perpetuating vital motion able to counteract the ordinary behavior of material particles.[77] This was as much a compromise of the strict Newtonian position as the views of Buffon, Lamarck, and Erasmus Darwin, but it allowed Cuvier to study animals objec-tively as machines while at the same time believing they had been created to fit their environments.

Cuvier was a great morphologist, the father of modern verte-brate paleontology, and a pioneer in comparative anatomy, and his great zeal as an investigator came largely from his belief in the purposeful adaptations of animals to their environments. He dis-sected in great detail, giving particular attention to the correlation of parts, since he was persuaded that every part correlated with the function of the whole. Even a single footprint can tell us a great deal, he observed; for example, animals with hooves must be herbivorous, because they have no means of grasping prey.

Lamarck had visualized the old ladder of being as a single esca-lator moving up toward man, but Cuvier's dissections failed to re-veal the unity of plan that Lamarck's hypothesis required. The di-verse forms of life could not be placed on a single moving stair. Instead, Cuvier described four main organic types — *Vertebrata, Mollusca, Articulata,* and *Radiata* — each one independent of the others, bearing no more resemblance to them than it did to plants.[78] His last group has been modified, but he effectively de-throned the notion of a single great chain of being, opening the way for later ideas of divergent evolutionary directions. It was a crucial step, allowing his successors to picture the evolution of life as a bush instead of a ladder.

It was Cuvier's great interest in fossil bones that linked his

[77] Georges Cuvier, *Lectures on Comparative Anatomy*, tr. by William Ross (London, 1802), I, pp. 4–5, cited in Greene, *op. cit.*, p. 169.

[78] Georges Cuvier, *The Animal Kingdom, Arranged in Conformity with Its Organization*, tr. and ed. by H. M'Murtrie (New York, 1831).

name with geology as well as with comparative anatomy. During his career, rock formations of the Paris Basin were being quarried, and he could pore over the bones that were recovered. Once he wrote of this time: " I found myself as if placed in a charnel house surrounded by mutilated fragments of many hundred skeletons of more than twenty kinds of animals, piled confusedly around me. The task assigned me was to restore them all to their original positions. At the voice of comparative anatomy every bone and fragment of a bone resumed its place." [79] His concern for fossil bones was climaxed in 1812 with his *Researches on Fossil Bones*,[80] where he showed that there were indeed many extinct species and that fossils seem to show an order as they occur in rocks. He was eager to discover what had undone all these strange animals from the past, and in his studies he had the key that would have unlocked millions of years of evolutionary history for his gaze. But he did not turn the key. Instead, he elaborated the version of catastrophism that has been linked with his name.

In a series of great cataclysms, he said, there had been wholesale destruction of species, and new forms had arisen, somehow, from the survivors. Although he himself believed that the earth had been repopulated each time from a few animals which survived the catastrophes, his disciples soon spoke of repeated divine creations of life occurring after each disaster. The causes of these ancient upheavals and their exact dates remained obscure in Cuvier's mind, to be sure, but his theory seemed adequate to account for facts that seemed inexplicable on Hutton's theory. For example, entire carcasses of mammoths had been found apparently " quick-frozen " in Siberia; how could the slow processes of uniformitarian geology account for this? [81] Cuvier wrote: " If there

[79] From an article in the *Edinburgh Review*, Vol. 65 (1837), p. 23, cited in Eiseley, *op. cit.*, p. 84.

[80] The full title was *Researches on Fossil Bones, Reestablishing the Character of many Animals, of which the Species have been destroyed in the Revolutions of the Earth.*

[81] For a more recent version of catastrophism, see Immanuel Velikovsky, *Worlds in Collision* (London: Victor Gollancz, Ltd., 1950), esp. pp. 36–38, where he suggests that a sudden climatic change must be postulated in order to explain the preservation of " quick-frozen " mammoth carcasses. The initial impact of Velikovsky's ideas on the scientific com-

is any circumstance thoroughly established in geology, it is, that the crust of our globe has been subjected to a great and sudden revolution, the epoch of which cannot be dated much further back than five or six thousand years ago; that this revolution had buried all the countries which were before inhabited by men and by the other animals now best known . . . that the small number of individuals of men and other animals that escaped from the effects of that great revolution, have since propagated and spread over the lands then newly laid dry; and consequently, that the human race has only resumed a progressive state of improvement since that epoch, by forming established societies, raising monuments, collecting natural facts, and constructing systems of science and learning." [82]

The great authority of Cuvier's views in the early nineteenth century extended to his ideas on the human species and its races, a subject of increasing public interest in pre-Civil War America. In his *Essay on the Theory of the Earth* (1815), he reaffirmed his belief that man barely antedated Noah's Flood, calling attention to the tradition of a great deluge among the Aztecs and the Incas.[83] He recognized three races (Caucasian, Mongolian, and Negroid) and supposed that they were merely varieties of a single created species, differing only because of their isolation since the Deluge. The Caucasian race was most beautiful and highly cultured, he noted, while the Negroid race was so degraded as to approach the level of animals.[84] These views on race were quickly seized by people who sought scientific justification for a doctrine of white supremacy; even though they were quite incidental to the main body

---

munity was nearly as explosive as the cosmic events that he proposes, and partly because response to his suggestions has been so polemical, their possible merits have not yet been carefully evaluated. As we shall point out later, extraterrestrial events surely must be considered among possible causes of events on earth, even though we may not wish to follow Velikovsky as far as he goes in this direction.

[82] Cuvier, *Researches on Fossil Bones*, cited in Charles C. Gillispie, *The Edge of Objectivity: An Essay in the History of Scientific Ideas* (Princeton University Press, 1960), p. 290.

[83] Cuvier, *Essay on the Theory of the Earth* (1st American ed., 1818), p. 146, cited in Greene, *op. cit.*, p. 237.

[84] *Ibid.*, p. 160, cited in Greene, *op. cit.*, p. 235.

of Cuvier's thought, in the United States they had more popular impact than his great work in comparative anatomy. A generation later, Darwin's work was received in America in similar fashion, as a contribution to the burning question of race.

7. THE GATHERING TIDE IN BRITAIN

Early British geologists were inspired as much by the book of Genesis as by observation, and ever since Burnet's *Sacred Theory of the Earth* in 1681, they had occupied themselves by using Newtonian principles to show how Noah's Flood explained everything that had happened to the earth since Creation. The popularity of this "Scriptural geology" lasted well into the nineteenth century, but by the 1830's there was some general agreement that long periods of time were involved in the formation of fossils, and even the most orthodox of Scriptural geologists were forced to devise some new *modus operandi* for the Creator. The answer was at hand, suggested by Cuvier — repeated "special creations," each separated from the others by long periods of time. This view became known as "progressionism," and its adherents envisioned a succession of organic worlds, each of which had ended abruptly when God induced some geological upheaval. These worlds were merely successive, however, not continuous or genetically derived from each other. Thus Hugh Miller, a leading exponent, wrote that the unity connecting these successive fossil worlds had nothing to do with parental descent, being, as he said, "of a higher and immaterial nature." [85] The immediate effect of progressionism was to give an increased place to supernatural intervention in nature — instead of one big miracle in the beginning, there had been a series of smaller miracles along the way; it was, as Lovejoy observes, a most singular way for creationists to add some "epicycles" to their system. [86]

Progressionism was deeply influenced by ideas from German

[85] Hugh Miller, *The Testimony of the Rocks* (Edinburgh, 1869), cited in Eiseley, *op. cit.*, p. 95.

[86] Arthur O. Lovejoy, "The Argument for Organic Evolution Before the Origin of Species, 1830–1858," *Forerunners of Darwin*, p. 365.

romantic philosophy, which in one of its important facets was a brilliant effort to glimpse the ways in which the past is incorporated into the present. Hegel, for example, believed that the " truth " of any event lay in how it functioned as a stage in the historical movement toward self-conscious Spirit, and romantic philosophers consistently maintained that the present furnished the only key for understanding the past. One of the earliest important expressions of this philosophy in the field of biology was given by Kielmeyer, Cuvier's anatomy instructor, who in 1793 formulated the so-called " biogenetic law," according to which lower organisms can only be understood as steps leading up to man.[87] Lorenz Oken put it quite succinctly: " Animals are foetal stages of man." [88] After Darwin's work appeared, this idea became attached to the name of Ernst Haeckel, but it has retained a peculiar fascination for biologists in the German tradition.[89] Even today this mode of thought lies behind the term " Mongolian spots," applied to the slate-blue areas of pigmentation that sometimes are found over the buttocks and backs of newborn Caucasian babies. The term reflects a false belief that Caucasian babies recapitulate in their fetal stages an adult characteristic of the " lower " Mongolian race.

When the romantic vision was fused with British geological progressionism, it became possible to think that fossils were " predictions " of man. Thus, Hugh Miller mused over the fossil footprints of an extinct reptile as " mute prophecies of the coming being," [90] and the Americans James McCosh and George Dickie were sure that the bipedal fossil footprints of birds (actually dinosaurs) were a sign that human beings would appear " in a subsequent and still distant epoch." [91] The net result of introducing these German ideas into British geology and biology was to discourage evolu-

[87] Alexander Gode von Aesch, *Natural Science in German Romanticism* (Columbia University Press, 1941), p. 121.

[88] *Ibid.*, p. 122.

[89] For a good discussion of the German transcendental school of biology see Russell, *Form and Function.*

[90] Miller, *The Testimony of the Rocks,* p. 193, cited in Eiseley, *op. cit.,* p. 96.

[91] James McCosh and George Dickie, *Typical Forms and Special Ends in Creation* (New York, 1857), p. 330, cited in Eiseley, *op. cit.,* p. 96.

tionary thought by lending spurious support to the progressionist viewpoint, and in the resulting wave of enthusiasm for Cuvier's version of catastrophism, his really important discovery of the divergent animal groups lay almost unnoticed.

It was Charles Lyell (1797–1875) who revived Hutton's ideas and was responsible for chasing the ghost of catastrophism at least to the back door of the house of science. Just when Cuvier was most famous and catastrophism was at its peak of influence, Lyell published his famous *Principles of Geology* (1830).[92] It was a thoroughly uniformitarian approach to geology, in which Lyell showed how sediments are being laid down and how rocks are broken up by such agencies as rain, ice, and sandstorm. He knew that the remains of plants and animals from different geological periods were found together in the fossil record, so he rejected Cuvier's idea of successive catastrophes as an unscientific speculation.

Lyell made a major advance by claiming that the uniformitarian doctrine must apply to organic forms as well as to rocks, so that the process of extinction and the appearance of new species must be part of the ordinary, everyday workings of nature.[93] But how could species originate in a world governed by natural law? He addressed himself to the only theory of origin by natural causes known to him, the *transformisme* of Lamarck, making the first comprehensive summary of Lamarck's views in the English language and ending with a rejection of Lamarck's explanation for evolutionary change. Considering this to be a refutation of the notion of evolution itself, Lyell then proposed that life originated in a number of " foci of creation " scattered around the earth, and that new species had been " called into being " from time to time as needed. He simply failed to see that this was only a new form of special creationism, completely incompatible with his uniformi-

[92] The full title was *Principles of Geology, Being an Attempt to Explain the Former Changes of the Earth's Surface, by Reference to Causes Now in Operation*. There were three volumes in the first edition, appearing 1830–1833.

[93] Charles Lyell, *Principles of Geology*, II, pp. 20 f. It was this second volume that Darwin received on board the *Beagle* during his voyage around South America.

tarian principles, and for years he refused to accept the notion that new species originated by descent. This ambiguity in his thought was a clear indication of the basic conflict that we have seen running through the lives of almost all the great men of science, the conflict between a Newtonian vision of nature and a Biblical faith in God's purposes in Creation.

By the 1840's every essential fact for a theory of evolution was available to science. Some scientists accepted evolution, and many others remained neutral, while admitting that evolution was a genuine possibility. Still, scientific orthodoxy agreed with Cuvier — the evidence for evolution was exciting at first glance, but detailed study showed the theory to be on shaky ground. However, while scientists remained skeptical of evolution, European thought was being deeply affected by other notions of change and development. The study of history was turning into a search for origins, and German " higher critics " were beginning to interpret the Scriptures in light of their textual sources. German philosophers were entranced with the notion of " becoming." The nebular hypothesis fascinated astronomers. Comte and Marx proposed developmental theories of human society. In a host of ways, the notion of change was permeating Western culture, capturing the imagination of people in spite of scientists who still paid attention to the static details of nature. British society in particular became fascinated by the vague and sweeping hints of evolution that stirred up conversation across the land.

This helps us understand the startling popularity of Robert Chambers' anonymous work *Vestiges of the Natural History of Creation* (1844). It was the first English-language book in fifty years to spin out a detailed theory of geological and biological evolution, and it was addressed to just those nonacademic readers who were most intrigued by its topic and most open to its thesis. Chambers (1802–1871) was an Edinburgh publisher, a personification of that age when science was still young enough to be grasped by an intelligent layman with humane interests. As early as 1837, he had written to an American friend of his vision of a single law that would embrace all human knowledge,[94] and from

[94] Millhauser, *op. cit.*, p. 28.

1840 to 1844 he studied everything and everyone who could help
him in his quest: Comte, Laplace, Newton, Lamarck, Von Baer,
even the gossip of village women. Reflecting the century-long enthusiasm for speculative systems that could organize the immense
new areas of knowledge, he was intent on producing a grand synthesis of mid-nineteenth-century science, where law was replacing
miracle. He seized on the notion of " development " as his grand
interpretive principle, making his " law of progress " as pervasive
and fundamental in *Vestiges* as the law of gravitation had been
for Newton. So anxious was he to give a completely persuasive set
of facts in support of his theory that he uncritically swept up old
wives' tales right along with ideas from Galileo and Newton, a
move which gained him no friends among the detail-minded scientists of his day!

Chambers was fully aware of the social consequences of writing
such a book, and he carefully kept his connection with it secret;
even the manuscript was penned by his wife, lest his handwriting
be recognized. He then mailed the manuscript to a friend in Manchester, who in turn submitted it to the publisher. In six months
it went through four editions, and there were six more during the
next ten years, by which time the book had run its course. Altogether some 23,750 copies reached the public.[95]

Chambers had two purposes in writing his book. He wanted to
rescue evolutionary theory from its grim association with the for-
eign name of Lamarck by giving it a firmer grounding than Lamarck had provided, and he wanted to show how evolution exemplified what he believed was a single grand law of progress governing the entire universe. He began with the widely accepted
nebular hypothesis, claiming that bodies in space were being
formed from a " universal fire-mist." Moving on to geology, he
found the law of progress behind the ascending fossil series. In
his section on biology he linked his theory to the Deist view of
God, claiming that creation occurred by law and not by divine
decree, but this left him with the problem of explaining the origins of life by purely natural means. The only way he saw to avoid
the notion of successive divine creations was to adopt the idea of

[95] *Ibid.*, p. 77.

spontaneous generation, but unfortunately his efforts to support belief in spontaneous generation far outran the evidence that his scientific critics knew so well, and they were quick to object.[96]

Finally, Chambers gave his " proofs " of evolution, pointing to the fossil series, to analogies of forms and functions, to embryological recapitulation, and to rudimentary and vestigial organs. When it came to *how* variations occurred, he followed the rather Lamarckian path marked out by Geoffroy Saint-Hilaire, proposing that variations took place by large saltatory jumps. Then, in line with his intention to show how all kinds of facts were illuminated by his " law of progress," he tried to show that evolution explained man's rise from savagery to civilization.

We may characterize Chambers' book as a kind of revised progressionism with Huttonian and Lamarckian principles, but its universe was still the old Deist universe of Design, constructed on shadowy faith in God's purposes; miracles of special creation were excluded only because God had ordained everything in the beginning. Yet the world of *Vestiges* was one where man was an animal and an animal was a machine, and where there was no place for a personal and living God. Chambers sensed that his theory had ruled God out of nature, and like Kant he was forced to postulate another realm somewhere beyond nature as the anchor for man's faith in God. In this vein he wrote: " It may be that . . . there is a system of Mercy and Grace behind the screen of nature, which is to make up for all casualties endured. . . . It is necessary to suppose that the present system is but a part of the whole, a stage in a Great Progress, and that Redress is in reserve." [97] Chambers' theory was both mechanistic and religious, admirably suited to a Victorian age that could believe simultaneously in starvation wages and a religion of love.

The reaction was electric. Many scientists voiced scholarly resentment of speculation that trespassed on their specialty, heaping scorn on Chambers for his errors in detail. Thomas Huxley was among the most vitriolic. Defenders of the faith lashed out at Chambers' " atheistic tendencies," one response being that of the *English Review*, which called evolution " one of the most mon-

---

[96] *Ibid.*, p. 93.   [97] Cited in *ibid.*, p. 113.

strous — we might add, one of the most disgusting — theories,
which ever insulted the dignity of man, or outraged the sacredness
of revelation." [98] A host of pamphleteers attacked the book, de-
nominational reviewers lambasted it, and ministers denounced it
from the pulpit; Bishop Wilberforce remarked that science was
only puffed up with pride when it began to conflict with religion.[99]
Vestiges was even attacked by Adam Sedgwick, a sort of " Grand
Old Man " of British geology, with whom Charles Darwin had
made a field trip in his youth. In 1844 his review appeared in the
influential *Edinburgh Review,* prompting Chambers to reply with
a second volume,[100] in which he urged his readers not to be distracted by minor errors in his argument. Even though half his examples might be wrong, he noted, nature still is a domain of law.

Vestiges was translated twice into German, and the first translator entitled his edition *Vestiges of Divinity,*[101] erroneously assuming it to be further evidence for natural theology. However,
the second translator was Carl Vogt, a radical freethinker who
had lost his position as professor at Giessen because of involve-
ment in the unsuccessful revolution of 1848. In the preface to his
translation, he combined his bitterness with an acute sensitivity to
the real implications of Chambers' views: " To the Constitutional
Party of Germany, whose influence should soon be limited to the
innocent reading of innocent books, I recommend this book in all
good will. It will find here a constitutional Englishman who constructed a constitutional God, who at first made laws as an auto-
crat but then of His own accord gave up autocracy, and, without
direct influence on the governed, allowed law to rule in His stead.
A splendid example for princes! " [102] Vogt opposed the idea of evo-

[98] *Ibid.,* p. 135.

[99] *Ibid.,* p. 136.

[100] Chambers, *Explanations, by the author of Vestiges of the Natural
History of Creation.*

[101] A. Seubert, *Spuren der Gottheit* (1846).

[102] Carl Vogt, *Natürliche Geschichte der Schöpfung des Weltalls, der
Erde und der auf ihr befindlichen Organismen, begründet auf die durch
die Wissenschaft errungenen Thatsachen,* aus dem Englischen nach der
sechsten Auflage (Braunschweig: Viewig, 1851), cited in Owsei Temkin,
" The Idea of Descent in Post-Romantic German Biology, 1848–1858,"
Forerunners of Darwin, p. 346.

lution at the time, but in later years he became a great disciple of Darwin, earning the doubtfully complimentary title of " Monkey Vogt." [103]

Chambers' work reached a wide audience also through the medium of literature, and one English historian comments, " *The Vestiges of Creation* was . . . a national sensation; translated into golden verses by Tennyson, evolution almost became a national creed." [104] One of the earliest literary reflections of Chambers' thought is to be found in Disraeli's *Tancred* (1847), where the hero is saved from a disastrous marriage to a silly young woman when he hears her gush, " You must read the ' Revelations '; it is all explained. But what is most interesting, is the way in which man has been developed. You know, all is development. The principle is perpetually going on. First, there was nothing, then there was something; then, I forget the next, I think there were shells, then fishes; then we came, let me see did we come next? Never mind that; we came at last. And the next change there will be something very superior to us, something with wings. Ah! that's it; we were fishes, and I believe we shall be crows." [105] Disraeli was no evolutionist! Also on the Continent, Schopenhauer read *Vestiges* in English and discussed it in his *Parerga und Paralipomena*,[106] chiding Chambers for equating everything metaphysical with Biblical theism and then trying to escape it by overstressing the purely physical.

It is impossible to overestimate the importance of Chambers' work in preparing the British public for Darwin. Because of the intense public discussion of *Vestiges*, most British clergymen had ample time to reflect over the real implications of evolutionary thought before Darwin published his work, and this very likely saved Darwin from an explosive and potentially disastrous reception. Chambers' book raised the issues, forced critics to take evo-

[103] Temkin, *loc. cit.*, p. 345.

[104] G. M. Young, ed., *Early Victorian England, 1830–1865* (Oxford University Press, 1934), II, p. 477. The themes of *Vestiges* appear in Tennyson's *In Memoriam*.

[105] Benjamin Disraeli, *Tancred* (John Lane, 1905 [1847]), p. 149.

[106] Arthur Schopenhauer, *Parerga und Paralipomena*, in *Sämmtliche Werke*, hrsg. Julius Frauenstädt (Zweite Auflage; Leipzig: F. A. Brockhaus, 1877), VI, p. 164.

lution seriously, and made it possible for Darwin's work to be received in an air of relative calm; Darwin himself wrote, " In my opinion it has done excellent service in this country in calling attention to the subject, in removing prejudice, and in thus preparing the ground for the reception of analogous views." [107]

As a result of the public discussion of *Vestiges*, many liberal theologians in Britain already were sympathetic with Darwin by the time Bishop Wilberforce made his famous attack on evolution in 1860, but in America, Darwin had no prophet who could precede him and absorb the kind of blows that fell on Chambers in England. Emerson and Lincoln read *Vestiges*, and a few scientists (e.g., Le Conte, Agassiz, and Gray) saw what was in the wind, but American theology in general was delayed in coming to terms with Darwin's theory. However, that story lies in our next chapter, and we must turn now to Darwin himself.

8. Charles Darwin: Evolution Without Purpose

In the work of Charles Darwin (1809–1882), the long-cherished theological argument of Design fell crashing to the ground, an event that portended far-reaching changes in theology and somewhat dismayed even Darwin. As a youth he tried his hand at medical studies in Edinburgh, but finding them unappealing, he went down to Cambridge to study for the ministry. Already natural history was more intriguing to him than the prospect of life as a country parson, so he never sought ordination. Instead, with the help of a teacher and his uncle, Darwin was appointed to the H.M.S. *Beagle* as ship's naturalist for a voyage of exploration around the world. In December, 1831, young Darwin set off on the journey that shaped his future and that of those who lived after him.

In his *Autobiography* he writes of the years just before the voyage, " I did not then in the least doubt the strict and literal truth of every word of the Bible," [108] and his faith in the creation of

---

[107] This appears in the historical sketch prefaced to the third and later editions of *The Origin of Species*.

[108] Francis Darwin, ed., *The Life and Letters of Charles Darwin*, I, p. 39. Hereafter this work will be cited as *LLCD*.

eternally fixed species was reflected by his great liking for Milton's *Paradise Lost*.[109] We have mentioned his enthusiasm for Paley's *Natural Theology*,[110] and it seems fair to say that Darwin began his duties as naturalist on the *Beagle* with an almost unquestioned faith in the traditional theological argument of Design. But Darwin also took along with him the first volume of Lyell's *Principles of Geology*, which persuaded him immediately that the uniformitarian principle should be applied to what he saw on his geological studies in South America.

He spent almost five fruitful years on the voyage, pouring into his notebooks a welter of facts which pressed him ever harder toward belief in the variability of species. In South America, for example, he found great armor-clad fossil animals resembling European armadillos; did their resemblance indicate common descent and variation? Finally in 1835, the *Beagle* reached the Galápagos Islands, situated on the Equator five hundred miles off the western coast of South America. As Darwin collected his specimens, he realized that the plants and animals on this barren volcanic archipelago differed from island to island; the inhabitants could even identify the huge Galápagos tortoises by the island of their origin. And the finches — why did they vary so much, if they had been created on the spot as one species? Darwin wondered what " center of creation " they belonged to, and he realized that the usual distinction between species and variety was vague and arbitrary.[111] He was beginning to realize that the traditional notion of creation left many facts unrelated, but he had not yet arrived at the belief in evolution, so he collected the finches indiscriminately, not bothering to separate them by island in a

109 He wrote, " In my excursions during the voyage of the *Beagle*, when I could take only a single volume, I always chose Milton." *LLCD*, I, p. 57.

110 At Cambridge, Darwin was required to study Paley, whose premises he assumed to be correct and whose argument delighted him as much as that of Euclid. He memorized the evidences almost word for word. *LLCD*, I, p. 41.

111 Charles Darwin, *The Origin of Species* (London: John Murray, 1859), p. 48. Hereafter this work will be cited as *OS*. For an excellent discussion of these birds, see David Lack, *Darwin's Finches: An Essay on the General Biological Theory of Evolution* (Harper Torchbooks, Harper & Brothers, 1961).

way which would have aided his future studies.[112]

It was the weight of his accumulated evidence which finally drove him to conclude that species varied, and his primary reason for writing *The Origin of Species* was to present his evidence.[113] Of course, Darwin knew that his grandfather and others had advanced theories of evolution, but we miss the point of his career if we rank him with philosophical or theoretical evolutionists. While he was formulating his own ideas, he had not read widely in the already-existing literature about evolution, and he was surprised when colleagues later pointed out how his own ideas had been anticipated by others.[114] Apparently he never realized that Lamarck had done yeoman service in applying Newtonian principles to biology, and he had not read Buffon at all.[115] Darwin's writing bore the stamp of his predecessors' thought, but his own work was remarkably free from the speculative style; it was, above all, a patient and comprehensive accumulation of facts, and only secondarily did he become interested in giving an *explanation* for his facts.

Returning from the voyage in October, 1836, he immediately set about the task of ordering his notes, leading up to the publication of his *Journal of Researches*. He became more and more interested in the question of variability, and after detailed studies of the changes in domesticated animals, he concluded that *selec-*

[112] Charles Darwin, *Journal of Researches Into the Geology and Natural History of the Various Countries Visited During the Voyage of H.M.S. Beagle Round the World* (London: Henry Colburn, 1839; new ed., D. Appleton & Company, 1897), p. 395.

[113] The opening sentences of *OS* emphasize this: "When on board H.M.S. *Beagle*, as naturalist, *I was much struck with certain facts* in the distribution of the inhabitants of South America, and in the geological relations of the present to the past inhabitants of that continent. *These facts seemed to me to throw some light on the origin of species* — that mystery of mysteries, as it has been called by one of our greatest philosophers." *OS*, p. 1, italics mine.

[114] After reading William Ogle's new translation of Aristotle's *On the Parts of Animals* in 1882, Darwin wrote to Ogle, "I had a high notion of Aristotle's merits, but I had not the most remote notion what a wonderful man he was. Linnaeus and Cuvier have been my two gods, though in different ways, but they were mere schoolboys to old Aristotle." *LLCD*, II, p. 427.

[115] *LLCD*, II, p. 228.

tion was the principle of change. He seems to have reached this viewpoint in 1837 or 1838,[116] and when he read Malthus' *Essay on Population* in October, 1838, he realized that the winnowing effect of overpopulation was just the factor he sought in applying selection in nature.

Darwin was extremely hesitant to submit his views prematurely to the scrutiny of other naturalists, and he rejected the continued urgings of his friends to publish. Year after year he delayed, convinced that only overwhelming evidence would persuade his scientific acquaintances that species varied. His great work would have been delayed even longer, were it not for the impulse provided by Alfred Russel Wallace (1823–1913), a young naturalist who arrived at a theory identical with Darwin's. Wallace had left in 1854 for eight years of exploration in Malaya, already familiar with the notorious *Vestiges*, and in 1855 he sent back a paper discussing the origin of species; this came to Darwin's attention.[117] Finally in 1858, during the height of a malarial fever, the answer to his questions about species variation flashed into Wallace's mind — it was in Malthus' essay, which he had read some years earlier. In two days he had sent off to Darwin an essay containing his new vision,[118] along with the request that Darwin forward it to Lyell for his consideration. Darwin was stunned, knowing that publication of Wallace's essay might mean that his own long years of patient toil would not be recognized. Nevertheless, he resolved to have Wallace's paper presented. Only at the insistence of Lyell and Joseph Hooker did he reluctantly submit a companion piece of his own, a short extract of the book on which he was laboring,[119]

[116] *LLCD*, I, p. 68.

[117] It was entitled, "The Law which has regulated the Introduction of New Species," *Annals and Magazine of Natural History*, 1855, pp. 185 f. The essay concluded, "Every species has come into existence coincident in both time and space with a pre-existing closely allied species." Cited in Bert James Loewenberg, *Darwin, Wallace and the Theory of Natural Selection, including the Linnean Society Papers* (Arlington Books, 1959), p. 19.

[118] "On the Tendency of Varieties to Depart Indefinitely from the Original Type."

[119] Its title was "Extract from an unpublished Work on Species by C. Darwin, Esq., Consisting of a portion of a Chapter entitled, 'On the Variation of Organic Beings in a state of Nature; on the Natural Means of

and the two were read jointly to the Linnaean Society of London in July, 1858. Both Darwin and Wallace had struck on the principle of natural selection as an explanation for evolution, and we can have only the highest regard for Wallace's continual willingness to give Darwin almost all the credit for the research that established the theory.

In 1859, Darwin published his book, still in the form of an abstract of the larger work which he had envisioned. Its full title was *On the Origin of Species by Means of Natural Selection, or the Preservation of Favoured Races in the Struggle for Life,* and the first edition of 1,250 copies was sold out on the day of publication.[120] The argument of the book began with two very important assumptions: (*a*) that the offspring of all living creatures tend to vary from their parents, and (*b*) that variations of all kinds may be inherited. Darwin had observed that breeders selected the best specimens to be the parents of each succeeding generation, so that by this process of " artificial selection " new varieties appeared. As an analogy he coined the term " natural selection " to indicate that over a vast period of time nature had been " selecting " plants and animals too. The accumulated inheritance of imperceptible favorable variations would, over the course of millions of years, account for the appearance of completely new forms of life. Carrying the analogy further, Darwin observed that the stock breeder culled unfit animals from his herd at breeding time; nature, he said, also removed its " unfit " during the " struggle for existence."

He assumed that animals tended to increase in numbers geometrically, outstripping the means of survival, so that the press of numbers inevitably produced a struggle for survival. In this situation, the balance could be tipped by even the tiniest advantage that one kind of creature might have over its neighbors, and it was the survival power of such variations that formed the basis of

---

Selection; on the Comparison of Domestic Races and true Species.' " Cited in Loewenberg, *op. cit.,* p. 32.

[120] *LLCD,* I, p. 71. Darwin attributed much of its initial success to the fact that Wallace's discovery forced him to hurry into print and thereby to keep *The Origin* of " moderate size." Its text ran to 490 pages.

natural selection. Here Darwin used the word " fitness " in a precise way to indicate a state of being sufficiently well adapted to the conditions of life so that the species continued to maintain itself by reproduction. Creatures that died or otherwise failed to reproduce their kind were " unfit," and it was a serious distortion when later writers almost equated " fitness " with " strength."

When Darwin began his search for an explanation of variability, he of course looked for the kind of causes that nineteenth-century Newtonian science recognized. This meant a search for efficient causes, purely natural and nonpurposive. In short, what he looked for was a way of fusing the anti-Aristotelian body of scientific thought with his own new belief in evolution. Evolution was a *fact*, of that he was persuaded, and it was to be *explained* without the concept of purpose. A few years later he wrote, " I had two distinct objects in view. First, to show that species had not been separately created, and secondly, that natural selection had been the chief agent of change, though largely aided by the inherited effects of habit, and slightly by the direct action of the surrounding conditions." [121] These two objects were logically distinct, as Darwin himself recognized, but it proved difficult in practice to keep them separate in his work. Darwin had become convinced of evolution about 1837, and the next twenty years were occupied both with the search for an explanation and the quest for further facts; therefore, it may not be surprising that in his book Darwin did not always distinguish clearly between the *fact* of variation and his theory of its *causes*.

This may help explain why Darwin was always concerned and a bit puzzled that certain of his critics focused their attack on his explanatory idea of natural selection, for he was personally much more concerned to establish the *fact* of evolution than to defend the idea of natural selection as its cause.[122] His final introductory sentence to *The Origin of Species* expressed his own position clearly: " I am convinced that Natural Selection has been the main

[121] Charles Darwin, *The Descent of Man and Selection in Relation to Sex* (D. Appleton & Company, 1871), I, p. 146.

[122] In 1863 he wrote to Asa Gray, " Personally, of course, I care much about Natural Selection; but that seems to me utterly unimportant compared to the question of Creation or Modification." *LLCD*, II, p. 163.

but not exclusive means of modification." [123] However, as he noted in subsequent editions, some passages caused his readers to believe he looked on natural selection " as an active power of Deity." [124] He insisted that he had only personified natural selection in a metaphorical sense, never intending to imply that it *induced* variation, and he pointed to his original definition: " This preservation of favourable variations and the rejection of injurious variations, I call Natural Selection." [125] Variations must first be given by nature, he insisted,[126] and only then can they be selected; speculation about the ultimate causes of variation was outside the scope of his theory of natural selection. Nevertheless, the title of his book indicated the importance of natural selection in his theory, and though he later believed he had attributed too much to it,[127] there can be little doubt that Darwin's style did encourage those who later made natural selection and the struggle for existence into metaphysical principles, crowning them king in place of the God whom they seemed to depose.

The Origin of Species represented the final stage in the " mechanizing " of biology, a last skirmish in the long advance of Newtonian science against the retreating Aristotelian vision to which the Biblical doctrine of creation had been linked; so when Darwin went considerably beyond Lyell by extending the uniformitarian principle to the origin of species, he knew that the notion of evolution would be received unfavorably by many.[128] Besides, he realized that his own explanation for evolution could not be proved conclusively. Consequently, he devoted a large portion of his book to a sympathetic discussion of the possible objections to his theory, admitting that some of them were forceful and persuasive.

[123] *OS*, p. 6.
[124] *OS* (6th ed., Doubleday & Company, Inc.; Dolphin Books n.d. [1872]), p. 89. They had noticed such passages as this on p. 42 of the first edition: " The accumulative action of Selection . . . is by far the predominant Power."
[125] *OS*, p. 81.
[126] *OS*, pp. 38 f.
[127] Charles Darwin, *The Descent of Man*, I, p. 91.
[128] Darwin used the word " evolution " only rarely, and I find it only once even in the sixth edition of *OS*, p. 472. He was accustomed to speak of " variability of species."

Most damaging, he conceded, was the scarcity of intermediate forms in the fossil record. Here he found support in Lyell, who had recognized that the fossil record was only fragmentary; the mere absence of intermediate forms, therefore, did not prove they had never existed.

At the point where the evidence was weakest, i.e., in demonstrating transitional stages by which the supposed organic changes had occurred, Darwin quite frankly appealed to his readers' faith in the general explanatory powers of his theory. Writing of the almost overwhelming difficulty of imagining that the eye had been produced by natural selection, he ventured that the reader, " if he find on finishing this treatise that large bodies of facts, otherwise inexplicable, can be explained by the theory of descent, ought not to hesitate to go further, and to admit that a structure even as perfect as the eye of an eagle might be formed by natural selection, although in this case he does not know any of the transitional grades. His reason ought to conquer his imagination; though I have felt the difficulty far too keenly to be surprised at any degree of hesitation in extending the principle of natural selection to such startling lengths." [129]

In spite of serious gaps in evidence, Darwin was completely persuaded that his theory accounted for a host of facts that the rival theory of creation left as utterly arbitrary, facts such as the homologies of animal forms, the sequence of fossils, the difference between Old World and New World animals, the varieties of creatures on islands, and the persistence of vestigial organs. Undoubtedly, the strongest argument for Darwin's theory was that in spite of large gaps in evidence, it could explain coherently a number of facts that remained arbitrary and unrelated on any other theory. Indeed, any other interpretation of the data seemed almost incredible to most scientists after they read Darwin.

In a classic summary of the method of scientific progress, he wrote in later editions, " It can hardly be supposed that a false theory would explain in so satisfactory a manner as does the theory of natural selection, the several large classes of facts above specified. It has recently been objected that this is an unsafe method of arguing; but it is a method used in judging of the common events

[129] *OS*, p. 188.

of life, and has often been used by the greatest natural philosophers. The undulatory theory of light has thus been arrived at; and the belief in the revolution of the earth on its own axis was until lately supported by hardly any direct evidence. . . . Although I am fully convinced of the truth of the views given in this volume under the form of an abstract, I by no means expect to convince experienced naturalists whose minds are stocked with a multitude of facts all viewed, during a long course of years, from a point of view directly opposite to mine. . . . Any one whose disposition leads him to attach more weight to unexplained difficulties than to explanation of a certain number of facts will certainly reject the theory." [130]

In the long run, Darwin's views of inheritance proved to be the most serious defect in his theory. He had always held the Lamarckian notion that environment had some measure of influence in stimulating variation,[131] and he believed that characteristics acquired by use can be inheritable; [132] in these views he merely reflected the commonsense attitude of breeders and field naturalists of his day. But his great concern was to show how " the whole organization becomes in some degree plastic," [133] and he believed that inheritance was a sort of blending of parental characteristics, much as one may blend blue paint and yellow paint to produce green.

Until the Mendelian theory of particulate inheritance was rediscovered, Darwin's theory was embarrassed by a criticism made in 1867 by Fleeming Jenkin. Jenkin observed that on Darwin's theory of inheritance any favorable new variation would soon be swamped out by continued backcrossing with the other animals of its species which did not share the variation.[134] In the final edition of *The Origin of Species* (1872), Darwin admitted the weight

[130] *OS* (6th ed.), pp. 470 f.

[131] For example, " We have reason to believe . . . that a change in the conditions of life, by specially acting on the reproductive system, causes or increases variability." *OS*, p. 82.

[132] For example, " I think there can be little doubt that use in our domestic animals strengthens and enlarges certain parts, and disuse diminishes them; and that such modifications are inherited." *OS*, p. 134.

[133] *OS*, p. 80.

[134] His essay was " The Origin of Species," *North British Review*, Vol. 46 (1867), pp. 149–171.

of this objection, and he could only suggest that " the tendency to vary in the same manner has often been so strong that all the individuals of the same species have been similarly modified without the aid of any form of selection." [135] Here he was drawing back very close to the older idea that variations happened by Design.

He was so troubled by the problems of genetics that he finally proposed a genetical theory of his own, calling it " pangenesis." [136] On this theory the germ cells each contained tiny " gemmules," particles of the body cells that were brought to them in the bloodstream. In this way, acquired changes in muscular strength or the length of an animal's hair could find their way directly into the germ cells, allowing the acquired variations to be inherited by the next generation. This was a very old idea, and even Darwin was not enthusiastic about it.[137] No doubt the notion of pangenesis slowed acceptance of his theory, but at the same time it did serve to stimulate the research in genetics that led to rediscovery of Mendel's work. In any case it did not detract greatly from Darwin's main point: animal species were descended from each other, and *some* natural causes must be invoked to replace the old argument that God had designed the world and its creatures.

Darwin always puzzled over the possible role of God in the world, and we have seen that he took the fact of variation as a given, the ultimate causes of which did not affect the substance of his argument. In the same way he took the existence of life as a given, explicitly disclaiming that his theory had anything to do with the origin of life.[138] However, in the last sentence of the book, he assumed that life had been " originally breathed into a

135 *OS* (6th ed.), p. 99.

136 This was presented near the end of *Variation in Animals and Plants Under Domestication* (1868).

137 He wrote to G. Bentham, " I am not at all surprised that you cannot digest pangenesis; it is enough to give anyone indigestion; but to my mind the idea has been an immense relief, as I could not endure to keep so many large classes of facts all floating loose in my mind without some thread of connection to tie them together in a tangible way." Francis Darwin and A. C. Seward, *More Letters of Charles Darwin* (D. Appleton & Company, 1903), II, p. 371.

138 *OS*, p. 207.

few forms or into one," [139] and in later editions he modified this
sentence to read, " originally breathed *by the Creator* into a few
forms or into one." [140] In 1860 he wondered further whether God
might have designed the laws of nature in such a way that evolution took place with the details " left to the working out of what
we may call chance." [141] But it was obvious that, whatever God's
relation to nature, Darwin's explanation of evolution did not allow God any part since the first " few forms or one." Whatever
the causes for variation might turn out to be, they would be natural and not supernatural or purposive.[142]

As Darwin had anticipated, the chief initial opposition to *The
Origin of Species* came not from theologians but from scientists.
Sir Richard Owen, England's leading anatomist, reviewed the book
for the *Edinburgh Review* in May, 1860, rejecting Darwin's theory
in favor of his own version of continued separate creations. Likewise, the Swiss paleontologist Pictet voiced the doubts of many
scientists in his March, 1860, review — Darwin, he said, went too
far beyond the available evidence.[143] Darwin later wrote that prior
to publication of *The Origin of Species* he had never conversed
with a naturalist who doubted the fixity of species,[144] and even
Huxley admitted that in 1860 Darwin's scientific supporters " were
numerically quite insignificant." [145] In spite of these humble beginnings, however, Darwin's ideas rapidly won the support of scientists everywhere. Huxley's enthusiastic interest led to the publi-

[139] *OS*, p. 490.

[140] *OS* (6th ed.), p. 478, italics mine.

[141] *LLCD*, II, p. 105.

[142] Writing to Asa Gray in 1861, he expressed his own sensitivity to the
problem of reconciling his Newtonian vision with belief in design: "I
must think that it is illogical to suppose that the variations which natural
selection preserves for the good of any being have been designed. But
I know that I am in the same sort of muddle (as I have said before) as
all the world seems to be in with respect to free will, yet with everything
supposed to have been foreseen or pre-ordained." *LLCD*, II, p. 170.

[143] Asa Gray, " Darwin and his Reviewers," *Atlantic Monthly* (October, 1860), reprinted as part of *Natural Selection not Inconsistent with
Natural Theology* (1861) and in *Darwiniana: Essays and Reviews Pertaining to Darwinism* (D. Appleton & Company, 1876), pp. 106, 136.

[144] *LLCD*, I, p. 71.

[145] *LLCD*, I, p. 540.

cation of his own *Zoological Evidences as to Man's Place in Nature* (1863), and in the same year Lyell adopted Darwin's viewpoint in *The Geological Evidences of the Antiquity of Man.* Lyell had consistently rejected the idea of evolution during a long and brilliant career, and undoubtedly his " conversion " hastened the acceptance of Darwin's ideas by many churchmen.

Darwin decided very early that human beings had evolved,[146] but in *The Origin of Species* he purposely avoided discussing man. He said only: " In the future I see open fields for far more important researches. . . . Much light will be thrown on the origin of man and his history." [147] Finally in *The Descent of Man* (1871), he took the inevitable step of applying his principle of natural selection directly to the species *Homo sapiens.* It was clear that Darwin was trying to explain the origins of man, his culture, and his spirit in terms of the same nonpurposive Newtonian vision that had already banished God from scientific thought.

[146] He wrote, " As soon as I had become, in the year 1837 or 1838, convinced that species were mutable productions, I could not avoid the belief that man must come under the same rule." *LLCD,* I, pp. 75 f.

[147] *OS* (6th ed.), p. 477.

II

THEOLOGY IN THE DARWINIAN AGE

1. The Twofold Threat of Darwinian Science

In the first chapter we tried to show that Darwin's tremendous impact on his world can be traced to the fact that his work combined the *notion* of evolution with a *nonpurposive explanation* of it. This meant that Darwinian science appeared to many Christians as a two-headed monster, each head breathing fire and threatening religious faith. In the first place, Darwin represented all those movements which were beginning to hint strongly at a world of change. Men always have recognized intuitions of change vying for first place with their intuitions of permanence at the heart of things, but traditional Christian faith had reconciled the two by speaking of an unchanging God governing a fundamentally unchanging world. Now Darwin's theory of evolution appeared, at a time when Western culture was already on its frantic rush toward the twentieth century, when technological and political changes were already reshaping the face of the planet into forms scarcely conceivable a century earlier, and when the stable doctrines of centuries were being swept away in the twinkling of an eye. How was the church to face such a world of changing ideas, changing values, changing understandings of its own place in the world? In the second place, Darwin represented the flower of that long tradition of Newtonian science that now was explaining the whole natural world and denying to it any purposiveness. What was to become of Biblical faith that the world was God's purposeful creation, and that man's primary responsibility was to order his life in terms of God's purposes? Either side of the Darwinian challenge would have posed problem enough for the church, but the tides of history had left both to be met by a single generation.

Darwinism struck at the roots of traditional doctrine in several related ways, all of which were frightening to a host of Christians raised to a literal faith in the Bible and for whom Paley's familiar argument about the watchmaker and his watch was the favorite illustration of the nature, purpose, and method of the creator. Perhaps the most fundamental threat, the one sensed earliest and most acutely by those whose attitudes led eventually to fundamentalism, was the very real possibility that a wave of evolutionary ideas would sweep away all the doctrinal foundations of Christian faith and leave the church awash in a shifting quicksand of relativism and atheism. In the broadest sense, Darwin's hypothesis raised doubts about the accuracy of the entire Bible, adding fuel to the fires already kindled by German textual critics. It struck specifically at the doctrine of creation, utterly overthrowing Paley's argument that creaturely adaptations were the reflection of divine design, and implying that God's original act of creation was a very modest affair indeed. Besides this, it jeopardized belief in original sin and man's need for redemption by proposing that human history began with man's rise from his animal ancestors instead of his fall from an original state of perfection.

What would become of these doctrines and of the faith in God that they represented? People all across the church were shocked into the realization that the same human scientific genius which already had trained telescopes on the mysterious reaches of space could now turn them around, as it were, so that God appeared only as a tiny figure at the other end, shadowy and scarcely impressive. The intellectual problem facing the church was immense: to link its Biblical faith in God and his purposes to an evolutionary view of a changing world, after long centuries in which this faith had been fused to the Aristotelian view of nature that nearly all of science had now abandoned.

No wonder, then, that theologians and religiously-minded scientists responded with a kaleidoscope of new theologies, and that the task is not yet finished. There have been about as many solutions as there are kinds of men — slow and tentative, fearful and defensive, joyous and hopeful — but all have sprung out of a struggle to bring faith in God's purposes into some tolerable relationship to the astonishing new Darwinian world. Some people have been able to salvage their faith in purposiveness only by utterly rejecting Darwinism and the whole historical consciousness that it represented. Some have tried bravely to see purposiveness in the Darwinian world or to anchor their faith in some ethereal realm which the evolutionary tide could not reach. Some have embraced evolution with a passion, explaining their traditional belief in God as an outmoded stage of evolution or making evolution into a new revelation for which God becomes merely the end point, the Omega but not the Alpha.

There have been at least three identifiable types of theological response to Darwinism in Europe and America, each reflecting a different theological tradition and style. It goes without saying that the types shade off into each other and that they have found varying emphasis in the lives and thought of individual men, but they are at least distinct enough to provide a framework for our discussion in the following pages.[1] The first kind of response was that shaped by traditional rational supernaturalistic orthodoxy and whose proponents remained fairly steadily in this tradition despite using a variety of weapons as they faced the Darwinian threat. The second was made by men who in varying ways were shaped by romantic liberalism and who tended to appeal to intuition and religious experience as their haven. The third was a reaction in terms of scientific modernism, where the dominant note was an attempt to recast traditional doctrines in a scientific and evolutionary mold. Attention to these three types of response will aid us in understanding the rather different relationships between Darwinian science and theology that are characteristic of Britain,

---

[1] These types are suggested by Sidney E. Mead in *The Lively Experiment: The Shaping of Christianity in America* (Harper & Row, Publishers, Inc., 1963), pp. 171–173. In more limited form they were discussed by Edwin Ewart Aubrey, "Religious Bearings of the Modern Scientific Movement," in *Environmental Factors in Christian History*, ed. by John Thomas McNeill, Matthew Spinka, and Harold R. Willoughby (The University of Chicago Press, 1939), pp. 368–370.

Germany, France, and America.

In order that the present chapter may have some obvious sense of leading up to later chapters, it seems wise to consider the theological responses to Darwinian science rather explicitly in the light of a distinction that will be centrally important in our effort to interpret evolutionary theory and the doctrine of creation with Whitehead's cosmology. The distinction involved is between subject and object, between subjective and objective categories. Already we have discussed the coming of modern science implicitly in these terms as a brilliant generalization of the objective aspects of nature known by sense perception (e.g., position and velocity) and a gradual elimination of subjective categories (e.g., purpose, value, feeling, intelligence) from the purview of scientific thought. If we attempt to carry this distinction over into our present discussion, focusing on the second head of our " two-headed Darwinian monster " for the moment, we must ask several questions of the men whose theological responses we study:

a. What relative weight did they give to subjective and objective categories as clues for interpreting reality?

b. Did they envision the reality of subjective categories as *in* nature or *apart from* nature? The former, we shall see, was typical of Britain; the latter, of the Kantian tradition in Germany.

c. If they believed subjective categories to be a real aspect of nature, how did they face the problem of reconciling this belief with the Newtonian doctrine that nature embodies only objective categories?

2. The Great Debate in Europe: Britain, Germany, and France

In 1855 the foundation stone was laid for the Oxford Museum of Science, with the Professor of Medicine delivering a prayer for the unity of science and religion.[2] In a very real sense this has remained the prayer of British theology, but only five years later the hoped-for unity was given a rude shock when the British Asso-

---

[2] H. M. and D. Vernon, *History of the Oxford Museum* (1909), cited in David Lack, *Evolutionary Theory and Christian Belief* (London: Methuen & Company, Ltd., 1961), p. 11.

ciation for the Advancement of Science met at the museum and Bishop Samuel Wilberforce engaged T. H. Huxley in their famous debate on evolution. Huxley was pressed into attending the session only at the last minute by Robert Chambers, anonymous author of *Vestiges*, but the Bishop concluded his attack on evolution by asking Huxley rather jokingly and yet half seriously whether he would trace his ancestry back to the apes via his grandmother's side or via his grandfather's side. Huxley murmured, " The Lord hath delivered him into my hands," [3] and the exchange between evolutionists and the church was fairly begun.

The Oxford encounter of 1860 was typical of the rather flamboyant manner in which a number of Darwin's theological foes took aim at his hypothesis of evolution, but Huxley's lifetime effort to ridicule his opponents exaggerates the role of ultraconservatives in the British church. There were from the very beginning a number of noted churchmen who gave Darwin's claims a fair and sympathetic hearing; men like Hort, Kingsley, and Temple were representative of this openness.[4] Bishop Temple, for example, believed rather optimistically that Darwinism " tended to make the Creation more wonderful than ever. For it shows not a number of isolated creations, but all creation knit together into a complete whole." [5] Even Bishop Wilberforce's initial hostility was tempered by a conciliatory tone when he attacked *The Origin of Species* in the *Quarterly Review* of July, 1860. He accepted the notion of natural selection but argued that it could not account for man's peculiar moral and spiritual attributes. Still, he maintained,

[3] Leonard Huxley, *Life and Letters of Thomas Henry Huxley* (London: The Macmillan Company, 1900), I, pp. 181, 188.

[4] Hort wrote to Westcott in March, 1860: " Have you read Darwin? . . . In spite of difficulties, I am inclined to think it unanswerable. In any case it is a treat to read such a book." *Life and Letters of F. J. A. Hort*, I, p. 414, cited in L. E. Elliott-Binns, *Religion in the Victorian Age* (London: Lutterworth Press, 1936), p. 167. In 1863, Charles Kingsley wrote, " Darwin is conquering everywhere, and rushing in like a flood, by the mere force of truth and fact." *The Works of Charles Kingsley: Letters and Memories*, ed. by his wife (The Co-operative Publication Society, 1899), II, p. 175.

[5] Ernest G. Sandford, *Frederick Temple: An Appreciation* (London: Macmillan & Co., Ltd., 1907), p. 301, cited in L. E. Elliott-Binns, *English Thought, 1860–1900: The Theological Aspect* (London: Longmans, Green & Co., Ltd., 1956), p. 38.

to oppose established scientific facts would be "the ever-ready feebleminded dishonesty of lying for God." [6]

However, the stage was already set for a great battle between orthodox Christian theology and the Darwinian science which was the incarnation of modern learning, and it is not hard to see why the British discussion about evolution soon ceased to be merely a conversation regarding a particular scientific theory. Biologists of Huxley's style saw it as a struggle for freedom of scientific inquiry, opposed by a rigidly dogmatic church,[7] while many churchmen saw it as a mortal struggle to protect belief in man's relationship to God against a growing wave of materialistic atheism and nagging agnosticism, championed by Huxley. The intensity of the conflict reflected both the real importance of the issues and the fact that truth lay on both sides of the argument.

The very heat of the debate over evolution tended to obscure the fact that this was itself but one facet of a larger effort in British theology to deal with advances in secular learning right across the board. During the years that Darwin was laboring over *The Origin of Species*, British churchmen were struggling to respond to the new developments in historical and philosophical thought that seemed to pose such a serious threat to Christian faith. At Oxford and Cambridge, for example, the utilitarian philosophy of John Stuart Mill was spreading a doctrine of determinism, and Herbert Spencer's semipositivistic evolutionary speculations were widely influential. In Germany, textual criticism of the Bible was already quite advanced.[8] Altogether, the middle years of the nineteenth century were years of soul-searching reappraisal when

6 Samuel Wilberforce, "Review of *The Origin of Species*," *Quarterly Review* (July, 1860), in R. B. Johnson, ed., *Famous Reviews* (1914), pp. 279 f., cited in Lack, *Evolutionary Theory and Christian Belief*, p. 15.

7 This belief in a perpetual struggle between reason and faith was highlighted in John William Draper, *History of the Conflict of Religion and Science* (1873).

8 Before 1860 not many British scholars were familiar with the work of their German opposites. For one thing, translation of D. F. Strauss's 1835 *Leben Jesu* had dampened the enthusiasm of many conservative churchmen for German scholarship. Strauss had concluded that the Gospels held too little reliable historical material for a factual portrait of Jesus, and he turned instead to the "idea" of the God-man which was realized in humanity.

many thoughtful people in Britain were torn by the conflict between their own quest for intellectual integrity and the faith that they had inherited. Even before *The Origin of Species* appeared, the issues were so tender that friendships often hinged on one's attitude toward the new learning. This disturbing situation prompted a group of liberal churchmen and theologians to force a confrontation with the problem, trying to break down the silence with which more conservative minds had greeted it. Thus appeared in 1860 the volume *Essays and Reviews,* producing an uproar in ecclesiastical circles. Bishop Wilberforce spearheaded an outcry of protest against the " dangerous views " and " liberal tendencies " reflected by the authors, and the wave of controversy spread so widely that Darwin's book received relatively little attention until Wilberforce got around to taking up the cudgel against it at the Oxford Museum debate the following summer.[9]

During the generation after *The Origin of Species,* while churchmen tasted and evaluated the new theory with typically British caution, a sizable stream of opinion continued to echo Bishop Wilberforce's early reluctance to extend the Darwinian hypothesis fully to man. Writing in this vein, the Roman Catholic Canon Hedley gave with reservations what seems to be the first fairly sympathetic printed discussion of Darwinism by a British ecclesiastical spokesman. In the *Dublin Review* for 1871 he said, " It is not contrary to faith to suppose that all living things, *up to man exclusively,* were evolved by natural law." [10] A noted Roman Catholic anatomist, St. George Mivart, was one of Darwin's most outspoken critics; although he accepted evolution and natural selection, he insisted that the soul was " absolutely created in the strict and primary sense of the word . . . by a supernatural act." [11] Likewise, Darwin's friend Wallace steadily maintained that supernatural intervention was required to account for man's higher nature.

[9] Dean R. W. Church wrote of *The Origin of Species* in 1861, " The book, I have no doubt, would be the subject still of a great row, if there were not a much greater row going on about Essays and Reviews." *Life of Dean Church,* p. 188, cited in Elliott-Binns, *English Thought,* p. 35.
[10] Lack, *Evolutionary Theory and Christian Belief,* p. 20. Italics mine.
[11] *On the Genesis of Species* (1871), cited in Lack, *op. cit.,* p. 21.

Some such response to Darwin's vision was made by large numbers of people in Britain and elsewhere, and a very similar attitude is expressed in the present Roman Catholic viewpoint as it was formulated in 1950 by Pius XII in the encyclical *Humani generis:* "The Teaching of the Church leaves the doctrine of Evolution an open question, as long as it confines its speculations to the development, from other living matter already in existence, of the human body. (That souls are immediately created by God is a view which the Catholic faith imposes on us.)" [12] This viewpoint has had a continuing place in Anglican theology as well, beginning with Aubrey Moore's position that the human soul was a divine gift,[13] and now represented in the work of the Anglo-Catholic theologian E. L. Mascall, who believes that man's soul was joined to his body at some point in the evolutionary ascent of the body.[14] This position is an example of conservatism in the best sense of the word, making a really significant gesture toward recognizing modern scientific thought, while steadily affirming the long-cherished faith that man is God's creature. Thus it accepts the basic notions of change represented in the theory of evolution, while still rejecting the final implications of Darwin's nonpurposive explanation.

Ultimately, however, this posture can only be defensive, a halfway house of explanation, for it requires us to accept a bifurcated nature as the price of salvaging religious faith. The pro-

[12] "Humani generis. Concerning Certain False Opinions," in *The Papal Encyclicals in Their Historical Context,* ed. by Anne Fremantle (Mentor Books, New American Library of World Literature, Inc., 1956), p. 287. This was a more flexible position than that taken by the Vatican Council of 1870, which not only recognized papal infallibility but anathematized all those who said that "the doctrines of the Church can ever receive a sense in accordance with the progress of science other than that which the Church has understood and still understands." Most contemporary Roman Catholic theologians agree on three points: (*a*) The evolutionary process is somehow an expression of God's will; (*b*) this process concerns only man's body, his spirit being a direct divine creation; and (*c*) the human race stems from a primordial pair. For a good discussion of the Roman Catholic view, see Ian G. Barbour, *Issues in Science and Religion* (Prentice-Hall, Inc., 1966), pp. 373–376.

[13] Aubrey Moore, *Science and the Faith* (1889).

[14] E. L. Mascall, *The Importance of Being Human: Some Aspects of the Christian Doctrine of Man* (Columbia University Press, 1958), p. 28.

posal boils down to this: nature as it evolved before the advent of man (and by implication, nature as it exists now, apart from man) is empty of subjectivity, but in man subjectivity becomes a real part of nature. This emergence of subjectivity in man remains as an ultimate irrationality, and we must be content to believe that its arbitrary entrance into the world is understoood only by God. In fact, the notion that subjectivity entered nature by divine fiat late in the evolutionary game is a version of " special creationism," since it amounts to the claim that God first created *objectivity* as a world of material particles and natural law, and then, millions of years later, he created *subjectivity* in human souls. Consequently, the soul's position in nature never can be explained, and we are unable to understand how a man's personality is related to its underlying physiological system.

The British church, both Protestant and Catholic, inherited a long-standing interest in natural religion, for a century being very directly shaped by parson-naturalists, and this tradition helps explain the fact that all through the controversy over evolution there were many churchmen in Britain who were determined to maintain a reasonable faith by working theological tradition and evolutionary theory into some common framework of thought. In terms of our image of the " two-headed monster," it was an acceptance of the *fact* of evolution coupled with serious efforts to modify Darwin's *explanation* by appeal to an inherited faith in God and nature's purposiveness. The Kantian philosophy and its separate realms for science and religion just did not appeal to most British people, for there was always an undercurrent of confidence that in the long run *some* coherent rational synthesis of science and faith was possible.

It was along these lines that the first substantial settlement with Darwinian science was reached, being symbolized rather dramatically by events at the 1887 meeting of the British Association for the Advancement of Science.[15] There the Bishops of Carlisle, Bed-

---

[15] The peak of the controversy had passed even earlier, and in 1882 Darwin was buried with great honor beside Sir Isaac Newton in Westminster Abbey.

ford, and Manchester preached sermons urging the church to square both itself and its thinking with science, and they provided a vivid illustration of the way that evolutionary thought could work a change in theology. The Bishop of Manchester even invoked the principle of evolution to help explain the fact of the controversy itself: " The sufficient answer to ninety-nine out of a hundred of the ordinary objections to the Bible, as the record of a divine education of our race, is asked in that one word — development. And to what are we indebted for that potent word? . . . To modern science, resolutely pursuing its search for truth in spite of popular obloquy and — alas! that one should have to say it — in spite too often of theological denunciation." [16] Small wonder that the agnostic crusader Huxley read the sermons with " a feeling of satisfaction which is quite new to me as a result of hearing, or reading, sermons." [17]

This conciliatory and adaptive mood in British theology was made even plainer in 1889 with the publication of the theological symposium, *Lux Mundi: A Series of Studies in the Religion of the Incarnation*, edited by Charles Gore, Principal of Pusey House, Oxford. The writers were teachers at Oxford, much influenced by the idealism of T. H. Greene, and they too saw a need for development in theology. The preface stated their intention " to put the Catholic faith into its right relation to modern intellectual and moral problems." [18] This they did by attempting to show that the theory of evolution enhanced the wonder of divine creation, illuminating nature as the arena in which God's purposes were gradually and ever more fully realized. Aubrey Moore wrote that Newtonian science had pushed the Deist's God farther and farther away, " and at the moment when it appeared as if He would be thrust out altogether, Darwinism appeared, and under the dis-

[16] The sermons were published together as *The Advance of Science* (1887). Huxley in the same year quoted from page 53 in his essay " An Episcopal Trilogy," reprinted in his *Science and Christian Tradition: Essays* (D. Appleton & Company, 1900), p. 131.

[17] Huxley, *Science and Christian Tradition*, p. 127. Here he applauded the Bishop of Bedford for repudiating the view that science and theology occupy wholly different spheres.

[18] *Lux Mundi: A Series of Studies in the Religion of the Incarnation*, ed. by Charles Gore (15th ed.; London: John Murray, 1904), p. vii.

guise of a foe did the work of a friend . . . by shewing us that we must choose between two alternatives. Either God is everywhere present in nature, or He is nowhere. He cannot be here and not there." [19] In his essay on "The Incarnation and Development," J. R. Illingworth voiced his enthusiasm for evolutionary thought in these words: "The Incarnation may be said to have introduced a new species into the world, a Divine man transcending past humanity, as humanity transcended the rest of the animal creation, and communicating His vital energy to subsequent generations of men." [20]

By interpreting Biblical ideas frankly in the light of secular scientific concepts, the *Lux Mundi* group made a real break with tradition in British theology. Yet they did attempt to maintain traditional doctrines, and their idealism was channeled principally into the effort to *reconcile* the inherited faith with modern science, not *revise* it. Their stress on the incarnation was very clearly an effort to use evolutionary thought in a quest for deeper understanding of the orthodox claim that creation and redemption must be seen together, and their efforts produced the most generally accepted solution to the "evolution and religion problem." There were, to be sure, a few extreme liberals in the church, men with extravagant expectations that a proper wave of Darwinism *ought* to sweep away all moorings in doctrine and ecclesiastical form — Charles Voysey even declared the doctrine of the incarnation to be idolatrous, but he soon left the Anglican fellowship (not entirely by choice) to become pastor of the Theistic Church in London.[21] All things considered, we can fairly view the British response to Darwinian science in terms of what we have called the tradition of supernaturalistic orthodoxy.

During the last part of the nineteenth century the Scottish writer Henry Drummond served the cause of rational religion with a flair that brought him an immense audience both in Europe and

[19] His essay was "The Christian Doctrine of God," *ibid.*, p. 73.

[20] *Ibid.*, pp. 151–152.

[21] His most radical ideas may be found in *The Sling and the Stone* (1870). See S. C. Carpenter, *Church and People, 1789–1889: A History of the Church of England from William Wilberforce to "Lux Mundi"* (London: S.P.C.K., 1959), p. 538.

in America, and the continued reprinting of his books [22] attested to the eagerness with which many Christians in the English-speaking world greeted his efforts to show that evolution was really God's purposive method of creating the human spirit. Drummond spoke for a generation of British writers who were persuaded that subjective categories somehow were fused with nature's objectivity, and he believed that science and religion were united by a common principle, " the Continuity of Law." [23] Thus he proposed as the first step in healing the breach between them " the disclosure of the naturalism of the supernatural," [24] trying to show by analogy how the natural laws discussed by scientists also applied to the spiritual realm of life.[25] His arguments were widely accepted, even though most scientists and some theologians realized that his parallels were forced and had been gained by extending scientific principles beyond the world of Newtonian science whence they came.

" Evolutionary ethics " raises the question whether human moral and ethical standards have evolved by purely natural means, and the problematical relationship between evolutionary thought and traditional British morality has drawn the attention of British writers repeatedly. Darwin himself believed that human morality had evolved from the social instincts of lower animals, and that the natural process tended toward the Golden Rule as a norm for human behavior.[26] But he did not see *how* natural selection could have led to a gradual raising of moral standards. Thus de-

[22] *Natural Law in the Spiritual World* went through thirty editions between 1883 and 1890.

[23] Henry Drummond, *Natural Law in the Spiritual World* (James Pott & Co., 1885), p. xiii.

[24] *Ibid.*, p. xxii.

[25] He noted, for example, that Darwin had seen two main factors in evolution, organisms and environments. In the spiritual life also, said Drummond, the Christian organism depends on his Christ-environment. Therefore, " Communion with God is a scientific necessity." *Ibid.*, p. 267.

[26] He wrote, " The moral sense perhaps affords the best and highest distinction between man and the lower animals; but I need say nothing on this head, as I have so lately endeavored to shew that the social instincts,— the prime example of man's moral constitution — with the aid of native intellectual powers and the effects of habit, *naturally lead to the golden rule,* ' As ye would that men should do to you, do ye to them likewise; ' and this lies at the foundation of morality." *The Descent of Man and Selection in Relation to Sex* (2d ed. rev.; London: John Murray.

prived of the chief natural factor that might account for the evolution of spirituality, Darwin confessed that the natural causes of man's higher spiritual qualities were " too complex to be clearly followed out," [27] and he could only propose, rather lamely, that the praise and blame of other individuals had tended to encourage socially acceptable behavior among man's primitive ancestors.[28] Here Darwin really was expressing his own personal style, a kind of reflexive faith that morality *must* be written into the heart of nature, even though his theory of evolution by natural selection did not provide a ready explanation.

In *The Ascent of Man* (1894), Henry Drummond addressed himself to the question in a way that was typical of efforts to develop a " Christian evolutionary ethics " by baptizing science's Newtonian " nature " with categories from the " supernatural." Drummond suggested that " the Struggle for the Life of Others " was as much a part of evolution by purely natural means as was the more famous " Struggle for Life," [29] and he roundly criticized Benjamin Kidd's *Social Evolution* for explaining human social progress by appeal to an extranatural and " ultra-rational " sanction.[30] Any such proposal was simply out of the question, said Drummond, because it destroyed the basic unity of reality.[31] He

---

1891), I, p. 194. Italics mine. This same view is defended sympathetically by Ritter in *Charles Darwin and the Golden Rule*.

[27] *The Descent of Man*, pp. 200 f.

[28] *Ibid.*, p. 202.

[29] Henry Drummond, *The Ascent of Man* (3d ed.; James Pott & Co., 1894), p. 13. Prince Kropotkin made the same point in *Mutual Aid: A Factor in Evolution* (Extending Horizons Bks., 1955 [1902]).

[30] Benjamin Kidd, *Social Evolution* (The Macmillan Company, 1894). Kidd, an English government clerk, tried to reconcile the competitive nature of British industrial society with a gathering trend toward legislative reform of social conditions. He was persuaded that progress in society hinged on relentless competition, but he realized also that the poor and oppressed cried out against being used as grist for the mill of natural selection in business. No rational solution for such a paradox seemed possible, and Kidd concluded that religion must provide society with " an ultra-rational sanction for the sacrifice of the interests of the individual to those of the social organism." (P. 116.) For an excellent discussion of this aspect of the Darwinian age see Richard Hofstadter, *Social Darwinism in American Thought* (rev. ed.; Beacon Press, Inc., 1955), Ch. 5.

[31] He regarded Kidd's appeal to something " ultra-rational " as a dodge, for " if Nature is the garment of God, it is woven without seam throughout." *The Ascent of Man*, p. 56.

saw that both Darwin and Kidd really ended by excluding man's "God-given spiritual qualities" from nature, and in his eagerness to show that God was active in nature, he enthusiastically attributed to the Darwinian process those very spiritual qualities which were excluded from it because of the Newtonian scaffold on which Darwin's theory had been erected.

T. H. Huxley had a clearer understanding of the real limitations of Darwin's scientific theory than did either Darwin or Drummond, even though Huxley was always Darwin's most vocal champion. In "Evolution and Ethics," his Romanes Lecture for 1893, he completely disagreed with Darwin's hopeful assertions about the natural evolution of the Golden Rule. "The thief and the murderer follow nature just as much as the philanthropist," he lamented. "Cosmic evolution may teach us how the good and the evil tendencies of men may have come about; but, in itself, it is incompetent to furnish any better reason why what we call good is preferable to what we call evil than we had before." [32] The neglect of such considerations had led, he noted, to a regrettable tendency for the "fanatical individualism of our time" to apply the analogy of natural selection to society, and it seemed painfully obvious to Huxley that this had disastrous results. "There is a general consensus," he said, "that the ape and tiger methods of the struggle for existence are not reconcilable with sound ethical principles." [33] "Let us understand, once for all," he continued, "that the ethical progress of society depends, not on imitating the cosmic process, still less in running away from it, but in combating it." [34] Certainly, he admitted, centuries would be required for man's newly gained ethical impulses to control his lower competitive nature, which had been honed to a razor-sharpness by millions of years of natural selection. But Huxley could close by appealing to his audience to join him in hope, "cherishing the good that falls in our way, and bearing the evil, in and around us, with stout hearts set on diminishing it." [35]

[32] T. H. Huxley and Julian Huxley, *Evolution and Ethics, 1893–1943* (London: Pilot Press, Ltd., 1947), p. 80.
[33] *Ibid.*, p. 64.
[34] *Ibid.*, p. 82.
[35] *Ibid.*, p. 84.

It was a very modest hope, by one to whom the Darwinian world seemed much less friendly and cooperative than it did to Darwin himself. Huxley had seen only too well that on Darwin's Newtonian assumptions there was no way to explain the facts of human morality, no way to understand the origins of human social values. In the end he, too, could only accept his own Victorian morality as a given, appealing to the innate good-heartedness of his listeners.

Most of the men who first engaged in the effort to rebuild theological understanding in Britain were seriously handicapped because the nonpurposive Newtonian vision that they sought to avoid had become so much an unquestioned item of their own common sense. Consequently, their efforts toward a new rational synthesis glossed over problems, fell short, or led into the blind alleys that we have discussed. Darwin, Huxley, Wilberforce, Drummond, the *Lux Mundi* group — all struggled for ways of explaining how their own experience of subjectivity could be real in a Newtonian universe, and in this impossible task they were bound to fail, as had a procession of brilliant men before them. But the failure was not immediately apparent, and during the late nineteenth century many Christians in Britain were satisfied with the varied ways these men affirmed that there *was*, after all, subjectivity in the universe and in the natural world of Darwinian science. However, every such claim was made with a degree of arbitrariness, and the evolutionary theologies gradually shrank before the increasingly able intellectual advances of a Newtonian scientific community.

Still, the very failure of these early efforts at a rational theology has, in the main, stimulated a search for the hidden assumptions that made them fail. Toward the end of the century, when the Germans Haeckel and Weismann had given an explicitly materialistic turn to Darwin's ideas, British churchmen did declare a truce (not a surrender!) with science; for a time the long-cherished ideal of a rational reconciliation of subjective and objective categories in nature seemed to be an elusive will-o'-the-wisp, and many British Christians agonized through the early years of this century. But after World War I there began a succession of impressive philosophical attempts to solve the problem, all speaking out of this British tradition and all attempting to formulate an evolutionary view of the world that could allow for belief in God and purposiveness at the heart of things. Here we think of Samuel Alexander's *Space, Time, and Deity* (1920), C. Lloyd Morgan's *Emergent Evolution* (1923), J. C. Smuts' *Holism and Evolution* (1926), and Whitehead's *Process and Reality* (1929); John Oman, William Temple, and Charles Raven are theological sons of this tradition.[36] No one would claim that the works of these men are of equal excellence or that they express the same religious vision of things, but they do mark the resurgence of that long British tradition of rationality in religion. The peculiarly British aspect of their search to understand is that it never seriously moved in the direction of Kantian or Hegelian idealism but focused instead on the effort to reconsider the whole philosophical tradition that spawned the problem.

We do not have space for a detailed discussion of happenings in Germany, but some brief comments are necessary if we are to follow the thread of our story. The German response to Darwinian thought has differed in an important way from the response we have called typical of Britain, principally because of the pervasive influence of Kant in shaping the common sense of German theological thought during the last two centuries. Kant's *Critique of Pure Reason* was a brilliant and intricate response to the Newtonian claim that nature was governed entirely by objective forces, and in it he grappled with the basic issue: how are human intuitions of *subjectivity* related to the *objectivity* in nature? But he took the Newtonian abstractions as statements about concrete reality, accepting the proposition that nature was composed entirely of objectivity in the form of enduring atoms. This meant that the problem took on a peculiar form: if the nature we can know through sense perception never at any time enjoys subjectivity, where is the subjectivity of the universe? British writers have tended to answer this question by a rather arbitrary insistence that nature is simultaneously objective and subjective, but Kant

---

[36] See John Oman, *The Natural and the Supernatural;* William Temple, *Nature, Man and God;* Charles Raven, *Natural Religion and Christian Theology.*

recognized in a stroke of genius that *the subjective and objective aspects of reality do not coincide.* It is impossible to exaggerate the importance of this discovery, and because of it all philosophy since Kant has been a response to his thought.

But Kant expressed his discovery in a way that had far-reaching implications for theology. He conceived his famous distinction between the " phenomenal " and the " noumenal," carving reality into two realms and affirming that the source of our intuitions of subjectivity lies beyond or outside of nature. Actually this proposal amounted to conceiving of nature on the model of a Newtonian atom, i.e., as a realm of reality that was enduringly *objective,* and then matching it with another realm that was enduringly *subjective.* Like two Newtonian atoms, Kant's two realms merely lay side-by-side in the universe, and there was no way to explain how they could be internally related to each other.

This philosophical settlement of the problem led to a separation and finally a divorce between natural science and theology, and German thinkers since Kant have almost consistently divided reality into two separate realms, (*a*) a realm of *objective* reality, to which they assign all of nature and which is the exclusive province of natural science, and (*b*) a realm of *subjective* reality beyond nature, to which is assigned human inwardness and which is the province of theology and philosophy. Consequently, even before *The Origin of Species* there was an immense gulf between the sensitivities of British and German thinkers. In England, Tennyson struggled valiantly to salvage his belief that subjectivity and objectivity occurred *in nature,* writing that it is " a time to sicken and to swoon, when Science reaches forth her arms " to snatch purpose from the world.[37] But in Germany the subjective and objective aspects of reality had been so fully wrenched apart that Helmholtz referred to the first half of the nineteenth century as a period during which " philosophers accused the scientific men of narrowness [and] the scientific men retorted that the philosophers were crazy." [38]

---

[37] Alfred Lord Tennyson, *In Memoriam.*
[38] H. Helmholtz, *Popular Lectures on Scientific Subjects,* tr. by E. Atkinson (London, 1873), p. 5, cited in Dampier, *A History of Science and Its Relations with Philosophy & Religion,* p. 292.

In the years preceding *The Origin of Species*, German biologists already were enthusiastically occupied with the task of grounding biology in a materialistic philosophy, and Büchner's *Force and Matter* was reprinted again and again.[39] Besides all this, the church in Germany had become identified with political conservatism, further alienating scientific liberals. In this hostile atmosphere, scientific materialists were determined at all costs to avoid any interpretation of evolution that smacked of Schelling's idealistic *Naturphilosophie*, and they embraced Darwinism as the symbol of anticlerical materialism. Ernst Haeckel (1834–1919) helped to make *Darwinismus* almost a new religion in Germany by 1900.[40] In a climate where science and theology already were at swords' points, it was practically impossible for churchmen to hold traditional orthodoxy together with Darwinian science in any sort of rational scheme. Theology's response to Darwin really had been settled by Kant long before *The Origin of Species* crossed the Channel, when he anchored religious faith on an inner witness to the moral law. Likewise, Schleiermacher's attention to " the feeling of absolute dependence " stands as vivid testimony to the radically subjective style of German theological thought as Darwin's work appeared.

Thus the prevailing type of response to Darwinism in German theology was that which we have called romantic liberalism, in this case resting on an ultimate duality of subjective and objective categories so that religious faith was anchored in a realm quite above the tides of objective scientific thought. Such a theological style may be seen, for example, in Ritschl's distinction between judgments of *fact* and judgments of *value*, a distinction which assumed that the subject matter of theology (value) was completely independent of the subject matter of natural science

[39] Louis Büchner, *Kraft und Stoff: Empirisch-naturphilosophische Studien in allgemein-verständlicher Darstellung* (Frankfurt a.M.: Meidinger, 1855). See Temkin's discussion in *Forerunners of Darwin*, pp. 325–355.

[40] This may be seen in his work *Die Welträtsel* (1899), Engl. tr. *The Riddle of the Universe* (London, 1900). Here Haeckel built a monistic materialistic philosophy on a Darwinian framework, claiming that all living movements may be explained in terms of the chemical properties of carbon.

(fact).[41] This German mode of thought continues to be influential in the form of notions that theology can or should be independent of scientific thought, or that " nature " and " human history " are somehow discontinuous.

Otto Zöckler, a contemporary of Darwin and author of what is still one of the best histories of the Christian doctrine of creation,[42] exemplifies the impact of this Kantian philosophy in nineteenth-century German theology. In his response to Darwinism, Zöckler was anxious to preserve the notion of divine freedom while accepting the notion of development in nature, and he did this by using the orthodox idea of *creatio prima* and *creatio secunda*, expressed in the Lutheran doctrine that God's creation, conservation, and governing of the world are an interrelated divine act. " *Creatio, conservatio, gubernatio*," he wrote, " compose a togetherness of divine acts which simply may not be separated." [43] He then proposed that God had created in the beginning a world that operated strictly according to the causal sequences observed by science, but that God was able to modify this sequence at will, introducing new organisms from time to time so that the whole process appears to us as a law-abiding evolutionary world. Of course this was a version of progressionism, but it was typically German in that Zöckler began by assuming that nature was purely objective and that God alone was the locus of subjectivity, i.e., novelty and purpose. Emphasizing that nature itself was devoid of purpose, he took as his text the words, " Without me you can do nothing." [44]

[41] Albrecht Ritschl, *The Christian Doctrine of Justification and Reconciliation* (Edinburgh, 1902).

[42] Otto Zöckler, *Geschichte der Beziehungen zwischen Theologie und Naturwissenschaft, mit besonderer Rücksicht auf Schöpfungsgeschichte* (Erste Abtheilung, Von den Anfängen der christlichen Kirche bis auf Newton und Leibniz, Gütersloh, 1877; Zweite Abtheilung, Von Newton und Leibniz bis zur Gegenwart, Gütersloh, 1879).

[43] Zöckler, article " Schöpfung und Erhaltung," in *Realencyklopädie für protestantische Theologie und Kirche*, Bd. 17, p. 702, cited in Günter Altner, *Schöpfungsglaube und Entwicklungsgedanke in der protestantischen Theologie zwischen Ernst Haeckel und Teilhard de Chardin* (Zürich: EVZ-Verlag, 1965), p. 7.

[44] Altner, *op. cit.*, p. 10. It is interesting that in Altner's very helpful study he continues to express the German style in the title of a chapter

This same assumption that subjectivity is located in some realm beyond a purely objective nature informs the work of Karl Heim, one of the most recent of those German theologians who have addressed themselves explicitly to the task of reconciling natural science and theology. In *Christian Faith and Natural Science*, Heim begins by drawing attention to the analysis of human subjectivity that modern existentialist writers have made, and then he proposes that the human ego and the body are " two different forms of existence [which] belong to two different spaces, spaces which possess fundamentally different structures." [45] However, Heim does not anchor subjectivity in a noumenal realm, as Kant did, for he is eager to show that the two different spaces are related. Referring to developments in modern physics and mathematics, he calls to our attention that the three-dimensional space known through sense perception is but one of many possible spaces which differ in their " curvature." [46] While we can know through science only the three-dimensional world of Euclidean space, we are led to infer the existence of a space which " lies completely outside the entire objective world. And yet this may still be a space in the true sense of the word, because in it too a multiplicity of entities are arranged in order according to a definite principle." It is this space, Heim proposes, in which " encounters take place between subjects." [47]

These two " spaces " thus are the loci of the objectivity and subjectivity of our world, and Heim goes on to observe that they both are characterized by a certain " polarity " or related over-againstness which unites them and from which our experience cannot escape. But what about the reality of God? Here Heim

surveying German theological response to Darwinism: " The Impossibility of a Synthesis." Discussing the work of men like Henry Drummond and Lyman Abbott, Ernst Benz observes regretfully that German theology was almost completely unaffected by British and American efforts to reconcile Christian faith with evolutionary science. See his *Schöpfungsglaube und Endzeiterwartung* (Munich: Nymphenburger Verlagshandlung, 1965), Ch. 9.

[45] Karl Heim, *Christian Faith and Natural Science* (Harper Torchbooks, Harper & Brothers, 1957), p. 121.

[46] *Ibid.*, p. 129.

[47] *Ibid.*, p. 140.

continues with his image of multiple " spaces." We must not expect to find God in the perceptible nature known to science, he
says, " For, as it says in the Old Testament, we cannot see God
and live. It follows that there must be some [other] space, just as
all-present as the three-dimensional space but completely unob-
servable." [48] This he calls the " suprapolar space," since it transcends the realm of polarity in which the earlier two spaces exist,[49] and it is in this way that divine subjectivity permeates the
world. Heim's proposal differs from Zöckler's, we note, in that
Heim really seeks to locate subjectivity *in* the world, by postulating realms of natural and divine subjectivity that exist in " polar "
and " suprapolar " relationship with nature's objectivity. But the
Kantian assumption ensures that Heim's " spaces " merely exist
arbitrarily alongside each other like Kant's two realms. Their relationship is purely external, and therefore quite unexplainable.

We shall recall this German style of response in our final chapter, but at this point we must move on to mention events in
France, where yet another direction may be seen. Until the time
of Bergson, there was virtually no contact between British and
French philosophy, a fact that may hark back to armed hostility
between the nations during the early part of the nineteenth century, and during the nineteenth century, Spencer was almost the
only British thinker known in France. This gulf between the two
nations was dramatized in the experience of Teilhard de Chardin,
great French evolutionist of our own time, who was unaware of
the whole Darwinian controversy until 1902, when he studied in
England! [50] The battleground between traditional orthodoxy and
modern knowledge in France was located, instead, in the great
struggle between Roman Catholic dogma and the critical study of
tradition, and nineteenth-century French theology was largely un-
troubled by evolutionary ideas except for a recollection of Lamarck's *transformisme*. French biology was still in the grip of
Cuvier's thought, and at first it was hostile toward Darwin as it

[48] *Ibid.*, p. 167.
[49] *Ibid.*, p. 162.
[50] Charles E. Raven, *Teilhard de Chardin: Scientist and Seer* (London: William Collins Sons & Co., Ltd., 1962), p. 33.

had been toward Lamarck; only around the turn of the century did serious rebuttal begin, with Bergson and Edouard Le Roy.

3. THE GREAT DEBATE IN AMERICA: VOICES FROM EVERY SIDE

Christian thought in America began in a strongly Calvinistic form with the Covenant Theology of the early Puritans, but by mid-nineteenth century this theology had lost its unity, allowing several significantly different currents to pour out into the stream of religious thought. Traditional orthodoxy had weathered the onslaught of rationalism and Deism in the eighteenth century by much the same accommodation in the direction of rational religion that we found in Britain. Paley's argument from Design was as popular in America as in England,[51] and many people assumed that any new discovery in biology was truly " scientific " only if it fitted into the cosmic drama of the Bible and could be explained rationally in terms of God's purposes. People in this current were " rationalists under the Scriptures," firmly convinced that the grounds for their religious faith could be harmonized with reason. Another current stemmed from the alliance between rationalism and a growing humanistic morality that emphasized man's freedom (" whosoever will . . ."). Flowing steadily away from the old " theological determinism " of Calvinism, which had been a Protestant Christian way of seeing the glory of God in the perfectly orderly movements of the universe, this newer current was seeing God's glory more and more in man, and it moved in the direction of Unitarianism.

Then there was a current of religious romanticism, American cousin to the idealism of Kant and Schleiermacher; and finally, a widening current of pietistic-revivalistic evangelicalism, sweeping westward with the frontier and becoming more and more hostile to the intellectual movements of the modern world after 1800. It is these last two currents that have carried the popular response of

[51] The Deist style found lively expression in America during the Revolutionary period. In 1784, Ethan Allen rejected revelation in *Reason, the Only Oracle of Man,* and in 1794, Thomas Paine published *The Age of Reason,* claiming that the word of God was to be found in the Creation. See Herbert M. Morais, *Deism in Eighteenth Century America* (Columbia University Press, 1934).

American religion to Darwinian science, so that while rational religion remained near to the hearts of most English Christians, the search for a rational synthesis of science and religion gradually lost its place as a dominant characteristic of American religious life.

When Darwin's book crossed the Atlantic, America was teetering on the brink of a disastrous civil war, and theological concern for the practical questions of slavery and political union far outweighed any burgeoning interest that the church might have had in natural science. Also there had been no *Vestiges* to prepare Americans for Darwin, and the United States was, as yet, relatively isolated from the results of German Biblical studies, so it was still possible for most people to take quite for granted the traditional view that God had created mankind some six thousand years earlier. In this atmosphere one burning theological question was whether God had created the white man as a natural superior of the Negro, and not a few Americans who read *The Origin of Species* did so in quest of help on this question. Only a few realized its ultimate implications about man's origins. Then during the Civil War, as the bodies of uncounted thousands of young men were returned for burial in town and village, American pastors and theologians found their thoughts turned to questions of judgment and salvation; the question of creation stirred few hearts.

The result was that clergymen quite generally ignored Darwin's work until the upheavals of the Civil War had passed, and serious theological discussion of the book was delayed for a decade. To be sure, there was an initial ripple of hostility to the idea of evolution, and several isolated theologians did make serious efforts to discuss the implications of *The Origin of Species,* chiefly by attacking Darwin's scientific methodology. But as few American clergymen knew anything about science, these theologians wrote for a limited audience, not as spokesmen for any genuine theological movement. Also, while the founders of American pragmatism at Harvard did pay close attention to Darwin from the beginning and made penetrating analyses of evolutionary thought,[52]

[52] Sometime around 1870 a group of America's most brilliant thinkers (the so-called "Metaphysical Club") was meeting for conversation at

this, too, was done largely out of the hearing of the church. Indeed, careful philosophical interpretation of evolutionary theory never has played more than a quiet piccolo in the orchestra of American religious life.

The typical response of churchmen, then, was one of neglect in the face of more pressing matters. But in the meantime American scientists were participating in a lively discussion of Darwin's theory, often serving up meaty dishes of popular theology along with their scientific judgments, and their headstart ensured that scientists would play a decisive role in shaping American responses to Darwinism. For this reason we shall begin our survey of these responses by a look at the thought of a scientist. In the pages to follow we shall try only to sketch the main types of response, focusing on a few typical figures, and indicating the long-run implications of their positions.

a. *The Response of Rational Supernaturalistic Orthodoxy.* Asa Gray (1810–1888) was one of America's leading botanists, author of a *Manual of Botany* (a household word for over fifty years) and professor of natural history at Harvard. During the years immediately preceding and following publication of *The Origin of Species* he was in continual correspondence with Darwin, and because of this exchange of letters, Gray was able to appreciate the full import of the finished work when it appeared. He read it immediately and published his review in the spring of 1860,[53] penetrating to the heart of Darwin's argument and clearly laying out its strengths and weaknesses, along with its implications for future scientific and theological thought. Darwin, he noted, was merely discussing the " how " of evolution, not the " why." [54] As

---

Harvard. These men were Charles Peirce, William James, Chauncey Wright, Oliver Wendell Holmes, Jr., Francis E. Abbot, and John Fiske. For an excellent discussion, see Philip P. Wiener, *Evolution and the Founders of Pragmatism* (Harvard University Press, 1949).

[53] Asa Gray, " Review of Darwin's Theory on the Origin of Species by means of Natural Selection," *American Journal of Science and Arts,* Vol. 29, No. 86 (March, 1860), pp. 152–184. This and twelve other essays by Professor Gray between 1860 and 1876 were collected in *Darwiniana: Essays and Reviews Pertaining to Darwinism* (D. Appleton & Company, 1876).

[54] Gray, *Darwiniana,* p. 53.

to the question of God's action in nature, Darwin's argument began by assuming that life had been " breathed into " some original forms, unmistakably suggesting divine creation, and logically this seemed to open the door for God to intervene as much as might be required. Gray, who always believed in a general providence, therefore trusted Darwin to be implying that " all was done wisely, in the largest sense designedly, and by an intelligent first cause." [55] This was an error, for as we have seen, Darwin did *not* believe explicitly in Design; still, Gray's review did catch the flavor of Darwin's own ambiguity on the point.[56]

Gray's unswerving belief that Darwin's hypothesis was compatible with belief in purposiveness at the heart of things was expressed in a series of articles entitled " Natural Selection not Inconsistent with Natural Theology." [57] Here his main point was clear: Darwin's theory was based on evidence derived from sense perception, while belief in a purposeful world originates as an inference from some other element of our total experience. " Design," he wrote, " can never be *demonstrated*. Witnessing the act does not make known the design. . . . The word of the actor is not proof . . . and the only possible way in cases where testimony is out of the question, is to infer the design from the result." [58] Since this was so, he concluded, theological belief in Design was still just as plausible as before Darwin's book appeared.[59] Thousands of readers agreed, and Gray never changed his mind during a lifetime of consideration.

He saw with great clarity a point that will be essential for our discussion later: whatever may be its source, belief in the pur-

[55] *Ibid.*

[56] See Ch. I, n. 142. Darwin spoke in Deist fashion of " laws impressed on matter by the Creator." *OS*, p. 488.

[57] There were three articles, appearing originally in *Atlantic Monthly* for July, August, and October, 1860; these were reprinted together as a pamphlet in 1861, then in *Darwiniana*. The same year he also wrote " Design Versus Necessity — Discussion between two Readers of Darwin's Treatise on the Origin of Species, upon its Natural Theology," *American Journal of Science and Arts*, Vol. 30, No. 89 (September, 1860), pp. 226–239, and reprinted in *Darwiniana*.

[58] Gray, *Darwiniana*, p. 70.

[59] *Ibid.*, p. 86.

posiveness of nature does not originate in observation of nature. But if Gray did not base his belief in Design on scientific evidence, where did he anchor it? Again he pointed clearly: " The sense that there is *reason why* is as innate as that there is *cause thereby*." [60] In other words, he was persuaded that human beings enjoy an inborn awareness of purposeful order in the universe, and that the very innateness of this awareness accounts for our ability to apprehend Design in nature without relying on the deliverances of sense perception. Very obviously, Gray's phrase " innate sense " indicated that in some fashion his awareness of order in the *objective* world depended on his own *subjective* experience. Whereas previously Gray's readers had believed themselves to have in the argument from Design a rationally persuasive argument for belief in God, based on demonstrable aspects of the external world, Gray's argument really left them with nothing but their own subjective conviction of purpose in nature. Apparently most of them did not realize this!

Asa Gray saw the world as a divinely created arena for man's scientific and religious activities, and the " innateness " of his belief in a " reason why " was for him a fact about the same creation that science investigated. Therefore he saw his (subjective) belief in Design as a basic and permanent category of human existence in the same (objective) nature that Darwin was explaining without purposiveness. But he did not feel the tension involved in his position, and in their exchange of letters Gray and Darwin never penetrated behind this starting point of Gray's reflection. Past the admission that Gray *did* believe in Design, and that Darwin did *not*, there was little to say. Darwin was only too acutely aware that his own scientific thought had led him away from belief in nature's purposiveness, but he could scarcely imagine what might persuade him of it again, unless it might be an angel come down for that purpose; [61] judging from this statement, Darwin nearly agreed with Gray that belief in purposiveness must be

    [60] Asa Gray, *Natural Science and Religion: Two Lectures Delivered to the Theological School of Yale College* (Charles Scribner's Sons, 1880), p. 86.
    [61] *LLCD*, II, p. 169.

" God-given." In any case, it lay beyond their power to explain, and neither man was able to shed much light on a deeper question: could or ought such " innate " belief withstand exposure to a consciously held nonpurposive Newtonian vision of reality?

Gray's " innate " conviction of nature's purposiveness was echoed by many American Christians who sought to maintain traditional beliefs during the next century, and perhaps we know it best in the form of Boston Personalism. This theological tradition, initiated by Borden P. Bowne (1847–1910), has kept consistently very close to the Bible and is also, in the words of one of its best known apostles, Edgar S. Brightman (1884–1957), " rational and proud of it." [62] Personalism rests on the assumption that the *subjective* categories of human personality are adequate to serve as our basis for understanding the world — hence its name, personal idealism — and Bowne seems to have agreed with Asa Gray that a sense for purposeful order in the world is one of the essential categories of human subjectivity. In this vein he wrote that the theological argument from Design " will always be a great favorite with common sense." [63] Contemporary Personalists such as Harold DeWolf and Peter Bertocci make a very similar assumption in believing that human beings naturally seek to *explain* their experience rationally; they argue that the world revealed to us by modern science is best explained by a personal God as Creator.[64] Here again, the quest for a " reason why " stems from a persuasion that the elements of experience find their meaning in terms of some subjective end or principle of organization.

However, positivistic scientists resist the notion that the elements of scientific experience are so coordinated, and modern literature bears witness to a desperate current of despair over meaning in modern life, testimony that many people either do not have, or have lost, that " innate sense " of purposeful order which

[62] From an article in *The Crozier Quarterly* (October, 1928), cited in Henry Nelson Wieman and Bernard Eugene Meland, *American Philosophies of Religion* (Willett, Clark & Company, 1936), p. 145.

[63] Borden P. Bowne, *Theism* (American Book Company, 1887), p. 77.

[64] See L. Harold DeWolf, *A Theology of the Living Church* (Harper & Brothers, Publishers, 1959), and Peter Anthony Bertocci, *Introduction to the Philosophy of Religion* (Prentice-Hall, Inc., 1951).

Gray and the Personalists assume. Since this is so, we must go on to analyze Gray's " innate sense " a bit further, distinguishing between two propositions, (a) that all people *experience* a purposeful world, and (b) that all people make *conscious judgments* to this effect. In Chapter IV we shall try to clarify this further, by maintaining that in affirming these propositions Gray was correct about (a) but wrong about (b). There we shall contend that modes of human consciousness (including consciousness of a " reason why " at the heart of things) are not " innate " or " natural " but are the product of a certain kind of cultural history.

Asa Gray and his intellectual descendants responded to Darwinian science by recognizing that their belief in Design rested somehow in human subjectivity, not in scientific demonstration. But many people who had been raised on a heavy diet of rationalism were unable to make this adjustment, and for them the failure of Paley's argument signaled the end of the line for a very long tradition of rational faith. In what became one of the great ironies of American religious life, this current of piety led directly to the present anti-intellectualism of much fundamentalism, and it is to this side of the orthodox response that we now turn.

Charles Hodge was professor of theology at Princeton from 1840 to 1878. He was by all odds the leading theological spokesman for conservative supernaturalistic orthodoxy, and in 1874 his book *What Is Darwinism?* launched a great reaction against the whole notion of evolution with this clear battle cry: " What is Darwinism? It is Atheism." [65] It was perfectly clear to Hodge from Scripture that the world existed as God's purposeful creation and that there was subjectivity in nature, but he was not willing to anchor his religious faith in human subjectivity alone. " Religion is a state of knowledge," he said firmly, " as well as a state of feeling." [66] With this conviction that faith must be related to knowledge of nature he began his careful evaluation of Darwinism, recognizing clearly (as Gray initially did not) that Darwin fully intended to exclude the notion of final causation

[65] Charles Hodge, *What Is Darwinism?* (Scribner, Armstrong, and Company, 1874), p. 177.
[66] *Ibid.*, p. 142.

from his explanation of evolution.[67] He also saw that it was not belief in evolution per se which led to atheism, but belief in Darwin's nonpurposive explanation,[68] and in the more careful sections of his work he realized that one might accept the notion of an evolving world without strangling over the Newtonian fabric which clothed it.[69] But in the long run Professor Hodge was unable to reconcile such a world of evolutionary flux with the fixed Calvinistic thought world that he had inherited; the idea of evolution seemed utterly incredible when compared with the traditional static view of creation. The distinction between the two heads of the " Darwinian monster " did not remain clear to him, and he attacked both, opposing the notion of evolution by a set of dubious scientific arguments while arguing that " any ordinarily constituted mind " must believe in Design.[70]

Although he did not intend it, Hodge's final rejection of Darwinian science, both conclusion and method, was an open invitation for his conservative readers to abandon the quest for rational coherence and to divorce religious faith from all modern knowledge of nature. The alternative, which so many adopted, was to anchor faith completely in human subjectivity, in the form of religious experience or arbitrary adherence to the letter of Scripture. Many readers took Hodge's book to be a refutation of the whole evolutionary hypothesis, and a large percentage of his spiritual heirs have fallen victim to the same error, but with much less sensitivity to the fact that belief in evolution per se is not a threat to faith in divine purpose. Modern fundamentalists thus characteristically attack the *fact* of evolution as they attempt to defend their faith in God's purposes — threatened by the Newtonian vision, they respond with a broadside against the entire modern world of change in which it appeared to them.

Their crusade has found fundamentalists indiscriminately opposing nearly the whole sweep of modern thought, so that they sometimes exhaust their energies on trivialities and are prevented from giving serious attention to the aspects of modern thought that really are hostile to faith. Here we think of their

[67] *Ibid.*, pp. 42, 52.   [69] *Ibid.*, pp. 50 f.
[68] *Ibid.*, p. 104.   [70] *Ibid.*, p. 59.

elaborate and ingenious efforts to refute the mounting tide of scientific evidence for evolution, as well as their continuing and sometimes successful crusade to ban the teaching of evolution in American public schools.[71] The astonishing proliferation of fundamentalist groups witnesses to the popularity of religion that avoids the complex issues of a changing world by an appeal to religious experience, but its increasing irrelevance and even hostility to modern life is the bitter fruit of rejecting a proud inheritance of rationality. Charles Hodge could say, " No sound minded man disputes any scientific fact," [72] but in fifty years the religious sentiments of many who looked on him as their spiritual father were more nearly expressed by a public prosecutor at the famous Scopes trial: " Who says we can't bar science that deprives us of all hope of the future life to come? " [73]

There was a certain prophetic grandeur in the way Charles Hodge rejected evolutionary pantheism: " The blasphemy of some of the German philosophers on this subject is simply unutterable." [74] Yet there is real pathos in the way some of his spiritual sons have dissolved Hodge's doctrinal standards in the changing hues of their own inner lights. In the long run, and ever more quickly in our time, to abandon the search for rational coherence in religion is to destroy faith or to allow it to become fatally diluted with mere emotion. We can only regret that Hodge did not succeed in linking his deep piety with the intellectual currents of his time.

There was only one really skillful American attempt to develop a scheme of ideas capable of clarifying both traditional faith and evolutionary science, but in a way that contrasted sharply with events in Britain, this American effort was made outside the church

---

[71] During William Jennings Bryan's great campaign, antievolution laws were passed by Tennessee, Mississippi, Arkansas, and Texas; bills were introduced and defeated in seven other states. There remains a lively public hostility to the teaching of evolutionary theory in some parts of the nation, and as recently as 1964 a vigorous campaign was waged in Arizona to place on the ballot a measure which would have banned the teaching of evolution as a fact.

[72] Hodge, *op. cit.*, p. 132.

[73] Gaius Glenn Atkins, *Religion in Our Times* (Round Table Press, Inc., 1932), p. 251.

[74] Hodge, *op. cit.*, p. 9.

and had virtually no impact on American religious life. It was the work of Francis E. Abbot (1836–1903), who spent his career constructing a positivistic religion of evolution. Abbot began as a respected Unitarian clergyman, but his radical style of thought brought him into conflict with his more orthodox colleagues so that he finally abandoned his profession to become one of the founders of the "Free Religious Association." [75] In *Scientific Theism* (1885) he presented the culmination of years of reflection, a distinguished attempt to reassess the whole modern philosophical tradition so as to show that nature is simultaneously both subjective and objective. He began by applauding the triumphs of science, moving on to observe that the whole scientific enterprise and its amazing practical successes rested on the assumption that scientists acquire in their work a real knowledge of a real world. Scientists act pragmatically, he said, as though an external world exists per se apart from human awareness, and as though they know this world per se. He proposed making these scientific assumptions the basis for metaphysics and theology.

Abbot realized that scientific understanding would have been impossible if the universe really were composed of nothing but isolated bits of stuff, and in an effort to overcome this abstraction [76] he proposed a philosophy which he called "Relationism." Its basic principle was that all the relations of objects in the external world are part and parcel of their very objectivity; thus the relation of a tree to a human observer could be regarded as part of its very treeness.[77] In this way Abbot hoped to avoid the extremes of empiricism and idealism, the latter then well known to him in New England transcendentalism.

When he used his notion of relationism to interpret evolution, he conceived the universe as an organism, *simultaneously and always subject and object*, a single living and growing whole.[78] For this reason he objected to idealistic interpretations of evolution as

[75] Wiener, *Evolution and the Founders of Pragmatism*, p. 42. See also Sidney Warren, *American Freethought, 1860–1914* (Columbia University Press, 1943), p. 35.

[76] We have referred to this as the notion of "simple location."

[77] Francis E. Abbot, *Scientific Theism* (2d ed.; Little, Brown and Company, 1886), pp. 25, 27.

[78] *Ibid.*, pp. 163, 184.

God " come-to-consciousness " in man, insisting that " the evolution of the universe as Divine Object is viewed as the work of the universe itself as Divine Subject. . . . The conscious could not possibly originate in the unconscious." [79] Here God was conceived as being, somehow, both the source and the outcome of the evolutionary process, but because God did not in any sense stand over against or outside the process, it was unclear in what sense he could be thought of as its source. Admitting that his system sounded pantheistic, Abbot defended it by saying that the teleology in his system was " the very essence of purely spiritual personality," therefore not a pantheistic category.[80] Still and all, when he said that God is " transcendent *in* the universe so far as it remains unknown," [81] it was fairly clear that Abbot had not succeeded in saving the Biblical vision of a God who transcends his creation.

What had happened? Abbot attacked the main problem, that of relating subjectivity and objectivity in the world, but he was not quite successful in escaping the notion of " simple location." Like Kant, he naïvely accepted the commonsense view that the ultimate entities of the universe endure through time, so he was forced toward a belief that things still exist in their subjective discreteness while being related to other things. Where Kant's genius had recognized that we must somehow conceive of objectivity and subjectivity separately, Abbot fused them together and claimed that the whole universe is simultaneously noumenal and phenomenal.[82] Logically, this was only the most explicit of that long series of attempts to fasten subjectivity onto the idealized objective particles of the Newtonian universe, and when Abbot extended his proposal to the idea of God, he was forced to conclude that God's reality *is* his relation to the world. This meant that it was not possible to think of God at all in abstraction from the evolving universe, and in the long run Abbot ended up by saying that the evolution of the world *is* the evolution of God, and therefore, our increasing scientific knowledge of the world *is* our growing knowledge of God.

[79] *Ibid.*, p. 167.
[80] *Ibid.*, p. 211.
[81] *Ibid.*, p. 213. Italics mine.
[82] *Ibid.*, p. 107.

Instead of reconciling the new evolutionary notions of change with the Biblical intuitions of God's permanence and transcendence, Abbot had created a theology where God disappeared into the whirling flux. He had moved a long way from Calvinism, through Unitarianism to a new gospel, so that he could close with a proud appeal for his readers to come sit on a strange new mourner's bench: " Scientific Theism is more than a philosophy: it is a religion, it is a gospel, it is the Faith of the Future, founded on knowledge rather than on blind belief, — a faith in which head and heart . . . will kneel in worship side by side at the same altar, dedicated not to the ' Unknown God,' still less to the ' Unknowable God,' but to the KNOWN GOD whose revealing prophet is SCIENCE." [83] Here was an American version of the " unutterable blasphemy " spoken by Schelling and so vigorously opposed by Charles Hodge. No wonder that many spiritual sons of Professor Hodge preferred to abandon the ship of rationalism in theology, rather than to be on board when Abbot ran it onto the rocks!

b. *The Response of Romantic Liberalism.* We turn now from these men, all of whom we have tried to see against a background of rational, supernaturalistic orthodoxy, to those who greeted Darwinism in ways that more strongly reveal their kinship with what we have called the current of romantic liberalism in theology. In one way or another these men anchored their faith in God and nature's purposiveness upon inward experience, the deliverances of their own religious consciousness. In this they were building on foundations laid by Horace Bushnell and New England transcendentalism, for, thanks to the influence of Bushnell, this romantic theology had remained within the church where it could become a powerful current in American religious life.[84] Francis Abbot's rational theology failed, but it contained several notions that became pivotal elements in romantic evolutionary theology — the idea of divine immanence, and the idea of a gradual realization of cosmic purpose. Together these ideas seemed to furnish a satisfying way of reconciling Christian faith and Darwinian science. Thus in the romantic citadel of inwardness, protected from

[83] *Ibid.*, pp. 217 f.   [84] Mead, *The Lively Experiment*, p. 172.

the Darwinian tide, these notions became almost the common sense of innumerable Americans by 1900.

This optimistic evolutionary theism was summed up in John Fiske's aphorism, " Evolution is God's way of doing things." [85] Fiske was the greatest popularizer of evolutionary ideas in America, a prolific writer and devoted disciple of Herbert Spencer, but one who served up his master's evolutionary speculations in a more palatable form by combining them with the idea of an immanent God. His serene reliance on subjective categories as the clue for interpreting all of reality led him to the same buoyant confidence in his system of thought that can be found in Kant and Hegel,[86] and in a way reminiscent of Abbot, he said that each strand in the surging web of modern knowledge made " more and more clearly visible the living garment of God." [87]

The problem of facing Darwinian science seemed perfectly easy of solution: abandon the crude idea of an external God and then think of the universe as an evolving organism with an indwelling principle of life, the immanent God.[88] Fiske thus tried to show that the notion of a God " inside " the world was a " higher " idea of God than the old-fashioned Deist idea of God " outside " the world,[89] soundly criticizing Augustine's doctrine of original sin because it depicted humanity as cut off from all relationship with God.[90] He knew it was hard to account for human perversity and evil if God was the indwelling pulse of change in the world, so he suggested that evil was merely the experienced contrast with good.

---

[85] He was persuaded that after man appeared on earth, " the dominant aspect of evolution was to be not the genesis of species, but the progress of civilization." John Fiske, *The Destiny of Man Viewed in the Light of His Origin* (24th ed.; Houghton, Mifflin and Company, 1897 [1884]), p. 30.

[86] Speaking of his philosophical conclusions, he said they were " the fruit of a wide induction from the most vitally important facts which the doctrine of evolution has set forth; and they may fairly claim recognition as an integral body of philosophic doctrine fit to stand the test of time." *The Idea of God as Affected by Modern Knowledge* (Houghton, Mifflin and Company, 1887), p. 164.

[87] *Ibid.*, p. 45.

[88] *Ibid.*, p. 131.

[89] *Ibid.*, pp. 89 f.

[90] *Ibid.*, p. 94.

We are never conscious of anything, Fiske observed, except as it stands in contrast with something else; thus if we are to be conscious of goodness in the world there must be some contrast which levers it up into consciousness, and we call this contrast, " evil." [91] This was an acute observation about human awareness, but it also betrayed Fiske's Kantian vision of reality by implying that good and evil were real only in human consciousness; he avoided the question whether good and evil were objectively real, as well as the question *why* there should be good and evil at all.

Fiske's writings express his almost jubilant certainty that science had confirmed Matthew Arnold's definition of God as " an eternal Power, not ourselves, that makes for righteousness." [92] However, his credulous identification of God with the natural process of evolution was basically an expression of the romantic intuition that objective categories of natural science find their reality somehow in the subjective experience of human awareness. In this way his bark of faith could sail serenely over waters that he believed were not really troubled by the " two-headed monster," and his immense following testified to the appeal of such views.

A more careful voice speaking from the romantic tradition was that of Joseph Le Conte, distinguished geologist and naturalist in post-Civil War America. Le Conte went west to help found the University of California after the war, and during his long career there he brooded continually about the relations between his religious and scientific thought, finally publishing his reconciliation in 1888 as *Evolution: Its Nature, Its Evidences and Its Relation to Religious Thought*. Le Conte knew that the reaction against evolution was really a reaction against its materialistic implications,[93] and in Hegelian fashion he was persuaded that truth could be approached only by a rational philosophy which ex-

---

[91] John Fiske, *Through Nature to God* (Houghton, Mifflin and Company, 1899), pp. 25, 34.

[92] Fiske, *Excursions of an Evolutionist* (15th ed.; Houghton, Mifflin and Company, 1893), p. 298.

[93] Joseph Le Conte, *Evolution: Its Nature, Its Evidences, and Its Relation to Religious Thought* (2d ed. rev.; D. Appleton & Company, 1898), p. vi.

plained the conflict between the traditional doctrine of creation and Darwinian natural science by transcending their differences.[94] Thus he saw partial truth in the pious view that God created man in 4004 B.C., and partial truth in the materialistic view that man " just growed " by natural processes without God.[95] His goal was to transcend these two dogmatisms and yet to affirm the joint reality of divine agency and natural processes. Therefore, he proposed a synthesis: divine agency by natural process. This led him to his formulation of evolution as " continuous *progressive change, according to certain laws,* and by means of resident forces." [96] The resident force was God.[97]

One difference between Fiske and Le Conte is significant. Even though their views led them to similar conclusions, Le Conte was trying with much greater seriousness than Fiske to find room in his scheme for the objective reality of nature, and he was not so willing to brush it under the carpet of human subjectivity. As a scientist he did not feel comfortable simply *identifying* nature's objectivity with the subjectivity that he intuited inwardly. Instead, he conceived of evolution as a process in which objective and subjective categories were independently real in nature, so that there was both an " unconscious evolution by natural laws, *inherited from below,*" and a conscious purposive " higher evolution, *inherited from above.*" [98]

Le Conte was the first American scientist to use the idea of emergence in his evolutionary thought, and it was here that he came closest to a successful reconciliation of religion and Darwinian science. As early as 1860 he had proposed three laws of organic succession, according to which evolution progressed steadily upward through successive reigns of mollusks, fish, reptiles, and mammals.[99] The continuity of the whole process rested in the emergence of each level from the preceding one solely by means of natural causes, i.e., by means of efficient causation. However, at the highest level in the evolutionary process he recognized human purposiveness. To explain this, he carefully limited the category of final causation to man and specifically to man's consciousness:

[94] *Ibid.,* p. 290.   [96] *Ibid.,* p. 8.   [98] *Ibid.,* pp. 26 f.
[95] *Ibid.,* p. 292.   [97] *Ibid.,* p. 301.   [99] *Ibid.,* p. 16.

" Organic evolution is by a *pushing* upward and onward from *below* and *behind*, human progress by a drawing upward and onward from above and in front by the attractive force of ideals." [100]

Le Conte clearly viewed human purposiveness as emergent from the natural process, even though he had defined the natural process in purely Newtonian terms that made it logically impossible for purpose as a metaphysical category to emerge. This ambiguous attitude toward the relation of efficient and final causation can be seen where he speaks of emergent purposiveness in these words: " Last, and only with the appearance of Man, another entirely different and far higher factor *was introduced.*" [101] Here there are echoes of Bishop Wilberforce and *Humani generis*, affirming that purposiveness was " introduced " into nature only when human consciousness appeared. Like so many others, Le Conte was groping here for a rational way to transcend the Newtonian vision, but finally he defeated himself by basing his thought within it. As had Kant, he rested in the idea of a realm of revelation beyond the realm of scientific knowledge,[102] speculating that " in all cases the psychical lies behind the physical." [103] Mechanics, he said, is but the mode of operation of the divine mind, and creation is one continuous act.[104]

Le Conte's understanding of evolution as a moving process stirred by the purposes of an immanent God led him to a view of Jesus that was typical of men in the romantic liberal tradition. In his view, " the Christ " was the most powerfully attractive ideal that draws mankind onward toward its evolutionary goal. Since he was thinking of a God totally immanent in nature, Le Conte could say that the ideal human is divine, and therefore we all — the whole human race — must someday realize this same ideal, the divinity which was found in Jesus. This, he said, would be the evolutionary attainment of " the fullness of the stature of Christ." [105]

His view of evil was very like Fiske's, in that evil is the price of arriving at good, and what we take to be physical evil is " only

[100] *Ibid.*, p. 88.

[101] *Ibid.*, p. 86. Italics mine.

[102] *Ibid.*, p. 333.

[103] *Ibid.*, p. 339.

[104] *Ibid.*, p. 348.

[105] *Ibid.*, p. 364.

seeming evil, but real good." [106] Therefore, evil is but the dominance of the lower over the higher, and sin is "the humiliating bondage" of a higher level of evolution to a lower level.[107] Le Conte had defined the human stage of evolution in terms of man's consciousness, and in terms of his Cartesian dualism this bondage to a lower level could only mean that the source of human sinfulness resides outside the realm of will and conscious purpose, in the mechanical Newtonian parts of man's organism. Therefore, man is not responsible for the fact of his sinfulness, only for striving to enter "a higher spiritual evolution" away from sin.[108]

John Fiske and Joseph Le Conte were not clergymen, but the romantic ideas that they expressed were echoed by a number of influential ministers, all of whom helped to fulfill Fiske's prophecy that the last part of the nineteenth century would be known to historians as an era when orthodoxy was decomposing.[109] Minot J. Savage (1841–1918), a prominent Unitarian minister, was among the first to espouse Fiske's evolutionism and propose his own version of progressive salvation worked by an immanent God. Savage accepted a cosmic evolutionism, beginning with the universal "fire-mist" that Robert Chambers had proposed in *Vestiges* and moving toward our world where "the moral grandeur of one like Jesus towers like a mountain," and where "the imagination must confess that it has no colors bright and grand enough to paint the possibilities of the ages to come." [110]

He was persuaded that human ideas of God evolved, too, from a primitive idea of God's transcendence to the advanced modern idea of God's immanence, so that "to the highest thought of men, God has become a power, whose centre is everywhere, and his circumference nowhere." [111] Likewise, he contrasted the less-evolved "Jewish" theory of human nature (self-abasement) with the "American" theory (self-respect), observing that only the latter

[106] *Ibid.*, p. 367.

[107] *Ibid.*, p. 330.

[108] *Ibid.*

[109] Fiske, *Excursions of an Evolutionist*, p. 269.

[110] Minot J. Savage, *The Religion of Evolution* (Lockwood, Brooks, & Company, 1876), pp. 50 ff.

[111] *Ibid.*, p. 55.

could avoid making God into a moral monster.[112] Evil, he said, was "only human maladjustment to laws that, when known and kept, are the true servants and the mighty helpers of humanity." [113] Therefore, the answer to social problems was moral education, for "when men are morally wise enough, they will know it is always best to do right." [114]

Savage's doctrine of God's immanence so nearly identified God and truth with the actual state of affairs that at one point in his discussion of evolution he asserted blithely, "Christianity, one of its products, is also true." [115] In the same fashion, expressing a reluctance to interfere with the "divinely ordered" evolutionary process, he rather offhandedly dismissed the gathering signs of the social gospel: "In the light of human nature, as thus revealed, may be seen the futility of some of the present prominent notions about reform, as in matters of temperance, social vice, and the repression of crime. You cannot legislate character." [116]

This curious expression of social conservatism was quite common among all breeds of evolutionists, and in the case of social Darwinism it took a fairly brutal form, justifying the oppression of the poor as necessary for the process of natural selection. But in the case of Savage and other romantic liberals, it took the form of faith in a rather Lamarckian inheritance of acquired ethical ideals. Here they were supported by the scientific views of Edward D. Cope (1840–1897), the most prominent spokesman for neo-Lamarckism as the century closed. Professor Cope saw in evolution a key for resolving the dispute between idealists and realists, and he was persuaded that evolution was utterly incomprehensible apart from some interaction of subjectivity and objectivity in nature. He made an important proposal, to which we shall recur in Chapter IV: "Movements inaugurated in conscious states may be performed, so soon as learned, in unconsciousness, and become a part of the mental furniture of the animal." [117]

[112] *Ibid.*, pp. 75, 80.
[113] *Ibid.*, p. 110.
[114] *Ibid.*
[115] *Ibid.*, p. 215.
[116] *Ibid.*, pp. 89 f.
[117] E. D. Cope, "The Foundations of Theism," *The Monist*, Vol. III, No. 4 (July, 1893), p. 629.

Again, "The fact that the process may be now reflex does not exclude the fact of the influence of consciousness at the inception, and its necessity for the continuance of the habit." [118]

In evaluating Cope's proposal, we will miss its meaning unless we realize that he used the word "consciousness" to mean any aspect of subjectivity, not merely self-consciousness or awareness; and that like Le Conte, he was anxious to give proper weight to the real objectivity in nature. This was his way of affirming (a) that the subjectivity and objectivity in nature are independently real, and (b) that the subjectivity in nature is instrumental in forming its objectivity. Cope was grappling for a way to understand the possible relationship of final and efficient causation in nature, but clergymen like Savage rather too quickly supposed that the way was now open for belief that the consciously acquired ethical standards of the fathers somehow passed over into the genetic inheritance of the sons. Here was a rationale for faith in evolutionary moral progress! It was a view that focused on the eventual improvement and salvation of the whole human race, but it had much less to say about the immediate salvation of individuals, and it offered little support to people caught up in a time of unbelievable social change.

Evolution as "God's way of doing things" seemed to the romantic liberals such an obvious fact that gradually they began to pay less attention to the deeper questions involved in relating their theology to scientific thought. Thus Henry Ward Beecher (1813–1887) gladly made evolution the grand cosmic principle on which to base his evangelical preaching at Plymouth Church in Brooklyn. He was persuaded that man's knowledge of God comes chiefly by means of moral intuitions which have evolved through human history, and he made evolution the exegetical principle as he sought to discover the ever-higher conceptions of God that appear in the Bible as its history passes.[119] Since he believed that "religion is simply right living," [120] he eagerly explained each man's

[118] E. D. Cope, *Primary Factors in Organic Evolution* (The Open Court Publishing Company, 1896), pp. 499 f. See also his *Origin of the Fittest* (1887).

[119] Henry Ward Beecher, *Evolution and Religion* (Fords, Howard, & Hulbert, 1885), pp. 26, 56–68.

[120] *Ibid.*, p. 14.

gradual moral sanctification as an evolutionary process,[121] apparently forgetting that Darwin's hypothesis implied very little about developments during the life of a single individual. Even more confidently, Beecher proclaimed that " evolution is accepted as *the method* of creation by the whole scientific world," [122] a claim that would have astonished the growing number of scientists who were by then agnostic about the whole question of creation.

Lyman Abbott (1835–1922), Beecher's successor to the Plymouth Church pulpit, rode the flood tide of romantic evolutionary theism in his book *The Theology of an Evolutionist* (1897), and his style was formed by the belief that " we are to look for the experience of God in our own times and in our own souls." [123] This freed him from the need to erect a coherent and historically oriented scheme of ideas, so that he could sail smoothly around the threat of Darwinian science by saying that it did not conflict with his inward experience of God. " All nature and all life is one great theophany," [124] he said, and he was certain that in this evolving theophany modern religion was much advanced beyond all earlier kinds. Consequently he tended to see little of distinctive value in the Hebrew tradition. But then, showing how safe his faith in Jesus was from the assaults of logic, he said he could not imagine a higher state of evolution than Jesus.[125] Drawing further on notions from evolutionary thought, he wrote that God's grace comes to those who throw themselves into the struggle for virtue — grace is not, he said, " an easy bestowment of virtue on an unstruggling creature." [126] Nevertheless, with an immanent God at work bringing our redemption through evolution, our salvation is assured and belief in immortality seems almost unavoidable.[127]

In the minds of men like Savage, Beecher, and Abbott, evolution truly became " the grandest generalization of our age, if not

[121] *Ibid.*, pp. 39–43.

[122] *Ibid.*, p. 50.

[123] Lyman Abbott, *Reminiscences* (Houghton, Mifflin Company, 1915), p. 462.

[124] Lyman Abbott, *The Theology of an Evolutionist* (Houghton, Mifflin Company, 1897), p. 9.

[125] *Ibid.*, p. 66.

[126] *Ibid.*, p. 112.

[127] *Ibid.*, p. 161.

of any age," [128] and they extended Darwin's ideas lavishly, by analogy, to every conceivable aspect of reality and every side of theology. On the positive side, their romantic evolutionary theism encouraged a progressive and humane outlook on life and provided an acceptable anchor for faith to multitudes of American Christians who were baffled by the intellectual problems raised by Darwinism. But in the long run it could satisfy only those who were already fellow-swimmers in the pool of religious experience, and it could not be self-sustaining. It now seems that men like Fiske, Beecher, and Abbott achieved their fame very largely because their speaking and writing echoed a confidence in divinely intended social progress that was then deeply rooted in Western culture. No doubt this confidence lasted past 1900 as a dominant element of the Western consciousness, but the romantic liberal reconciliation could not survive the shattering impact of two world wars and the spiritual " shaking of the foundations " that we see around us now. Altogether, not so many people still have Asa Gray's " innate " conviction of purpose in the world, while the objective methodology of science has continued to produce impressive — and sometimes horrifying — successes. Belief in purposiveness at the heart of things slips away in history, as Darwin so painfully knew, and the romantic liberals unwittingly put down their anchor in a religious consciousness that soon would weaken and leave them adrift in stormy seas.

c. *The Response of Scientific Modernism.* Long before Lyman Abbott was preaching with evolutionary fervor in Brooklyn, the founders of American pragmatism had laid the groundwork for an approach to Darwinism which avoided any such extremes of enthusiasm. We have noted briefly that these men were meeting at Harvard just after the Civil War, and their scholarly response to Darwin continued to travel mainly in academic circles, rather isolated from the churches. Of course, this isolation was not complete (ideas do escape from the classroom!), but still, popular religion did not come to reflect their thought.

Chauncey Wright (1830–1875) was a key figure in this early group at Harvard, which included John Fiske, Francis Abbot,

[128] *Ibid.*, p. 177.

Charles Peirce, and William James. He opposed any effort to make evolution into a metaphysical principle, being equally antagonistic to Francis Abbot's use of evolutionism as a basis for theology and to the German tendency to discuss Darwin in terms of philosophical materialism. Wright's position was basically the same as Kant's, separating the realm of subjectivity quite sharply from the realm of objectivity, and acknowledging that Darwinian science was purely objective.

He was intensely concerned to protect scientific inquiry from the meddling of dogmatic theology,[129] and his philosophical position offered him a haven from which to make trenchant criticisms of the logic of both science and natural theology. As early as 1865 he had pointed out that science can never disclose purpose in nature and that theologians merely dilute the purity of religious truth when they try to make science support belief in Design.[130] Certain that people arrived at belief in a purposive universe on other grounds, he determined to show that faith could be in principle utterly independent of science. Here he expressed himself in a way that would have been approved by Rudolf Bultmann two generations later, writing that nothing in science or philosophy can rebuke religious faith, " unless it be the dogmatism which would presumptuously interpret as science what is only manifest to faith, or would require of faith that it shall justify itself by proofs." [131]

Wright brilliantly criticized the positivism of Comte by pointing out that " subjective motives " (e.g., awe, curiosity) were not only the original stimulus for scientific investigation, but " objective motives " by themselves were at all times a weak stimulus for research. The modern " objective " spirit of science, he noted, could hardly have had any persistent influence on the direction of inquiry until after a large body of systematic and well-digested scientific truth had been generated in response to " sub-

129 Wiener, *op. cit.*, p. 65.
130 Chauncey Wright, *Philosophical Discussions*, ed. by Charles Eliot Norton (Henry Holt and Company, 1878), pp. 36, 39. This appeared first in " Natural Theology as a Positive Science," *North American Review* (January, 1865).
131 *Ibid.*, p. 41.

jective motives "; and even then the " objective " attitude never can supersede the " subjective " attitude.[132] Positivism was correct, he said, in pointing to the successive appearance of its three phases in the development of the human mind — Theological, Metaphysical, Scientific — but they only *begin* in succession, and thereafter they *coexist* independently. For this reason, said Wright, Spencer had no business proclaiming that science now should dictate rules for the study of history, society, laws, and morality.

At a time when John Fiske was calling Spencer's work " of the calibre of that which Aristotle and Newton did," [133] Wright saw with prophetic vision that Spencer's immense following meant only that he was trumpeting the note of Universal Progress, which Wright called the " key-note of modern civilization." [134] He observed that all cosmological schemes are strictly teleological, since they involve speculations about what we have not observed and supply a principle of order derived ultimately from our own minds.[135] This being the case, he concluded that Spencer's grandiose system was merely a mask for his own form of religious sentiment (moral idealism), which illustrated " his incompetency for the further development of his encyclopedic abstractions." [136]

It is against the background of Chauncey Wright's razor-sharp thought that we should try to see the work of William James, whom Whitehead has called " that adorable genius." [137] James and his friends were tremendously impressed by the fact of evolution, and pragmatism was in no small way an attempt to express their discovery that human reason had evolved for practical ends, that the function of ideas was to help man adjust to a changing world.

---

[132] *Ibid.*, pp. 47–52.

[133] Fiske, *Excursions of an Evolutionist*, p. 295.

[134] Wright, *op. cit.*, p. 69. He went on: " Faith that moral perfectibility is possible, not in remote times and places, not in the millenium, not in heaven, but in the furtherance of a present progress, is a faith which to possess in modern times does not make a man suspected of folly or fanaticism. He may forget the past, cease to be religious in the conventional sense of the word, but he is the modern prophet."

[135] *Ibid.*, p. 71.

[136] *Ibid.*, pp. 91–96. For a good recent study of Wright, see Edward H. Madden, *Chauncey Wright and the Foundations of Pragmatism* (University of Washington Press, 1963).

[137] Whitehead, *Science and the Modern World*, p. 2.

Therefore, much hinged on how a certain idea or belief worked out in practice, just as a good deal depended on how an evolved change in a bird's wing affected the bird's success in natural selection.

James was concerned to establish the validity of subjective categories *as a part of nature*, and his essay " Does ' Consciousness ' Exist? " was an explicit attempt to show that Kant failed to save subjectivity by establishing it in a transcendental realm outside of empirical nature. Kant, he said, had " undermined the soul " when he made the ego transcendental.[138] James proposed instead that there is one primal stuff of reality and that it should be called " pure experience," with subjectivity and objectivity its " terms." [139] This was, of course, a way of affirming that all reality is essentially both subjective and objective, but James meant more precisely that both " subject " and " object " are abstractions from the concrete reality, " pure experience." Here he resembled Bergson, whom we shall discuss in more detail later.

Since James was persuaded that subjective and objective categories were real and inseparable aspects of nature, he objected vigorously to Wright's dispassionate separation of " subjective motives " from " objective " thought. Wright believed, for example, that a state of suspended judgment on religious questions was the only reasonable attitude, and James wrote " The Will to Believe " chiefly to oppose this view.[140] Here he tried to make a place for subjectivity in nature by the empirical method: we must take the complex and spontaneous variations of our *inner* life as empirical facts which are just as real as the facts of the *outer* world. Supporting this view, James observed that, in things which matter most to us, we ordinarily discover ourselves simply holding a belief without knowing why, and that when we want to see the *worth* of something we consult our hearts, not science.[141] His point was that subjective factors inevitably lie at the root of our deepest convictions — even the most " objective " scientist finally is con-

[138] William James, *Essays in Radical Empiricism* (Longmans, Green & Co., Inc., 1912), p. 1.

[139] *Ibid.*, p. 4.

[140] Wiener, *op. cit.*, p. 46.

[141] James, *op. cit.*, pp. 94, 103.

sulting his heart when he acts on the assumption that it is good to establish facts or to correct false belief. James linked his views specifically to evolution by noting that the subjective categories (such as purpose) had appeared in the same natural evolutionary process that had produced the objective categories of scientific thought, and he summed up his views on their essential togetherness by statements such as, " Faith in a fact can help create the fact." [142] His Gifford Lectures, *The Varieties of Religious Experience*, were a similar effort to stake out a place for subjectivity *in nature* by pointing to the undoubted importance of religious experience as a factor in human existence. The essence of religion, he said, is to be found in the feelings and conduct of people,[143] and our own immediate religious experience is certainly less abstract than a science that takes no account of anything private.

In making " pure experience " the concrete fact, James fused subjectivity and objectivity in a way which had the most interesting implications. For one thing, it opened up fascinating possibilities for understanding the phenomena of psychical research, a field in which James was a leader. Here he could think of the external world somehow present as an aspect of one's subconscious experience, and he spoke of a man's conscious life as continuous with a " wider self." [144] In line with this, he suggested that God's action in human experience comes in the form of powerful intrusions from what we ordinarily call the subconscious; Jungian psychology has made much of this idea. But James's position made it very difficult for him to conceive of God as being real apart from his practical existential impact in human experience. He did not believe that God (or anything else, for that matter) could exist without making a difference in facts, and he readily classed himself with those " crass " supernaturalists who believed that God has a causal efficacy right along with other factors which to-

[142] *Ibid.*, p. 106.
[143] William James, *The Varieties of Religious Experience* (Modern Library, n.d.), pp. 490, 494. Emphasizing that religion is centered in feeling, he wrote, " See how the ancient spirit of Methodism evaporates under those wonderfully able rationalistic booklets (which every one should read) of a philosopher like Professor Bowne." P. 492, note.
[144] *Ibid.*, p. 505.

gether causally determine the details of the real world.[145] He wrote: " That which produces effects within another reality must be termed a reality itself, so I feel as if we had no philosophic excuse for calling the unseen or mystical world unreal. . . . God is real since he produces real effects." [146]

Once William James had claimed that religious experience qualified as a datum for science, the empirical strain in academic religious thought moved steadily into prominence. Henry Nelson Wieman (1884–   ) has attempted to give an accurate empirical description of Christian faith, focusing on events in a way which resembles James's insistence that subjective and objective categories are abstractions from the concrete actuality of experience. Like James, he believes that we identify God conceptually only after experiencing the effect of God's reality in the events of life, and this function of God in human life is expressed in the title of one of his books, *The Source of Human Good.*[147] Wieman's effort to rescue subjective categories thus turns on his conviction that in serving the creative process which increases human good, we are serving God. Even less than William James is he able to think of God as transcending the process, and, in the long run, the creative process must provide its own call on our loyalties. Here we seem to be thrown back on an " innate conviction " of loyalty to the process, very much like the " innate " belief in nature's purposiveness that we have found in Asa Gray and Boston Personalism.

Shailer Mathews also tried to revive a wavering theological orthodoxy by bringing the guns of science to its defense. He said that modernism represented the elements of " change " in Christendom in contrast to the " stand-patters," [148] and, because he believed Christianity to be a moral and spiritual movement, he did not feel bound by the theological formulations of any one age. Just as William James had seen consciousness as a variable function of an underlying experience, Mathews saw theological doc-

---

[145] *Ibid.,* pp. 510 f.

[146] *Ibid.,* p. 507.

[147] Henry Nelson Wieman, *The Source of Human Good* (University of Chicago Press, 1946).

[148] Shailer Mathews, *The Faith of Modernism* (The Macmillan Company, 1924), p. 17.

trine as a changing function of certain rather simple Christian convictions, " the permanent element of our evolving religion." [149] These convictions, he assumed, boiled down to belief in God, good will, and personal survival after death. With this attitude, Mathews could hardly regard theological reflection as an avenue to truth, and his pragmatic style was captured in a single phrase: " The way to get together is to work together." [150] Building society will be " an accomplishment of the evolutionary process," [151] said Mathews, and in his dedication to the social process we see an almost complete victory of evolutionary notions of flux over traditional notions of divine stability.

[149] *Ibid.*, pp. 72–76.   [150] *Ibid.*, p. 175.   [151] *Ibid.*, p. 173.

III

THE MODERN SCIENTIFIC THEORY
OF EVOLUTION

1. A Century of Research

We have mentioned earlier that the latter part of the nineteenth century was a time of intensive study by scientists anxious to establish the *fact* of evolution as suggested by Darwin. This search for evidence was necessary on two counts: (*a*) Darwin's evidence, impressive as it was, needed a good deal of elaboration, especially when it came to establishing fossil series, and (*b*) the current of theological hostility toward the notion of evolution almost compelled scientists to take up the gauntlet, especially when it came in the form of suggestions that Darwinism was " bad science." The resulting advances in comparative anatomy and embryology produced forests of family trees, as investigators became engrossed in unraveling the phylogenies of organisms. Documenting their constructions from the increasing successes in paleontology, some of them grew their family trees on rather shaky ground; Ernst Haeckel (1834–1919) was one of those enthusiastic Darwinians whose genealogical diagrams now produce some amazement.[1] Another facet of Darwinian thought appeared as the detailed study of adaptations, in an effort to show that the hypothesis of natural selection could account for all the amazingly complex organic adaptations that previously had been explained in terms of Design; a favorite example was the problem of accounting for the evolution of the mammalian eye. In a sense this

[1] Charles Singer, *A History of Biology to about the Year 1900: A General Introduction to the Study of Living Things* (3d ed. rev.; London: Abelard-Schuman, Ltd., 1959), p. 488.

took on the flavor of a " biological theodicy," justifying the benevolent workings of natural selection to man with the enthusiasm that theologians were accustomed to use in defending the purposes of God.

As the century drew to a close, biologists became dissatisfied with the increasingly speculative nature of Darwinian science, and the time was ripe for a study of the *causes* of variation. Until this problem was investigated, there could be no way of settling what had become the major dispute in the evolutionists' camp by 1900 — the argument between neo-Darwinians (who saw natural selection as the chief or only factor in evolution) and neo-Lamarckians (who emphasized both the role of an organism's responses to needs produced by its environment, and the inheritance of acquired characteristics). The debate was muddied considerably by the fact that Darwin himself had assumed the Lamarckian inheritance of acquired characteristics.

During the 1890's this controversy revolved around the work of the neo-Darwinian August Weismann (1834–1914). He was disturbed by Darwin's improbable notion of pangenesis and opposed it by postulating an immortal " germ plasm " which was isolated from the other cells in an organism and which preserved the species by dividing and being passed on to the next generation quite unaffected by any changes that the environment might have induced in the rest of the body.[2] His sharp distinction between germinal and somatic cells was overdrawn, but it did help biologists to distinguish between genetic variation and noninheritable somatic variation, a distinction Darwin could not yet make. Of course, this distinction sharply opposed Lamarck's idea that organisms could bequeath variations that had arisen as the *total* organism responded to needs presented by the environment, and Weismann stoutly opposed every Lamarckian strain in Darwin's thought. He sought to prove his point by cutting off the tails of newborn rats, showing (not very surprisingly) that the deformity never was passed on to the next generation.[3] Here he was not re-

2 August Weismann, *Essays Upon Heredity* (2 vols.; Oxford University Press, 1892).

3 Eric Nordenskiöld, *The History of Biology* (Tudor Publishing Co., 1928), p. 565.

ally testing Lamarck's theory, which concerned only the inheritance of variations that arose to aid animals in new environments, since we may doubt that Weismann's rats felt any need to lose their tails! But he was always eager to show that evolution could be explained in terms of natural selection alone, and his enthusiasm even led him to adopt the idea that body cells " struggled for existence " among themselves. On the other hand, several evolutionists were strong defenders of neo-Lamarckism, emphasizing the importance of the environment and the organism's inner response as factors in evolutionary change. These men also found in neo-Lamarckism a salutary principle for social progress; among them was the American paleontologist Edward D. Cope.

Darwin's original hypothesis had assumed that in every generation all the characteristics of animals varied on a continuum in every direction; thus animals bred from the largest member of a litter should tend to vary in size around this new norm. In this way, Darwin believed, natural selection over a long period could pile up massive changes in any characteristic. But, near the end of the century, the Cambridge biologist William Bateson (1861–1926) became dissatisfied with Darwin's view, and he accumulated examples of discontinuous variation or " saltation," publishing his results in 1894.[4] He suggested that large-scale change, not Darwin's continuous but small-scale variation around a norm, provides the raw material of evolution. Hugo de Vries (1848–1935), professor of botany at Amsterdam, also believed that Darwin was wrong in his views on variation in nature. After years of studying a colony of American evening primroses, he published his *Mutationslehre* (1901–1903), saying that new species arise suddenly by gross changes which he called " mutations." The " mutation theory " rapidly gained ground, and during the same decade the Danish investigator W. L. Johannsen (1857–1927) showed by careful experiments with beans that natural selection could not operate if there were only the kind of variation postulated by Darwin. No matter whether he bred from the largest or the small-

[4] William Bateson, *Materials for the Study of Variation, Treated with especial Regard to Discontinuity in the Origin of Species* (The Macmillan Company, 1894).

est beans in a self-fertilizing bean population, he was unable to develop beans with a range of weights different from his original beans.

By 1910 it seemed that discontinuous " jumps " somehow must be among the major causal factors in speciation, and if this were so, the factors of natural selection and geographical isolation might be much less important than Darwin had thought. But the problem of tracing the causes of saltatory variation to the germ plasm was obviously great, and Darwinians found themselves perplexed. This period of puzzlement had two results — it pushed Darwinians more directly toward developing the science of genetics as they tried to establish a naturalistic explanation for mutations; but also it lent some credence to the claims of those who began to say that Darwinism was dying. Once again, a temporary obstacle for science seemed to offer support for those who were prone to find God lurking at the boundaries of scientific knowledge, and the temporary confusion among Darwinians encouraged some churchmen to use the notion of mutation in justifying their belief in repeated divine creations. In 1900 Mendel's work was rediscovered, giving further impetus to the idea that mutations were the main cause of evolutionary change,[5] and by 1914 Bateson was persuaded that genetical change occurred *only* by large mutations. But he believed that each mutation was merely a loss of some germ plasm; evolution appeared to him as a process in which an original bundle of genetic material slowly was stripped away so that new forms appeared.[6] This made natural selection seem even more trivial as a factor in evolution, so that the theory of natural selection reached a low of popularity during the period from 1900 to 1925. As things turned out, early genetical studies nearly killed interest in studying the causes of evolution.

As the years went by, however, it became clearer that the various streams of biological research were coming together again in

---

[5] Interestingly, the discovery was made by three men working independently of each other: Correns, De Vries, and Tschermak. See F. S. Bodenheimer, *The History of Biology: an Introduction* (London: Wm. Dawson & Sons, Ltd., 1958), p. 142.

[6] Julian Huxley, *Evolution: The Modern Synthesis* (Science Editions, John Wiley & Sons, Inc., 1964), p. 24.

a newer form of Darwinism. By 1930 it was possible for Fisher to reconcile the facts behind the chromosome theory and the mutation theory with the older notions of gradual evolutionary change through natural selection,[7] and in 1931 the physiologist J. B. S. Haldane delivered a series of lectures entitled " A Re-examination of Darwinism." He published them under a title symbolizing the way biologists were returning to the question which interested Darwin: *The Causes of Evolution*.[8] As Huxley observed, the new form of Darwinism was a modified Darwinism operating with a host of facts unknown to Darwin,[9] but it was still Darwinian in its ideal of a nonpurposive explanation for evolution.

Since 1930, elements from various earlier explanatory schemes have been fused into a very broad unified theory that has come to be called the " synthetic selectionist theory." Mayr refers to it as a " synthesis of mutationism and environmentalism," [10] and events of recent years have fully borne out Huxley's 1942 prediction that the time was ripe for a grand synthesis of work in genetics, developmental physiology, ecology, systematics, paleontology, cytology, and mathematical analysis.[11] The volume of biological knowledge represented in the present synthetic theory of evolution is now so staggering in its detail that one writer expresses an almost eschatological hope when he says we must await the coming of another Darwin, someone who will be able to extract an essence from this huge pile of facts.[12]

2. General Aspects of the Modern Synthetic Theory

Evolutionary science during the closing decades of the nineteenth century was devoted to a successful gathering of proofs that evolution really has occurred, but we still hear it asked, " Is evo-

---

[7] R. A. Fisher, *The Genetical Theory of Natural Selection* (Oxford: Clarendon Press, 1930).

[8] J. B. S. Haldane, *The Causes of Evolution* (Harper & Brothers, 1932).

[9] J. Huxley, *Evolution: The Modern Synthesis*, p. 27.

[10] Ernst Mayr, *Animal Species and Evolution* (Harvard University Press, 1963), p. 1.

[11] In the preface of *Evolution: The Modern Synthesis*.

[12] Ben Dawes, *A Hundred Years of Biology* (London: Gerald Duckworth & Co., Ltd., 1952), p. 285.

lution a fact, or only a theory? " This question, raised sometimes
by persons who object to the teaching of evolution in public
schools, reveals a lack of understanding for scientific methodology and the nature of historical judgments; it fails to distinguish
between actual past events and our present judgments as to the
nature of those events. A very large portion of evolutionary theory attempts to give historical explanations for certain events in
the past, and the acknowledged criterion of truth is whether our
beliefs about certain happenings in the past history of the earth
correspond with the actual events themselves. Now, beliefs about
the past can be formed only by observing certain presently existing artifacts (e.g., markings in rocks), then making interpretive
judgments in the light of some general understanding. Therefore,
when someone asks, " Is evolution a fact? " he is combining two
questions. The first is this: have those who are best qualified to
make these interpretive judgments about the artifacts agreed that
belief in evolution corresponds with actual events in the past?
Clearly the answer to this question is " yes," for almost every rep-
utable scientist is persuaded that belief in evolution corresponds
with actual past events. We are then justified in saying that *belief*
in evolution is about as well agreed upon scientifically as belief
that the earth rotates on its axis once in twenty-four hours. The
second question is this: are these men correct in their judgment?
Obviously this question cannot so easily be answered, for we must
first agree on which basic understanding of reality in general is
most nearly adequate to serve as the ground of our judgments.
Therefore, those who maintain that evolution is " merely a theory " really are telling us only that they use an interpretive scheme
of ideas which differs from that of modern science, but they usually do not make this explicit; they then feel free to propose some
alternate hypothesis (usually special creation) to account for the
artifacts.

It goes almost without saying that no one could ever have wit-
nessed any major evolutionary change, for events of this magnitude (often called macroevolution) require immense periods of
time. The only evolutionary events we actually can observe are
the small-scale genetic changes called microevolution, which hap-

pen more rapidly. Hence we are compelled to infer the causes of macroevolution on some basis other than observation. If we do this, should we conclude that the causes of present microevolutionary events also were sufficient causes for past macroevolutionary happenings? It will not be surprising that even well-informed biologists disagree at this point, and the admitted leap between what evolutionists can observe in the present and what they do infer about the past undoubtedly encourages some people to propose special creation instead. Nevertheless, most modern investigators are persuaded that the whole phylogenetic tree, from the earliest forms of life to the more than two million present species of animals and plants, can be explained adequately (at least in principle) solely in terms of the causes observed or postulated for presently observable microevolutionary events.

Evolutionary science is so complex and fast-moving that even the most expert observer cannot write a description that is still accurate by the time his last page is finished, so as we try here to present a brief summary of the present theory it is with knowledge that specialists will cringe at certain omissions. We may hope only that our effort is relatively free from distortion and misplaced emphasis. Fortunately, the Darwin centennial year (1959) stimulated a good deal of writing on evolution, and we have excellent recent studies to draw on, notably those of Dobzhansky, Grant, Mayr, and Rensch.[13] Let us begin by pointing up some central ideas in the modern theory of evolution, ideas that need to be borne in mind if we are to avoid serious errors of interpretation. Criticism of these ideas will be reserved until the next chapter.

a. *Evolutionary biology studies populations, not types.* Dobzhansky, whose work in genetics has done so much in clarifying the details of evolution, writes, " Evolution is a change in the genetic composition of populations." [14] Mayr believes that the re-

[13] Theodosius Dobzhansky, *Mankind Evolving: The Evolution of the Human Species* (Yale University Press, 1962) ; Verne Grant, *The Origin of Adaptations* (Columbia University Press, 1963) ; Ernst Mayr, *Animal Species and Evolution* (Harvard University Press, 1963) ; Bernhard Rensch, *Evolution Above the Species Level* (Columbia University Press, 1960).

[14] Theodosius Dobzhansky, *Genetics and the Origin of Species* (3d ed.; Columbia University Press, 1951), p. 16.

placement of typological thinking by population thinking in biology is the greatest conceptual revolution that has taken place in that science, and he goes so far as to lay nearly every major dispute in evolutionary study to a disagreement between a " typologist " and a " populationist." [15] Now, what do we mean by these terms? The typological approach to biological species sees the " type " (e.g., " dog," " goldfinch," " man ") as a real entity, whereas for the populationist the type is only an average obtained when we take a spatial or temporal cross section of some evolving animal line. We tend to visualize organisms as individual examples of some type rather than as members of a variable population that endures through time; but in spite of the obvious advantages of this view when we are seeking to identify an animal morphologically, it is precisely this habit that must be suspended when we come to consider evolutionary change. Very clearly, nominalism has won out over idealism and romanticism in biology, and we must guard ourselves against the longtime habit of thinking that evolution advances by producing a new " type " of individual. Individuals do not evolve, only populations do.

A moment's reflection will show that concern for individual creatures is a real novelty on earth, but this concern for the individual, so much a part of the Western culture in which science arose, has been read back erroneously into the dimmest recesses of the evolutionary past. It has taken us a long time to learn that while a single sparrow may be very important to God, the sparrow is not very important to evolution: events in heaven (the way God lovingly views a sparrow) are not the same as events on earth (the way a sparrow contributes to the gene pool of the next generation of sparrows in its population).

b. *The present theory is a synthesis of earlier causal theories, still seeking to explain evolution in terms of purely natural causes.* Grant's recent statement is typical of this attitude as he calls evolutionary theory " an attempt to explain the historical unfolding of life on the earth as a result of the operation of natural causes, some of which reside in living organisms themselves and others in their environments." [16] We know, for example, that the scope

<hr/>

[15] Mayr, *op. cit.*, pp. 5 f.   [16] Grant, *op. cit.*, p. 3.

of genetic mutation may be controlled both by intrinsic factors and by such extrinsic factors as X-rays; and it is now agreed that the environment serves as the primary factor in natural selection. Also Grant's definition is very carefully phrased where he says that the modern theory is an *attempt* to explain in terms of natural (i.e., nonpurposive) causes. Certainly this is still the basic explanatory ideal, even if it is not reached in fact, and the modern theory seeks to avoid, wherever possible, any notions of a purposive relationship between organisms and their complex environments. Instead, it tries to clarify the selective effects of environments on the gene pools of animal populations, and explanation at this level has been quite fruitful.

c. *Evolutionary change is not primarily a genetic event but occurs principally through geographical factors of speciation.* Until recently it was believed that when we discovered the causes of genetic mutation we would know the reasons for evolutionary change, but geographical isolation has proved to be much more important than mutation in the production of new populations. Evolution now is seen as a two-stage phenomenon (genetic variation, and sorting of it by natural selection), but the second factor is vastly more significant, and here geographical isolation is decisive. Among other things, this means that the fascinating details of the genetic code are only of secondary importance for investigating the causes of evolutionary change. We must remember, however, that the causes of stability also are exceedingly important factors in the total evolutionary process, and at this point genetic factors are supreme.

d. *The modern theory is not reductionistic.* Perhaps this may be surprising to those who have supposed that evolutionists were dedicated to explaining the events of evolutionary history (and sometimes history in general!) by reducing every explanation to the concepts of physics and chemistry. On the contrary, however, very few evolutionary biologists seek to do this or even see it as desirable. The bitter disputes between mechanists and vitalists that marked biology during the late nineteenth century and early twentieth century have passed from the scene, and there is increasing agreement over the futility of " explaining away " nonphysical factors, especially in seeking to understand human evolution. Some biologists believe that cultural factors have played the major role in human evolution since Cro-Magnon man appeared about thirty-five thousand years ago, and in discussing human evolution a number of biologists even introduce the idea of purpose. This is, we should note, an important departure from the nonpurposive explanatory ideal generally upheld while thinking of prehuman evolution, and it suggests that one of two things may be true: (a) perhaps different explanatory models apply at different stages of evolutionary history, or (b) some more comprehensive explanatory model is required to provide a coherent explanation of evolution. Later we shall defend the second of these alternatives, but at the moment we must ask why this major shift in biological modes of thought has occurred during the past century.

Very likely there are several reasons. For one thing, it is a modest retreat from the attitude of men like Herbert Spencer and T. H. Huxley, who made extravagant and unguarded metaphysical extrapolations from biological thought.[17] Then too it may reflect a widespread recent suspicion of the whole metaphysical task, an attitude encouraged by the success of positivism in science and expressed particularly in the notion that scientific theories are merely human devices helpful in gathering facts beneath a conceptual umbrella. This "instrumentalist" view of scientific theories, which sees them principally in terms of their usefulness in further research, specifically disclaims that they correspond with actual events in the world; the "truth" of a theory is defined entirely with regard to its experimental fruitfulness.[18] More importantly, however, it appears that evolutionary biologists have been struck with the really notable results obtained by doing their work in terms of concepts that are derived directly from the study of liv-

[17] T. H. Huxley's grandson Julian was a victim of the same malady, often speaking of evolution as though it were the sufficient grounds of his own brand of humanistic piety. A typical comment: "Man's true destiny is . . . to be the chief agent for the future of evolution on this planet." Julian Huxley, "The Emergence of Darwinism," *Evolution after Darwin*, Vol. I, ed. by Sol Tax (The University of Chicago Press, 1960), p. 19.

[18] See, e.g., Philipp Frank, *Modern Science and Its Philosophy* (Harvard University Press, 1950), and *The Validation of Scientific Theories*, ed. by Philipp Frank (Beacon Press, Inc., 1957).

ing organisms and their behavior; thus "organismic biology" has been a steadily growing branch of science since 1900. Von Bertalanffy, for example, believes that although organisms and their processes might in principle be describable in terms of concepts from physics and chemistry, "organismic" concepts are necessary if we are to describe the ways in which physicochemical processes are organized in living creatures. It is simply no help in studying living things, he observes, to approach them either with a "machine model" of explanation or with the "vitalist model" that opposes it. Only by developing concepts directly from biological data can we hope to gain understanding of living organisms.[19] Some such attitude is characteristic of most present-day evolutionary biologists. Mayr, for example, points out that the differences between species cannot be expressed in terms of the genetic code. Even if we could reduce our concepts in this way (which we cannot), it would be fruitless for further research, like trying to express the differences between the Bible and *Paradise Lost* in terms of letter frequencies. "The meaningful level of integration," writes Mayr, "is well above that of the basic code of information, the nucleotide pairs."[20] A similar view is held by the German zoologist Rensch, who points out that evolutionary studies can advance only by attention to regularities that develop in living matter at a level far above the genetic code. Rensch even proposes the term "bionomogenesis" to indicate that modern evolutionary theory depends on formulating laws which relate to biological phenomena directly.[21]

Here the point is that each level of generalization in science exhibits certain simplicities which stand out only at that level, e.g., certain simplicities about the flight of a sea gull would be utterly obscured if in our thinking we refused to abstract from considering the individual cells. Therefore, such high-level abstrac-

[19] Ludwig von Bertalanffy, *Modern Theories of Development: an Introduction to Theoretical Biology*, tr. and adapted by J. H. Woodger (Harper Torchbooks, Harper & Brothers, 1962), p. 46. This work appeared first in 1928 as *Kritische Theorie der Formbildung*, and it served as a kind of manifesto for organismic biologists during the next generation.

[20] Mayr, *Animal Species and Evolution*, p. 544.

[21] Rensch, *Evolution Above the Species Level*, p. 321.

tions as " gene loci " and " geographical races " continue to be useful in research quite apart from the question of their ultimate metaphysical reference,[22] and biologists can agree on the main elements of the modern synthetic theory, even though they may disagree in terms of metaphysics or be uninterested in examining the metaphysical basis of their methodology and explanatory ideals. In fact, satisfaction with their general notions has encouraged biologists to disclaim metaphysics, very much as Newton did, and the present attitude is one of hesitancy to link the notions of evolutionary biology with *any* metaphysical scheme, even that of traditional materialistic determinism.

3. THE ORIGIN OF LIFE

It is important to remember that the biological theory of evolution is strictly limited in its subject matter to changes in living forms after there was some life on earth, and in this restricted sense, evolutionary theory really says nothing about the origin of life itself. Strictly speaking, we cannot say " scientifically " that life even originated, for we have no present evidence that life develops from nonliving material. Also, the present " layer " of life on earth probably has destroyed any observable conditions under which life may have once originated from inorganic matter. There have been suggestions that living spores were transported to earth from outer space by some sort of cosmic current,[23] but even this proposal still leaves us with the ultimate source of life unexplained. Of course, general theories of cosmic evolution, such as Kant's, were in vogue long before Darwin applied the notion of evolution to living creatures, and there are still today plausible reasons for suggesting that life and even planetary systems have originated by some process that may be described appropriately as evolutionary. However, we cannot make these judgments by de-

[22] See the discussions about reduction of concepts in Ernest Nagel, *The Structure of Science: Problems in the Logic of Scientific Explanation* (Harcourt, Brace, & World, Inc., 1961), and Stephen Toulmin, *The Philosophy of Science* (London: Hutchinson & Co., Publishers, Ltd., 1953).

[23] J. B. S. Haldane, " The Origin of Life," *New Biology*, 16 (1954), pp. 12-27.

duction from what we have learned in studying the evolution of life on our planet — nothing we know about gene mutation implies that life began from a "natural selection" of struggling atoms! This is only to say that theories of cosmic evolution are openly speculative in nature, and we must be careful about implying that "science tells us" of the origin of our planet or the life we find on it. Science tells us a great deal, enough so that scientists and philosophers can construct cosmological schemes that help us in our quest for understanding; but we should remember that cosmology occupies a somewhat awkward position midway between scientifically verified facts and completely unverified philosophical speculation. Probably we should place imaginative efforts to reconstruct the origin of life somewhere between science and cosmology, and it is clear that while theology may relate itself to cosmological reflection, we are not entitled to erect a theological doctrine of creation on the supposition that it can be verified scientifically.

With these things said, let us now take a running look at the history of our planet as it has been reconstructed by scientists. From studies of radioactive materials, the age of the earth has been set at about five billion years, and Oparin's image is helpful as we try to imagine what this means. He suggests that we visualize the history of the earth recorded in ten volumes of five hundred pages each, so that each page covers a million years.[24] Our discussion of the fossilized remains of animals and plants preserved since the Cambrian era, five hundred million years ago, would appear in the tenth volume. About half of this period was required for plants to become fully terrestrial and for amphibious animals to appear, but then evolution of terrestrial animals took place more rapidly. About sixty to seventy million years ago the reptiles reached the height of their development, and it was another thirty-five million years before their dominance was superseded by that of birds and beasts. The entire history of man is confined to the very last page or two of the very last volume! As to the first origin of life, we may conjecture that primitive forms appear somewhere in the

24 A. I. Oparin, *Life: Its Nature, Origin and Development*, tr. by Ann Synge (Academic Press, Inc., 1962), p. 91.

eighth or seventh volume, around a billion years ago; there are some fossils from the Riffian era (pre-Cambrian), and we might guess that the very earliest forms of life would antedate these by a volume or two. Some recent studies even suggest that life existed on earth more than two billion years ago, and very likely the evolutionary distance from these first forms to simple bacteria-like creatures was as great as that which now separates the amoeba from man.

It is dangerous to place too much reliance on presently existing creatures as clues to the evolutionary past, but a brief look at the smallest forms of present life does reveal a series that can be at least suggestive of events in the past. The simplest known forms of life are complex individualized systems containing nucleoproteins, capable of metabolism and reproduction. Bacteria range in size from 0.5 to 10 microns, a micron (mu) being one thousandth of a millimeter. Smaller than these are the rickettsiae, which produce illnesses such as typhus; they are about 0.2 to 0.7 mu in size. Even smaller are the complex viruses, one causing equine encephalomyelitis being only about 50 millimicrons (mmu) in size; this is below the threshold of the ordinary light microscope. Bacteriophages, which are parasitic on bacteria, range in size from about 12 to 140 mmu. Finally we come to the smallest of all, the simple viruses, including the poliomyelitis virus and the tobacco mosaic virus. The latter is so minute that it can be discussed in molecular terms — but even it has a molecular weight something like 46 million! We need to remember that this series is not a phylogenetic series, for some of these organisms may be descended from more complex ancestors, but at least it should be clear that even the " primitive amoeba " is a very sophisticated creature far removed from the first beginnings of life. One interesting discovery possibly relating to the origin of life is that of Miller, who obtained amino acids such as glutamic acid and alanine by electrical discharges in a mixture of methane, ammonia, hydrogen, and water vapor, types of gas which are thought to have existed in the primordial atmosphere of earth.[25] This may indi-

---

[25] S. L. Miller, " A Production of Amino Acids Under Possible Primitive Earth Conditions," *Science*, 117 (1953), pp. 528 f.

cate that early forms of life passed through the stage of amino acids, but much more investigation is required before we dare make any solid conclusions.

4. GENES AND MUTATIONS, THE RAW MATERIALS OF EVOLUTION

In 1909, Johannsen coined the word " gene " to designate the supposed particles responsible for the phenomena of Mendelian inheritance. He also distinguished between " phenotype " (phenomenon type) and " genotype " (genetic type) ; the genotype is believed to remain unchanged throughout the lifetime of an animal, but the phenotype, which comprises all its observable characteristics, varies in response to changing conditions in the environment. The original " genes " were purely hypothetical, but between 1910 and 1935, T. H. Morgan and his workers carefully developed the present idea that a gene is a portion of material in the chromosome.[26] It is remarkable that the chromosomes of all higher plants and animals are strikingly similar to each other, and this fact serves as persuasive evidence of the unity of life on our planet.

Most people by now have heard the expression " cracking the genetic code," even though it harks back only to 1953, when Watson and Crick proposed the double-helix model of chromosome structure.[27] They suggested that in all creatures the carrier of genetic information is a double-stranded coil of deoxyribonucleic acid (DNA), a polymer which may be imagined without too much distortion as an immensely long, coiled extension ladder. Each " crossbar " is a hydrogen bond that holds together the opposed segments of the ladder " legs," and it is these bonds which are broken when the DNA splits longitudinally in order to reproduce itself. The legs of the ladder are composed of long chains of nucleotides, each of which consists of a nitrogen base (purine or pyramidine), a 5-carbon sugar (deoxyribose), and phosphoric

[26] More recently we have discovered that the genotype is determined not only by chromosome genes but by plasmagenes in the cell cytoplasm as well, although the latter seem to have little effect.

[27] J. D. Watson and F. H. C. Crick, " The Structure of DNA," *Cold Spring Harbor Symp. Quant. Biol.* 18 (1953), pp. 123–131.

acid. The important point is that only two purines (adenine and guanine, A and G) and two pyramidines (cytosine and thymine, C and T) are involved as nucleotide bases. The adenine base in one leg of the ladder is always bonded to a thymine base in the other leg, and guanine is always linked with cytosine, so that the two legs of the ladder are exact complements of each other. In this way, when the DNA molecule splits into two threads, each ladder leg can rebuild a whole molecule by " selecting " from the cell environment the proper complementary bases. The genetic " alphabet " consists of the four " letters " (A, G, C, T) arranged in varying combinations along the ladder — e.g., AT, GC, TA, GC, CG, etc. — and the exact sequence of nucleotide pairs is believed to determine the formation of amino acids in the cell protoplasm. Present evidence indicates that three successive DNA-bases form a symbol determining formation of an amino acid, and the potential genetic information that can be stored in this system is nearly beyond belief. If we suppose, for example, that a given gene section of the DNA ladder contains ten base pairs of nucleotides, a simple calculation reveals that the possible number of permutations of these four " letters " is 4^{10}, or 1,048,576. Dobzhansky estimates that a human sex cell contains upward of one hundred thousand genes, and this number of genes may contain over four billion nucleotide pairs. Although many combinations would be genetic nonsense, the possible number of different genetic endowments from a single ovum exceeds the number of atomic particles in the universe! [28]

During the early Mendelian period of genetics, when genes were conceived of as tiny discrete particles on the analogy of Newtonian atoms, there arose a one-gene-for-one-character attitude — as though there were a single gene for body size, one for hair color, and perhaps even a gene for intelligence. However, discovery of the DNA structure has destroyed this naïve view, making it clear that genetic processes are extremely complex. One important newer view is that genes interact with each other; thus it is very nearly true that each character of an organism is affected by all the genes, and that every gene affects every character. In fact,

[28] Dobzhansky, *Mankind Evolving*, pp. 27, 38.

it usually is difficult to say with precision just which portion of the DNA chain we mean by speaking of a single gene, even though we retain the concept for thinking about events above the level of individual nucleotides.

Here we must introduce the term " pleiotropy," referring to the capacity of a gene to affect more than one feature of the phenotype. Every gene so far studied has turned out to be pleiotropic in some way. In the flour moth *Ephestia kuehniella*, for example, it was found that a gene affecting pigmentation of the eye has ten other known physiological and morphological effects, because mutation of this gene produces an inability to synthesize kynurenin, a necessary precursor of the essential amino acid tryptophane. Here the pleiotropic action of the gene seems to be due to its effect on every biochemical process in the moth's body that involves the kynurenin-tryptophane reaction.[29]

One of the most fascinating examples of genetic pleiotropy concerns human sickle-cell disease, a condition in which the red blood cells are sickle-shaped and fragile, producing anemia. This abnormality follows a single mutation affecting the hemoglobin molecule. For some time we have known that people homozygous for this condition (with two mutant genes) have a severe anemia, usually dying before adolescence. People heterozygous for the condition (with one normal and one mutant gene) are almost normally healthy, although the trait may be diagnosed by examination of their red blood cells. Now it has been found that people heterozygous for sickle-cell trait have an elevated resistance to falciparum malaria, and that the worldwide incidence of sickle-cell genes corresponds fairly well with the areas where falciparum malaria is endemic. We may conclude that, through natural selection, a balance has been achieved between sickle-cell disease and malaria; in those parts of the world human populations have evolved a resistance to malaria, but one which costs the death of up to 3 percent of their children.[30]

Having made these comments about individual genes, we must point out that evolutionary theory advances largely by neglecting

[29] Mayr, *Animal Species and Evolution*, pp. 159–161.
[30] Dobzhansky, *Mankind Evolving*, pp. 151–156.

factors below the total genotype and phenotype of animals. This is one of the most obvious examples of how organismic thinking now dominates the field of evolutionary genetics, while the classical atomistic view of genetics now seems limited to a few biochemistry laboratories. There, some researchers still hold a sophisticated version of the ancient preformationist idea in the form of belief that each gene produces one enzyme and that the body is, somehow, completely preformed as enzymes in the sex cells. All earlier versions of preformationism have been false, however, and there seems no reason to suppose that this biochemical reincarnation of the ideal will fare differently.

The word " mutation " no longer is used to designate gross saltatory genetic events such as were postulated by De Vries and more recently by Velikovsky in his version of catastrophism. Instead, it is restricted in meaning to the small-scale genetic events we have discussed, and gene mutation may be regarded as an " error " in the process of copying some part of the DNA ladder before the chromosomes divide. There are also several kinds of chromosome mutation (duplications, translocations, inversions) that may alter the basic genotype; some mutations even involve whole sections of chromosomes, but a change in a single nucleotide pair qualifies.

Critics of the mutation theory, erroneously assuming that evolutionary change is caused solely by mutations, sometimes point out that most mutations are harmful. This is true enough, but it is not so startling as first appears. Mutations occur repeatedly, and natural selection acts like a fire that burns down the haystack of mutations, making it easier to " find " the valuable ones and fix them in the genetic pattern.[31] The possible changes at any gene locus are limited in number, and since there has been plenty of time for the better mutations to occur and become fixed in the genotype, *any* change is likely to be a backward step.

The frequency of gene mutations varies from site to site along the chromosomes and from animal to animal. In general, the more slowly organisms reproduce, the higher their rate of mutation, suggesting that the rate of mutation itself may be subject to natu-

[31] *Ibid.*, p. 139.

ral selection. The fruit fly *Drosophila* has a mutation rate 100 to 1000 times that of the ubiquitous colon bacterium *Escherichia coli*, while the rate in mammals seems to be higher than in *Drosophila*.[32] Some idea of the frequency of mutation in human beings can be gotten from studies of achondroplastic dwarfism, an easily observable human malformation which has been traced to the mutation of a single gene. This mutation occurs continually in about forty-two persons per million, and the proportion of achondroplastic individuals in the population remains relatively constant only because these people have fewer children on the average. However, smaller and less obvious mutations probably occur more often, and Dobzhansky estimates that about 20 percent of all people carry one or more newly mutated genes.[33]

All of us have heard it said that the basic stuff of evolution is random genetic mutation, and sometimes this has been taken to imply that " chance alone " is the dominant factor in producing evolutionary change. Lecomte du Noüy represents those who object to modern evolutionary theory on the grounds that natural selection is uncreative and that chance alone could not account for the evolution of higher forms of life. In *Human Destiny* he calculated that if life first appeared on earth by chance, it would require 10^{242} billion years for a single molecule of high dissymmetry to be formed by thermic agitations in primitive conditions.[34] From this he concluded that a scientific theory of evolution based on chance happenings could not explain much about higher organisms, and he believed it was necessary to propose a teleological " antichance " factor. In reply to Du Noüy's argument, the modern selectionist can point out that " chance alone " is much less important in evolution than Du Noüy supposed. It is true that almost all mutations are random in the sense that they occur as unpredictable statistical phenomena whose causes are not presently known, but mutations merely joggle the genetic *status quo* and cannot produce any kind of evolutionary trend. Actually a much

[32] Mayr, *op. cit.*, pp. 173, 416.
[33] Dobzhansky, *Mankind Evolving*, p. 47.
[34] Pierre Lecomte du Noüy, *Human Destiny* (Longmans, Green & Company, 1947), pp. 26–38.

more important source of randomness in evolution is found in the selective equivalence of different genotypes — many different genotypes may be capable of producing the same phenotype, and since it is this phenotype which then is acted upon through natural selection, " chance " may determine which of a number of equivalent genotypes will be selected.[35] Chance also plays a role in the dispersal of animal populations, but it is no longer regarded as the decisive factor in evolutionary change.

Similarly, the modern selectionist can avoid Du Noüy's appeal for a teleological " antichance " factor by pointing to the creative aspect of natural selection. Simpson illustrates this by the analogy of a man who tries to draw, simultaneously, the letters C, A, and T from a huge bag of alphabet letters, in order to spell " CAT." [36] If he could draw out only three letters at a time and had to discard them whenever they were not the proper combination, he might never finish — or he might draw out all the C's in wrong combinations before ever finding them together with A and T. This is the model of natural selection to which Du Noüy objects, and on which " chance alone " could never account satisfactorily for evolution. But now suppose that each time the man drew out a C, an A, or a T in a wrong combination he threw them back in the bag and discarded the letters he did not want. And suppose that whenever he drew out two of the sought-after letters at the same time, he could clip them together and throw them back in the bag. Before long he would have a supply of clipped CA, CT, and AT combinations in the bag, plus a number of individual C's, A's, and T's needed to make up the desired word CAT. Using this system the man has achieved what would have been a highly improbable goal; this is the way natural selection operates, precisely by *reducing* the element of chance. (In fairness to Simpson, we must avoid the temptation to make this analogy teleological by assuming that it requires some " Great Speller " whose purposes are merely achieved through natural selection; the analogy holds as a description of what has happened in natural selection even if we

[35] Dobzhansky, *Mankind Evolving,* p. 213.
[36] G. G. Simpson, " The Problem of Plan and Purpose in Nature," *Scientific Monthly,* 64 (1947), pp. 481–495.

avoid all notions of evolutionary goals.)

We have noted that the biochemical details of mutation are not of central importance for the continuing study of evolutionary advance, because natural selection acts principally not on individual genes or even on entire genotypes but on phenotypes, which reflect the interaction of genotype and environment. Thus the general form of evolutionary theory will be unaffected by any further light that may be shed on the ultimate causes of gene mutation, and this has important implications for any theological attempt to discuss the role of divine causation in the evolutionary process.

In particular, this means that it will prove unfruitful to propose that God acts in evolution by " nudging " the mutation process in one direction or another; such a proposal really is unsatisfying from both the scientific and the theological standpoint. Scientists will object that it never can be put to the test and thus is on the level of earlier proposals for an unseen vital force that acted by limiting the mechanical Newtonian forces. Theologically, we have two reasons for objecting: (a) the proposal is a modern version of an old idea, the " God of the gaps," attempting to save a place for God by postulating his action only at the point where natural scientific knowledge is still vague, and (b) it has the same defects as Deism, i.e., locating God's relationship to the world so far from the level of human historical existence as to make God practically absent from our lives.[37]

---

[37] William G. Pollard recognizes this in *Chance and Providence: God's Action in a World Governed by Scientific Law* (Charles Scribner's Sons, 1958). Here Pollard seeks to show how God's providence is continually effective in history, which requires showing that God somehow takes part in the determination of every event. Pollard does not wish to abridge the explanatory power of scientific thought, so he seeks to show that divine causation occurs *in addition* to the causes studied by science. To do this, he proposes that what we observe as " accident " and " chance " reflect this divine causation. He reaches this conclusion by noting that in most natural processes the factors in causation allow for the system two or more alternative responses (p. 37). The Heisenberg principle of indeterminacy, he points out, shows that *in principle* we cannot predict which response the system will make — " chance " is not to be traced to any lack of information about the relevant causes, and we are not at liberty to propose some additional causal agency, the effects of which (if known) would eliminate our need to attribute " chance " and probability to natural

5. Species and Natural Selection

Reminding ourselves that biologists no longer think of species as " types," we may grasp the present understanding of a species as *an interbreeding population that is distributed both in space and in time*, so that evolutionary change can be seen as a change in the genetic composition of an animal population. Earlier definitions of species relied on sometimes arbitrary morphological and typological considerations, but this modern definition of species is based on more readily observable facts. Consequently, taxonomy slowly has changed over to the biologically defined concept of species, and biologists now use such terms as " polytypic species," " monotypic species," and " sibling species," the last referring to species which are morphologically similar but do not interbreed. Since morphological differences are mainly secondary by-products of an underlying genetic discontinuity between species, the older morphological definitions are no longer quite so helpful.

This brings us to one of the central assumptions of modern evolutionary theory: *change in a species always reveals the pre-existence of a genetic basis for the change.* We note that for all who pursue the nonpurposive ideal of explanation, this assumption is equivalent to saying that evolutionary change can be explained completely by preexisting efficient causes. On the other

---

events. He then suggests (p. 66) that the key to the Biblical idea of providence is found in the appearance of chance and accident in history, e.g., an event which was for Israel an act of God was to others merely good luck and could be explained fully in terms of natural causes.

However, it is not clear just how Pollard can affirm (p. 94) that events are at the same time under the full sway of both natural and divine causation, which would seem to mean that the same event may be fully explained in terms of natural causes *and* in terms of divine causation. He asserts (p. 124) that there is a real paradox of freedom and providence, and this, along with his detailed description of the concept of complementarity in modern science (pp. 142–152), suggests that he does not see a way to penetrate behind such a dual affirmation to a deeper level of understanding. Pollard is correct in stating that present scientific evidence indicates the inadequacy of classical notions of causation to explain events, and his intention is authentically Biblical when he wants to show that divine causation occurs *continually* and *in the world*. But in the world he finds only natural causes and chance, i.e., no subjectivity, which prevents him from achieving his goal.

hand, we recall from our discussion of theological responses to Darwinism that the chief stumbling block in the way of any such explanation is the appearance of design in nature. Birds really are admirably suited for flying and fish for swimming, and biologists do not cease to marvel at the intricacy of these adaptations merely because they may explain them in terms of a Newtonian cosmology. Indeed, the British geneticist Waddington writes that the major demand made of modern evolutionary theory is that it present a " really convincing alternative " to the old notion of intelligent design.[38] Can evolutionary theory do this? Can we understand the astonishing complexity of the human eye and the elaborate life cycle of the malaria parasite as the results of a long process of tiny changes, each of which merely revealed the preexistence of genetic possibilities? Apparently, this claim asks for a measure of faith approaching that demanded by the traditional claim that every species was designed by God exactly as we see it. In either case we are asked to believe in a great reservoir of possibilities, and modern evolutionary theory does resemble a new religious creed by asking us to have faith that all genetic possibilities appeared logically " in the beginning." In order to evaluate this claim fairly we need to move on to a brief discussion of the modern conception of natural selection.

Natural selection still is seen by most biologists as " a blind, mechanical, automatic, impersonal process," [39] but some important recent changes in the theory certainly have widened its explanatory powers. First of all, we have seen that natural selection " favors " or " rejects " phenotypes, not genotypes or individual genes. This means that some genes may have little or no evolutionary importance, and it means that environmental factors are important causes of evolutionary change by virtue of their effects on creatures. Second, we now view natural selection as a statistical phenomenon of whole population gene pools, and it is this which lends credence to the claim that evolutionary change can draw from a nearly inexhaustible reservoir of variability.

[38] C. H. Waddington, " Evolutionary Adaptation," *Evolution After Darwin*, Vol. I, p. 382.
[39] Dobzhansky, *Mankind Evolving*, p. 128.

When typological thinking was common in biology it was easy to assume that natural selection was an " either/or " phenomenon: either a " type " was adapted to its world and survived, or it was not adapted and perished. But we now know that evolutionary change depends on the contributions that many organisms make to the gene pools of succeeding generations of their populations, and this cannot be viewed as an " either/or " situation. Instead, evolutionists make use of statistics to help them evaluate the probability that a given gene will remain in the gene pool. Here analysis has shown that if a gene is superior selectively to its alternate by as little as 0.1 percent, it will tend to accumulate in the population's gene pool.[40]

Mayr points out that many of the arguments used against natural selection fail to take into account its statistical character. Some have argued, for example, that many young animals are killed accidentally or in ways which have nothing to do with selective fitness. But even if 90 percent of the animals in a given generation meet accidental death, selective factors still very largely determine the success of the survivors in contributing genes to the gene pool of the next generation.[41] Again, some have argued that the earliest changes in the direction of a new structure, such as the eye, could hardly be of selective advantage. The present answer is that since the total phenotype is selected, all that really matters is that an eye rudiment not be overly harmful; also the rudiment might appear as a trivial by-product of some mutation that in another way contributes toward selective fitness, i.e., through genetic pleiotropy.

Some early Darwinians, apparently struck with the violence of mating battles and the ferocity of beasts of prey, tended to over-emphasize the importance of physical struggle in evolution. However, careful observation shows that overt conflict among animals is an infrequent occurrence, and although nature is far from the adaptive paradise that some old arguments from design pictured, Tennyson's vision of nature " red with tooth and claw " is greatly overshadowed by the astonishing ways in which natural selection

[40] Mayr, *Animal Species and Evolution*, p. 191.
[41] *Ibid.*, p. 186.

has led to methods of *avoiding* competition. This takes place chiefly by creatures becoming adapted to different " ecological niches," and this process has been recognized increasingly as a very important factor in natural selection. The niches of two species need differ only minutely in order to allow them to avoid competing by living, as it were, in different worlds. For example, the American wood warbler avoids competing with other birds simply by searching for its meals in other places, and species of European hawks and owls which normally both feed on meadow voles avoid competition in lean years by falling back on different species of secondary prey.[42] Innumerable such intricacies force us to realize that the natural environment provides a virtually unlimited number of niches to which a species may become adapted so as to find itself " favored " by natural selection. We are only now beginning to realize how vast are the possibilities of specialized adaptation, and under these circumstances it seems wise to suppose that almost any characteristic of an organism — no matter how odd it may seem to us — could be adaptive in *some* complicated niche.

There is still some discussion among biologists as to whether through natural selection acquired characteristics may be inherited. However, in modern terms this means asking whether phenotypic modifications can produce a change in the gene pool of an animal population, and the issue is considered apart from the quite separate question of purposive causation. We may summarize the arguments on each side, focusing on experiments by Waddington, who found that if eggs of normal fruit flies are treated with ether vapor soon after being laid, a number of them develop with a double thorax. After about twenty generations of artificial selection from those flies which developed with double thorax in response to ether, Waddington produced a stock of flies in which double thorax developed quite frequently even though the eggs were not treated with ether.[43] Is this a case of inheritance of acquired characteristics? One theory which would avoid this conclusion is that proposed in 1902 by Lloyd Morgan

[42] *Ibid.*, pp. 79 f.
[43] Waddington, " Evolutionary Adaptation," p. 394.

and Baldwin ("Organic Selection"), according to which a new gene mutation finally appears at random to duplicate and replace the effect of an original response to some environmental stress. Waddington believes, however, that development of the flies normally resists canalization toward double thoraxes, but this resistance is reduced gradually by his artificial selection until only a very minor mutation is necessary to divert the course of development toward formation of double thoraxes. The developmental process has been "set," as it were, on a hair trigger, and any of a number of different gene mutations (all random at the nucleoprotein level) may produce the phenotype of double thorax; Waddington thus does not suppose that his ether treatment *causes* the mutations of which he speaks. Mayr presents a slightly different interpretation, noting that a single genotype can produce different phenotypes under different environmental circumstances, and suggesting that the ether treatment merely permits the manifestation of genetic capacities that normally do not reach the threshold of expression in the phenotype.[44] Regardless of how this issue may be decided, we note that both men assume the ether treatment merely brings to light some preexisting genetic possibility; neither introduces the category of purpose.

One other example may be cited: many animals, including the ostrich, are born with calluses where their bare skin touches the ground; these calluses appear in the embryos — long before they are required. Some opponents of natural selection have argued that this is best explained as the inheritance of a trait that arose in ancestors, who developed calluses as a reaction to friction. In response to this criticism, the modern selectionist can point out that many organs, including the eye, develop in the embryonic stage where they have no obvious use. But more to the point, the selectionist suggests that in the gene pool of the ancestral ostrich population there already were genes that could favor formation of calluses if the population ever moved into an ecological niche where calluses would be helpful, perhaps a rocky terrain where lack of protection could lead to injury. In the new niche, selection would favor the accumulation of these genes in the population,

----

[44] Mayr, *op. cit.*, p. 189.

leading finally to the probability that they would "penetrate" (show up in the phenotype) oftener and earlier in the development of individual organisms.[45] This explanation is the more credible when we realize that to speak of a "preexisting gene for callus formation" does not mean thinking of an inert particle of genetic material waiting silently for millions of years until ostriches required calluses. It means only that given the fantastically complex entity that is a developing ostrich at the stage of embryonic development where callus formation might be a next step, there was some genetic mechanism that could turn the wheel of development slightly toward this novel characteristic. It is quite possible that the same biochemical structure which in ostriches is "a gene for callus formation" might be in elephants "a gene for curly tusks" or in streptococci "a gene for penicillin resistance." In summary, it is clear that modern selectionist theory gains greatly in explanatory capacity because it deals with populations numbering thousands or millions; in this light we do more readily feel its plausibility and its claim for an almost infinite "storehouse" of ready genetic channels for adaptation. Any interpretation of evolutionary theory must give proper weight to these discoveries.

6. The Origin of New Species and Structures

Evolutionists commonly agree that new species arise in several related ways. First, there is what Simpson calls "phyletic evolution,"[46] steady cumulative change within an animal population so that a new species develops from an older one without any splitting or multiplying of species; some fossil series illustrate this mode of change. Second, there is "true speciation";[47] this occurs whenever differentiation within a population proceeds to the point where it diverges into two species. Third, there is what Rensch calls "kladogenesis" (from *klados*, branch).[48] This refers to the diversification of a given type of organism (species, genus,

---

[45] *Ibid.*

[46] G. G. Simpson, *The Major Features of Evolution* (Columbia University Press, 1953), p. 10.

[47] Mayr, *op. cit.*, p. 428.

[48] Rensch, *Evolution Above the Species Level,* p. 97.

etc.) in its adaptive zone by branching or splitting, a phenomenon known as " adaptive radiation." Most of our comments in this section will concern kladogenesis, about which our knowledge is most complete, and we shall consider, primarily, animal evolution. Let us note some general features.

One of the main aspects of kladogenesis is this: *diverging evolutionary lines usually show an intense initial radiation of forms,* an " explosive radiation," in the early part of their phylogeny. In general, however, only a limited number of the branches continue to develop into a second phase, where animal forms acquire numerous specialized adaptations and sometimes maintain a single direction of evolution over a long period. During this phase there may be repeated evolution of some structures, and in related forms there may be parallel evolution of analogous structures. Finally there tends to be a degenerative phase and the formation of " excessive " traits, leading toward extinction. This sequence is not, by any means, universal (reptiles existed in the Carboniferous period but did not begin to split much until the Triassic), but the sequence is striking enough that a number of people have suggested that phylogenetic lines exhibit " youth " and " old age " just as individual creatures do; some have postulated an " immanent force " to explain the phenomenon.[49] The analogy is only suggestive, however, for it rests on the dubious notion that a species can be considered as a single entity; it is much simpler to view the slowdown of phylogenetic radiation during a phase of specialization as caused by the gradual filling of available habitats.[50] When an animal population enters a specialized adaptive zone, the move is likely to be correlated with the development of some new and specialized structure, as when the feathered wing developed as a means for flying through the air.

According to the present theory, three factors are involved in the production of such evolutionary novelty, and it may be well

[49] O. H. Schindewolf, *Paläontologie, Entwicklungslehre und Genetik* (Berlin: Bornträger, 1936), and A. Vandel, *L'Homme et l'evolution* (Paris: Gallimard, 1949).

[50] Rensch, *op. cit.,* p. 123.

to summarize them here. These new structures may begin as incidental phenotypic by-products of genetic pleiotropism, or some existing structure may be modified toward more intense and specialized function. But most importantly, as noted by Darwin, existing organs may change their function. For this, two conditions are required, resembling at a higher level the multiple and interactive effects of genes: some existing organ must be preadapted to a degree for more than one function, and some bodily function must be duplicated by more than one organ. For example, many primitive fish had two independent organs of respiration, gills and primitive lungs. The early bag-like lungs evolved into the complex lungs of four-footed land animals, while the original gills were converted into endocrine glands and accessory organs of the digestive system. But in more recent fish, the gills are elaborated and the primitive lungs may be converted into a swim bladder or accessory sense organs.[51]

A second major feature of kladogenesis: *evolution is not reversible for any major phylogenetic step.* Almost without exception, organs that have become reduced in the course of phylogeny never regain their original strength, and organs that disappear do not reappear. Even the apparent exceptions to this rule really reinforce it. For example, armored plates have appeared twice in the phylogeny of some turtles, but each time from a different anatomical source. Originally the armor came from bone, but one group of land turtles returned to the sea during the Jurassic and Cretaceous periods, and their heavy plates were reduced to a thin layer of bony material. When a line of these marine turtles again took to the land, armored plates reappeared, but this time in the dorsal skin *above* the old vestigial armor.[52] Clearly, evolution is a historical process, i.e., change is always limited by the past.

It is important to note that *almost every known form of asexual organism seems to be descended secondarily from sexual forms.* True, an asexual organism can produce a new species solely by mutation — parthenogenesis might appear superficially to be a more " primitive " kind of reproduction, and mutation

[51] Mayr, *op. cit.*, pp. 602–604.   [52] Rensch, *op. cit.*, p. 124.

alone might appear to be the primordial cause of evolutionary change; but genetic recombination has such immensely high value in natural selection and is so widespread among the lowest known organisms that we may reasonably suppose sexual reproduction to be one of the early " discoveries " of life. If this be true, natural selection must have appeared as a factor in evolution at the same time.[53]

When we consider the modern definition of species in terms of reproductive isolation, it is not hard to see why *geographical isolation is the principal factor in speciation.* Rensch comments that " all alleged cases of speciation without prior geographic isolation must be considered with great skepticism," [54] and the theory of geographic speciation is now at the center of evolutionary biology. Curiously, field naturalists were emphasizing this factor in evolution for over fifty years before laboratory scientists were able to provide a genetic explanation for it; this lag may reflect the typological and macromutational attitude of some early geneticists who worked primarily with individual creatures and thus easily were led to reinforce their typological concepts. Also rediscovery of Mendelian particulate inheritance made geographical isolation seem relatively unimportant in evolutionary divergence, so that men like Bateson and De Vries ignored it. Even in 1930 Fisher still implied that finding the causes of mutation would give us the causes of evolutionary change, and during the 1930's he and Dobzhansky continued to work out the problems of mutation and selection as such; only after this work was done could population geneticists begin to develop our present genetic theory of speciation.[55]

In addition to the obvious sorts of geographical barriers — seas, islands, rivers, ice fields, deserts, mountains, lakes — there are innumerable factors of isolation that reflect the habits and preferences of creatures. One Tasmanian songbird jumped the two thousand kilometer gap between Tasmania and New Zealand in 1856 and has become New Zealand's most common native songbird, yet

[53] Mayr, *op. cit.*, p. 412. Exceptions to the rule of sexuality seem to be the blue-green algae and most bacteria. See G. Ledyard Stebbins, *Variation and Evolution in Plants* (Columbia University Press, 1950), pp. 156 f.

[54] Rensch, *op. cit.*, p. 46.

[55] Mayr, *op. cit.*, p. 517.

a close relative with similar flying ability refuses to cross even a few kilometers of open sea near its home in the central Solomons.[56] Thus the sea is a factor of geographical isolation for one species of bird but not for the other. When we reach man, however, there are no factors of isolation at all, for man can go anywhere and live anywhere on the planet. This fact makes it nearly certain that *Homo sapiens* never will diverge into two species.

Having mentioned these general points, we can move on to what is, perhaps, the biggest disagreement among present evolutionary biologists: *can the causes of microevolution by themselves account for events of macroevolution?* Most biologists believe they can, but several respected scientists such as Schindewolf, Goldschmidt, and Cuénot continue to believe that some sort of large-scale " jumps " must be postulated in order to explain the major phylogenetic advances.[57] Evolutionary advance by such jumps has been called " macrogenesis," and since we cannot observe any major phylogenetic change, arguments for macrogenesis must rest on the effort to show some inadequacy in the modern selectionist theory. Most believers in macrogenesis are typologists, impressed that in the fossil record new types appear abruptly and in apparent discontinuity with their ancestors. Now, many fossil records do show a sudden appearance of new structural types, and this observation led Cuvier to propose the theory of catastrophes that has been one of the main weapons of anti-Darwinians ever since. Also, it must be admitted that the intermediate stages of animal phyla dating back into pre-Cambrian times remain unknown, so that the branches of the evolutionary tree do not seem to connect with the trunk; some gaps in the fossil record are huge, such as that between Recent forms of cyclostomes (eels and hagfishes) and their Paleozoic ancestors, the ostracoderms.[58] On the other hand, there are many " living fossils," and most of the " missing links " be-

[56] *Ibid.,* p. 567.
[57] See Schindewolf, *op. cit.,* and *Grundfragen der Paläontologie* (Stuttgart: Schweizerbart, 1950) ; R. B. Goldschmidt, *The Material Basis of Evolution* (Yale University Press, 1940), and " Evolution as Viewed by One Geneticist," *American Scientist,* 40 (1952), pp. 84–98; L. Cuénot, *Invention et finalité en biologie* (Paris: Flammarion, 1941), and *L'Evolution biologique, les faits, les incertitudes* (Paris: Masson, 1951).
[58] Rensch, *Evolution Above the Species Level,* p. 266.

tween major categories of vertebrates have been found in the years since Darwin wrote — a very remarkable fact, considering that we have found fossil remains for but 1 in every 5000 species that have existed! [59] Then too, the gaps in our fossil series correspond fairly well with gaps in the geologic record itself, which means we should not expect to find the remains of animals that would link the major animal phyla; these ancestral forms must have lived in pre-Cambrian times, the rock formations of which almost always are secondarily deformed by heat and folding.[60]

Goldschmidt is the only modern advocate of macrogenesis who actually specifies just how it might have operated, but his supporters agree that some massive genetic reconstruction or " systemic mutation " is required.[61] This notion of wholesale mutation seemed more plausible in the days when geneticists believed that each gene controlled a single characteristic and that new evolutionary types were produced by the appearance of mutant individual animals; but now we recognize that evolution is not primarily a genetic event, mutation merely supplying the population gene pool with variations which then, through recombination and gene flow, are dealt with by natural selection. Under these circumstances, how would a " hopeful monster " produced by macromutation find a mate and establish the reproductive isolation that we now know to be required for the origin of a new species? Any such major genetic upheaval almost certainly would be lethal, disrupting the finely tuned physiological processes that are controlled by the genes. Besides, to propose massive mutation is like asking us to believe that we could tear down the beautiful mosaics of Ravenna and produce a more delightful pattern by scattering the pieces across the floor with a shovel. Is it any harder to believe in a single special creation?

Some adherents of macrogenesis have invoked " cosmic forces " to help explain evolution, a proposal complicated not only by the fact that we have only begun to understand the nature of extraterrestrial forces but also that for many people the distinction be-

[59] Mayr, *Animal Species and Evolution*, p. 436.
[60] Rensch, *op. cit.*, p. 269.
[61] Mayr, *op. cit.*, p. 438.

tween "cosmic force" and "divine intervention" is very shadowy. In principle, however, there is no objection to suggesting that extraterrestrial events form part of the natural environment in which evolution proceeds, and it may well prove fruitful to consider such causes in explaining certain features of extinction that continue to puzzle us. For example, a number of marine animal groups (including the Dinosauria) disappeared very quickly in the late Cretaceous period, and it is at least possible that variation in the level of ultraviolet radiation may have been among the factors causing these extinctions. But here we are without evidence, and we must beware of invoking factors about which we know very little. Also, the periods when many forms of land animals became extinct do not coincide with periods of great marine extinction,[62] which speaks against any oversimple theory that cosmic catastrophes explain mass extinction. In any case, we have no evidence of extraterrestrial factors spurring evolutionary advance.[63]

One of the least understood aspects of evolution is the speed at which phylogeny moves, and the question is often raised: has there really been enough time in the geologic history of the earth to produce by evolution the millions upon millions of species of animals and plants that are known to have lived? The answer is "yes," and a simple calculation will show why. It is not unusual for a new species to arise from its predecessor in less than a million years, but, to be conservative, let us suppose that a single species produces only four new species every three million years. If only half of these go on to further speciation, there could be sixty-five thousand species after only fifty million years, and the sum would double every three million years.[64] Now, we know that all present animal phyla except the vertebrates already existed in the Cambrian

[62] Rensch, *op. cit.*, p. 238.
[63] Immanuel Velikovsky uses this argument in his proposal of "cataclysmic evolution," *Earth in Upheaval* (London: Victor Gollancz, Ltd., in Association with Sidgwick & Jackson, Ltd., 1956), pp. 223–227. He speaks of "simultaneous mutation of many characteristics . . . with a new species as a resultant," which indicates that he is thinking of speciation in terms of the production of a new type from previous individuals.
[64] Mayr, *op. cit.*, p. 585.

period (six hundred million years ago), and the vertebrates probably originated during this period or the succeeding Ordovician
(five hundred million years ago). The average phylogenetic age of
thirty-three classes of Recent animals with adequate fossil records
is four hundred and sixty million years, the phylum Pisces being
something like five hundred million years old; thus if we allow
for the average vertebrate to produce at least one generation per
year, about five hundred million generations have been available
for the evolution of our present vertebrate forms from their ancestors.

One of the unsolved problems for evolutionary theory is why
some animal forms remain virtually unchanged for millions of
years, while others display astonishing bursts of speciation; the
coelacanth fish, for example, have hardly changed at all since the
end of the Carboniferous period and were believed extinct for
fifty to sixty million years until one was caught in 1938! The famous lungfish can be studied over a stretch of some three hundred
million years, and during the last one hundred and fifty million
years it, too, has remained essentially unchanged.[65] Even a single
species of the fairy shrimp is known to have endured for one hundred and eighty million years.[66] On the other hand, fossil records
show that mammals can evolve quite rapidly. The British red deer
evolved into a separate species during the eight thousand years
since submergence of the English Channel, and even more remarkably, it assumed the phenotype of the New Zealand Carpathian
deer in only a few generations after being introduced into that
country.[67] In general, land animals have evolved faster than
aquatic forms, and the terrestrial orders are not so old. Recent orders of fish average two hundred and seventy million years in age;
reptiles, one hundred and eighty-five million years; birds, sixty-
five million years; and mammals, sixty-five million years. Most
recent genera of mammals, e.g., *Bison* and *Camelus*, date back
only to the Pliocene period, some seven or eight million years, and
the well-known woolly mammoth appeared on the scene for about

[65] Simpson, *The Major Features of Evolution*, p. 24.
[66] Mayr, *op. cit.*, p. 577.
[67] *Ibid.*, p. 578.

two hundred thousand years in the interglacial period which ended only one hundred and twenty thousand years ago.

We tend naturally to stress similarities among creatures as we seek a unifying explanation for evolution, but if we hope to escape the mistake of viewing evolution in a narrowly idealistic or one-sidedly teleological way, we must emphasize also the amazing diversity in nature. Evolution is a history of continued and almost unbelievable " experimentation " with forms of life and adaptation, and it has produced a diversity far exceeding anything that our forefathers dreamed of in their principle of plenitude. We may say very simply: *continuous production of novel forms has been the rule.* A few examples may help us to appreciate this variety and to realize how misleading it is either to regard some present creaturely form as " the goal " of evolution or to attribute to divine purpose something that is better explained by natural selection. Let us begin with the respiratory pigments, by which animals transport oxygen for metabolism. There are pigments containing iron, pigments containing copper, pigments containing vanadium; hemoglobin has developed in Vertebrata, in Annelida, in Mollusca, in Echinodermata, and even in the famous laboratory protozoan *Paramecium*. Red hemoglobin has appeared independently on several levels of the evolutionary scale and with different globin components; and among Mollusca we find not only hemoglobin but hemocyanin, pinnaglobin, and achroglobin. As for eating habits, among insects there are carnivorous, herbivorous, and omnivorous types; there are coprophages, bloodsuckers, keratin and wax eaters, xylophages, nectar suckers and pollen eaters, and even those which eat nothing at all during their short span of adult life. Finally, beetles have evolved fifteen different ways of squeaking, using different parts of their bodies! Surely, in the face of this orchestra of evolutionary devices, it is rash to believe that any one way of transporting oxygen, or eating, or squeaking is " the goal " of evolution.

Instead, the evidence suggests that evolutionary " goals " are innumerable and that nature tolerates the quirks of her creatures almost indefinitely. Even the complexly adapted human eye, used so often in the past as an example by those who wished to show the role of divine direction in evolution, is but one evolutionary "experiment" in vision. This type, the vesicular eye which has a retina, pigment layer, lens, and cornea, has developed independently in Coelenterata, Annelida, Echinodermata, Onychophora, Gastropoda, and Cephalopoda, as well as in the Vertebrata. Apparently it has proved to be the most useful "invention," since it is maintained in phylogeny where once it occurs, but even the second-best kind of eye (the compound eye of insects) has evolved several times, and some animals that have evolved vesicular eyes continue to possess more primitive flat eye grooves. Clearly, any effort to find either creaturely or divine purpose in the evolution of the eye must begin with the obvious importance of natural selection among these visual experiments.

Ceaseless evolutionary "probing" gradually produces animals fit for every new environment, but this same probing by natural selection also responds to the many unchanging aspects of nature. Thus it is no surprise that a camera resembles the human eye: the mode of light transmission is constant, and a lens is the best way to focus light, regardless of whether the lens is ground by a machine or grown by an organism. In other ways too, the basic physical conditions of our world sharply limit evolutionary possibilities. Take, for example, the magnitude of earth's gravity. We know that the weight of an animal body grows by the cube of its size, whereas the aerodynamic efficiency of wings and the weight-bearing capacity of bones grow only by the square of their cross-sectional area. Gravity being what it is, we can see why there is an upper limit to the size of flying creatures and why the bodies of large animals must be supported on top of columnar legs instead of being swung like those of insects between jointed horizontal legs.

Some organs that now strike us as marvelously adapted for their function turn out to have evolutionary histories which only the most dedicated teleologist could call "originally designed"; more often than not, we find that new organs have very humble beginnings in a gradual differentiation from some other organ system that had evolved long before. The human ear is a splendid example. In the middle ear are three tiny auditory ossicles, the malleus, incus, and stapes, which transmit vibrations from the eardrum to the inner ear. Investigating their evolutionary history, we find that the malleus is descended from the articular bone, which joins lower to upper jaw in fish, amphibians, and reptiles. The incus originated from the quadrate, and the stapes is the result of a gradual transformation that began with the hyomandibular bone of fish, joining the jaw to brain case. Thus all three human auditory ossicles evolved from bones whose original functions had nothing to do with hearing, and the tympanic cavity itself is derived from what was, in earlier forms of life, a part of the breathing apparatus.[68]

In summary, we must agree that modern selectionist theory has made impressive strides toward its goal of explaining evolutionary change in terms of natural efficient causes, and selectionists stand on rather solid ground when they hesitate to introduce the notion of purpose (either creaturely or divine) as an additional causal factor. Any effort to show a role for purpose in evolution must take very seriously the complex chains of causation that have been revealed by selection theory.

7. TRENDS IN EVOLUTION

During the nineteenth century, paleontologists accumulated considerable evidence of long-term trends in phylogeny, perhaps the best-known example being the family tree of the modern horse, which stretches back to the four-toed *Eohippus* of Lower Eocene times some fifty million years ago. And more recently it has been possible to trace even man's fossil ancestry with some degree of assurance back over twenty million years.[69] The continuity in evolution is impressive, for in spite of the innumerable minor types of creatures that have perished in evolutionary dead ends, none of the basic phyla ever has become extinct. Thus it is not surprising that continuity is cited frequently as evidence for some guiding agency in the overall direction of evolution.

[68] Rensch, *op. cit.*, pp. 60–68, 275–277.
[69] W. E. LeGros Clark, *The Fossil Evidence for Human Evolution* (2d ed.; University of Chicago Press, 1964), p. 11.

At other levels, too, we cannot doubt that there has been prog-ress in evolution, for many evolutionary inventions remain as a fixed point of departure for later developments, once they have appeared on earth. For example, we know of no other process re-sembling the formation of nucleoprotein molecules capable of re-duplication, and this biochemical invention is the basis of all life on earth. Likewise, the discovery of genes and the union of genes into chromosomes give every indication of being unique evolu-tionary events, and the appearance of sexual reproduction was an-other major evolutionary advance. Evolution of the cell could only have occurred at a time when biochemical plasticity was al-ready quite far advanced, and in its turn we must see the cell as another evolutionary breakthrough that defined the possibilities for further development of living forms on our planet.

On a higher level, there are noticeable long-term trends toward multiplying the number and types of creatures, toward creatures with larger bodies, and toward creatures with more complex nerv-ous systems and visual organs. In land animals we find a definite trend toward larger brains, and in the widest sense no one seri-ously doubts that man is higher in the evolutionary scale than a worm. But the question remains: are these trends reason to infer the activity of some purposeful directive agency?

Modern selectionists reject all such suggestions as superfluous, noting that they very often reflect typological thinking. Our abil-ity to trace the horse's ancestry back to *Eohippus* really only dem-onstrates that evolution is a historical process, i.e., that every pres-ent animal *must* be descended ultimately from some ancestor in the remote past. The lines of descent are constructed by us after the fact, and the higher categories toward which animals have evolved all began as unimpressive local populations of a species, not as ideal types purposed in the mind of God or by nature. Thus straight-line (orthogenetic) trends need not represent the results of undeviating guided evolution; they merely reflect the canaliza-tion of a population's gene pool toward phenotypic expressions that are particularly " favored " by natural selection over a long period of time. In the long run, species are analogous to muta-tions — they are biological experiments, and the new ecological niche into which any species shifts probably will turn out to be an evolutionary dead-end street. Therefore, when we observe finely adapted animals with long fossil pedigrees, what we have found are the needles left over after the evolutionary haystack burned down. The fire might very well have burned in a quite different way, for all we know, leaving us with a world of complex creatures amazingly different from the ones we know. No one, say evolutionists, was planning horses before they evolved. Modern selectionist theory makes it nearly impossible to suppose that any modern creature, including man, is the ultimate realization of a single primordial purpose effective since the beginning of history. On the contrary, the evidence suggests that our present two million species of animals and plants are what evolution has " achieved " by repeatedly " making do " with whatever species happened to be on hand at the time.

For modern evolutionists the question about trends thus comes down to one central question: why does the haystack burn? Why is there evolution at all? But at this point we verge on metaphysics and are not asking a strictly scientific question. Evolutionists usually do not push beyond this point in explanation, and they are content to take as their ultimate " given " some more obvious fact, e.g., that we inhabit a planet on which evolution does take place, or that chemical compounds display some instability. Given these facts, they do not require any additional directiveness to account for the trends that we recognize as one aspect of evolutionary history. The present scientific attitude is much like Asa Gray's, where he suggested, in effect, that we should stop trying to find God behind the individual details of adaptation and see him behind the whole evolutionary process. But there is one great difference: Gray believed in a purposeful origin and ground for the whole process, while modern evolutionists usually do not.

8. THE EVOLUTION OF MAN

The history of man is a tiny fleck of foam tossing on a great sea of evolutionary history, and we learn by contrast a certain patience with our world when we regard the ancient face of the lungfish or the bony remnants of the brontosaurus. But it is man's evolution that calls forth our chief interest, and it is not patience with the course of evolution that we need so much as patience with human history. This is only to say what everyone admits, that human affairs have an importance which cannot be contained within any view of evolution that seeks to make man *merely* a product of evolution. But how are we to express this in the face of evidence that indicates man appeared on the planet as the result of a " make-do " process with no intrinsic long-term goals? We can begin by noting two important recent changes in thinking about human evolution. First, the abandoning of typological concepts and the approach by way of population genetics is as important here as in the rest of evolutionary studies. This means that the first " man " was not an individual but a whole population, diverging from a parent species of " pre-man." The view that the genus *Homo* began with a new type of individual now appears quite implausible, and to define as " man " certain individuals in a primitive population would be arbitrary. Also, the self-conscious stress on apparently nonphysical factors in human evolution must be recalled. For example, the population approach indicates that cooperation among individuals must have played a role in human evolution from remotest times, so that supporters of evolutionary ethics are not read out of the evolutionists' camp, and Mayr agrees with Julian Huxley in seeing no conflict between natural selection and human ethics.[70] Dobzhansky's book *The Biological Basis of Human Freedom* is carefully suggestive of this attitude.[71]

Now, what about man's ancestry? Bishop Wilberforce smilingly asked T. H. Huxley just which side of his family he could trace back to the apes, and his error crops up here and there in the notion that man is a descendant of a presently existing species of apes. This is certainly not the case, for man and the anthropoid apes both descend from some common ancestor who probably was as different from either of them as man is from the gorilla; analysis of animal hemoglobin patterns proves conclusively that man's

[70] Mayr, *op. cit.*, p. 651.
[71] Theodosius Dobzhansky, *The Biological Basis of Human Freedom* (Columbia Paperbacks, Columbia University Press, 1960).

ancestors (the Hominidae) branched off from the line of African apes (the Pongidae) long after their common African ancestors had diverged from the line (Cercopithecidae) which led toward present-day Asiatic forms such as the East Indian orangutan.[72] Mayr suggests that in seeking this common ancestor of the Hominidae and Pongidae we need to look for a creature that was not especially adapted either for life in trees or for travel on two feet, that had a smaller brain than man, but yet differed significantly from monkeys.[73] Fossil forms which resemble this postulated creature have been found in Miocene deposits in Africa, dating back some twelve to twenty-five million years. Only very rough working hypotheses can yet be devised concerning these remains, but we may guess that the evolutionary line which produced man separated from that which produced apes about eleven million years ago.[74] *Proconsul* probably stands close to this common ancestor of both hominid and pongid stocks.

By far the most important fossils bearing on man's evolution have been found in Africa since 1924 by Broom, Dart, Robinson, Leakey, and others. All these belong to the genus *Australopithecus*, "man-apes" that have teeth of an hominid pattern and pelvises indicating an upright posture. There is evidence that they used tools, but their cranial capacity was only about the same as that of modern apes (450–550 cc.), and they had very large jaws. These remains are dated variously at from 600,000 to 1,750,000 years, but new finds occur so frequently that even these approximations are quite likely to change. The oldest really human remains come from eastern Asia, Java, and northern China; all these belonged to the genus *Homo*, although they were not members of our species *Homo sapiens*. Java man (originally called *Pithecanthropus erectus*) and Peking man are now regarded as races of the same species and are labeled *Homo erectus erectus* and *Homo erectus pekinensis*, respectively. These men walked erect, and their femurs were indistinguishable from those of mod-

[72] E. Zuckerkandl, R. T. Jones, and Linus Pauling, "A Comparison of Animal Hemoglobins by Tryptic Peptide Pattern Analysis," *Proc. Nat. Acad. Sci.*, 46 (1960), pp. 1349–1360.

[73] Mayr, *Animal Species and Evolution*, p. 626.

[74] Dobzhansky, *Mankind Evolving*, p. 174.

ern man. Their brains (800–1200 cc.) were larger than those of
the australopithecines, but they had skulls somewhat resembling
chimpanzees or gibbons and teeth that showed a mixture of human and anthropoid characteristics. Some of these remains, notably the jaw of so-called Heidelberg man, may be as much as five
hundred thousand years old.

During the last Ice Age, which began some 120,000 years ago,
the famous Neanderthal man (*Homo sapiens neanderthalensis*)
lived in Europe, but even before that another race of men more
like ourselves (*Homo sapiens presapiens*) apparently lived there,
disappearing when the Neanderthalians appeared. Neanderthal
man is the best-known form of fossil man aside from modern man,
and it appears that he developed as the last great ice sheet extended into northern Europe. He was short, with massive bones, a
large brain (1450 cc.), a receding forehead. Thirty-five thousand
to forty thousand years ago, while the last glaciation was still at
its height, Neanderthal man was replaced rather quickly by a race
of men like us (the Cro-Magnons, *Homo sapiens sapiens*) who in-
vaded Europe, bringing with them a culture different from the
Neanderthal culture. But where did they come from? This is a
puzzling question. There is little to indicate that Neanderthal and
Cro-Magnon races overlapped in Europe, and we do not know
whether Neanderthal man became extinct before Cro-Magnon man
appeared there; perhaps the latter exterminated Neanderthal man.
Two caves on Mount Carmel in Palestine have yielded remains
suggesting that both races coexisted or succeeded each other
there,[75] but of course this does not solve the problem of the origin
of *Homo sapiens sapiens*. Presumably he originated in some isolated population of Africa or Asia — Ethiopia or Arabia or In-
dia? — but all we really know is that he appeared suddenly as an
invader of Europe some thirty-five thousand years ago. We must
await further fossil discoveries before we know much more than
this about our most immediate ancestors, but in the meantime, it
is possible to sketch a plausible pathway leading to the emergence
of modern man. Dobzhansky suggests that one species of *Australopithecus* became dependent on tool-making and tool-use, thus

[75] LeGros Clark, *op. cit.*, p. 72.

creating for itself a new niche with immense possibilities for further adaptation. The result was a tremendous spurt of evolutionary activity, and the species then became classifiable as *Homo* instead of *Australopithecus*. We know that *Homo erectus* lived over a great area stretching from Java and China to Europe and North Africa, a fact that would have encouraged the development of races,[76] and the simplest assumption is that there always has been but a single species of men, with a variety of races much as we find today.

The most startling fact about hominid evolution is the tremendous increase in brain size during the middle Pleistocene. The following table [77] summarizes the change:

	Cranial capacity in cc.
Australopithecines	450–550
Homo erectus erectus	770–1000
Homo erectus pekinensis	900–1200
Homo sapiens neanderthalensis	1300–1425
Homo sapiens sapiens (Recent)	1200–1500

When we consider that some estimates of the average rate of evolutionary change suggest a 1 to 2 percent change in a million years, it is astonishing to realize that the hominid brain has increased threefold in size in something like a million years! By any standard, this is a major evolutionary breakthrough. We know full well that the size of a living man's brain tells us very little about his intelligence, and the elephant with a 5000 cc. brain is less intelligent than a man, but still it seems foolish to deny that this tremendous increase in brain size was correlated with an increase in intelligence. What caused this breakthrough? We can only speculate, but everything else we know about evolution suggests that it must have been a complex of interrelated factors, among them upright stance, use of tools, development of symbolic language, perhaps even the development of monogamous family life. What we are dealing with is the emergence of a whole new way of life, which may be called human instead of animal, and it

[76] Dobzhansky, *Mankind Evolving*, p. 187.
[77] *Ibid.*, p. 200.

is perfectly proper to distinguish this as a new phase of evolutionary history.

This suggests an answer to another puzzling question: why has there been no significant change in the human body since Cro-Magnon man appeared some thirty thousand years ago? The impression we gain is that *Homo sapiens sapiens* nearly ceased to evolve organically after he entered a new " adaptive zone," the world of human culture with its endless possibilities for adaptive variety. However, it would be foolish to contend that organic evolution has stopped, just because no very striking changes in the human form have occurred for thirty thousand years. Ancient selective factors are still effective, and starvation continues to eliminate the less hardy and the oppressed in most parts of the earth. But it is equally true that the process of natural selection is more and more determined by human intelligence. The discovery of insulin, for example, has allowed countless diabetics to survive past the age of reproduction, thus largely eliminating the selective pressure against genes for diabetes mellitus. Undoubtedly, something that may be called " history " or " culture " is now the center stage for human evolution, and one of the main problems in evolutionary thought now is to understand the proper relationship between what Dobzhansky has called the " organic " and " superorganic " factors of human evolution.[78]

Responses to this problem already have swung from one extreme (identifying the two factors) to another (separating them sharply). Early Darwinians, exhilarated at unlocking their rich storehouse of information, often were unable to check their enthusiasm for the naturalistic categories of evolutionary thought. Most early anthropologists caught this virus and naïvely assumed that these same categories would explain human culture as well, and they proceeded to collapse " history " into " nature." Thus, men like Tylor studied types of human culture on the evolutionary assumption that they would reveal a single pathway from simple primitive savagery to complex civilization. In retrospect we can see behind this nineteenth-century view of culture not only a naturalistic bias but also the same typological thinking that led paleon-

[78] *Ibid.*, p. 18.

tologists of the same era to view man as the summit of a long orthogenetic evolutionary process that passed through its own series of morphological types. Early evolutionary anthropologists were too ready to categorize cultures as " higher " or " lower," but after a period of initial enthusiasm for notions of cultural evolution before 1900, it became more and more obvious that the scheme was forced. Franz Boas (1858–1942) did a great deal to eliminate this extreme view from anthropology, pointing out that existing " primitive " societies really are quite complexly organized and certainly not to be taken as simple antecedents of our own civilization. Boas even insisted that primitive and civilized men think in about the same ways,[79] which, of course, implied that it is methodologically unsound to explain human cultures by applying the categories of evolutionary thought derived from studying the prereflective parts of nature. Perhaps in reaction to the earlier views, theories of cultural relativism came into vogue between the two world wars; writers like Ruth Benedict pointed out the many ways in which human social standards were transient products of culture,[80] sometimes implying that changes in human society are completely independent of the other causal factors that help to explain evolution.

Evolutionists now take a more mediating position, and although it would be rash to say there is general agreement, we may take Dobzhansky's view as representative of much present thought. He points out that culture arose and developed in the human evolutionary sequence " hand in hand with the genetic basis which made it possible," [81] and for this reason it seems quite unscientific to exclude from the study of culture any consideration of its genetic basis. Nothing from the study of evolution warrants belief that man's biological evolution has ceased and that he only evolves culturally, even though the " superorganic " has been for several thousand years the dominant factor. Startlingly absent from most present discussions of human evolution are the old reductionistic

[79] Franz Boas, *The Mind of Primitive Man* (rev. ed.; Collier Books, 1963 [1911]).

[80] Ruth Benedict, *Patterns of Culture* (Mentor Books, New American Library of World Literature, 1946).

[81] Dobzhansky, *Mankind Evolving*, p. 75.

ideas that human mentality and culture are " nothing but " complex physicochemical processes, and the last sixty years have seen
a really significant move away from the earlier tendency for scientists to make explicit materialistic interpretations of their evidence. We may illustrate this changed attitude by the example of
views concerning schizophrenia. During the early years of this
century there was sharp disagreement between those who held to
the belief that schizophrenia was caused by " purely organic " factors, including genetic ones, and those who believed that it was
produced by " psychodynamic " factors. Now it seems that there
is at least some genetic predisposition to certain varieties of schizophrenia,[82] and the present approach to treatment takes into consideration that schizophrenia is a disease with a complex causal
background in which both " organic " and " superorganic " factors may play varying roles. Spurred by such views, most evolutionists believe that the " organic " and " superorganic " are in-
extricably bound up together as causes of man's evolutionary position, whatever may be their ultimate metaphysical status.

In terms of our earlier distinction between the objective and
subjective aspects of reality, this newer attitude seems to reflect the
admission that subjective categories are among the causal factors
in nature, at least as we think of human evolution. The present
scientific attitude thus bears a certain resemblance to the theological stance that arbitrarily introduces man's soul at a certain stage
in evolution, and the resulting question for a metaphysical interpretation is about the same: granted that subjective categories are
a real aspect of nature in the early stages of human evolution,
what are we to say about the reality of these subjective categories
in nature before man appeared?

[82] See F. J. Kallman, *Heredity in Health and Mental Disorder* (W. W.
Norton & Company, Inc., 1953).

IV

A WHITEHEADIAN INTERPRETATION
OF EVOLUTIONARY THEORY

" Civilized beings," writes Whitehead, " are those who survey
the world with some large generality of understanding." [1] Of the
scientists whose work we have been discussing, nearly every one
would agree that evolutionary science is an important part of civilized man's larger venture in understanding,[2] and in this spirit
we come now to the point of interpreting their work explicitly in

NOTE: Whitehead's works now have been republished in various paperbound editions whose pagination does not agree with the originals, and
since my own study of Whitehead has been largely from these newer editions, I have guessed that page references to these same paperbound versions will be more useful than references to the originals. The following
abbreviations will be used in citing Whitehead's works:

AI — *Adventures of Ideas* (Mentor Books, New American Library
of World Literature, Inc., 1955).

FR — *The Function of Reason* (Beacon Paperbacks, Beacon Press,
Inc., 1958).

MT — *Modes of Thought* (Capricorn Books, G. P. Putnam's Sons,
1958).

PR — *Process and Reality* (Humanities Press, Inc., 1957). This edition is identical with the 1929 original.

RM — *Religion in the Making* (Living Age Books, Meridian Books,
Inc., 1960).

SMW — *Science and the Modern World* (Mentor Books, New American Library of World Literature, Inc., 1948).

S — *Symbolism: Its Meaning and Effect* (Capricorn Books, G. P.
Putnam's Sons, 1959).

[1] *MT* 5.

[2] Strict positivists will not agree that evolutionary science provides understanding, but we must allow the argument of the whole chapter to be
our response to this view.

terms of Whitehead's cosmology. Our hope is that this approach may enable us further to widen our understanding by attention to what Whitehead calls the " vague beyond," [3] i.e., those insistent other facts of experience which press for inclusion in any system of thought we devise. Of course, we can never approach conscious understanding of the total background of our thinking, so that we must always proceed by judicious abstraction. But we can try to recognize the proper limits for abstraction by repeated attention to the concrete grounds of our thought.

Now, what is involved in understanding evolution? A full explanation would include a welter of judgments considering present and past events and using both historical and systematic modes of explanation, but for our purposes there are some clues that help us focus the problem a bit more sharply. To begin with, the phrases " survival of the fittest " and " adaptation to the environment " point us to factors of evolutionary *persistence*, the endurance of kinds of evolutionary order that have been realized in individual animals or species. Apparently, we must seek to explain these factors. But evolutionary history also has been a rather steady movement beyond things that merely persist. Although the sandstone cliffs of the Grand Canyon stand majestically while ages pass, the most ancient living *Sequoia* crumbles to dust in a few thousand years, the men who gaze at them will vanish in a century, and some insects flitting unseen in the forest will be gone tomorrow. Whatever biological evolution may signify, at least it is not life's endurance contest with the " everlasting hills "! Plainly we must seek also for some factors of evolutionary *advance*, for without them our present world, teeming with life of every variety, would be inexplicable.

With these points in mind, Whitehead suggests that the problem is to explain " how complex organisms with such deficient survival power ever appeared," [4] and to explain " the development of enduring harmonies of enduring shapes of value, which merge into higher attainments of things beyond themselves." [5] We must explain " the aim at forms of order, and the aim at novelty of order, and the measure of success, and the measure of failure." [6]

[3] *MT* 8.   [4] *FR* 5.   [5] *SMW* 96.   [6] *MT* 119.

All these phrases call to our attention the two complementary aspects of evolution — there is evolutionary *novelty* imposed on evolutionary *order*. Neither the novelty nor the order can be taken for granted; what we must explain are the factors that produce order or disrupt it, and the factors that produce novelty or stifle it, and the ways in which these factors are related. We must ask why new species originate, but we must ask also why old species continue.

1. The Concept of Final Causation in Evolutionary Theory

Whitehead proposes that we can best explain the evolution of living forms if we recognize a threefold urge of organisms, in which " the art of life is *first* to be alive, *secondly,* to be alive in a satisfactory way, and *thirdly* to acquire an increase in satisfaction." [7] Trying to account for this upward urge of life, he observes that what we call " reason " in human experience arose over the course of millions of years primarily as a practical tool with which man can direct an attack on his environment. Therefore, says Whitehead, in some degree there must be present in *all* creatures " a factor in experience which directs and criticizes the urge toward the attainment of an end realized in imagination but not in fact." [8] Even beyond this, we should assume that in a " lowly, diffused form " it constitutes the agency of evolutionary advance which we require if we are to understand why the cosmos ever evolved beyond some past state when it consisted only of uncoordinated occurrences in empty space. On this view the world is incomprehensible unless we use the category of final causation in explaining the entire history of our universe, including biological evolution on the planet Earth. But scientists almost unanimously object either (*a*) that the concept of final causation is not properly a scientific concept at all, or (*b*) that it can be used in scientific discourse only in a guarded metaphorical sense. Also, in most cases their objection rests on two well-established facts, neither of which can be brushed aside if we wish to find the proper place for concepts of final causation. First of all, the methodology

[7] *FR* 8.   [8] *Ibid.*

of modern science has been tremendously successful for two hundred and fifty years without notions of teleology, and the fact of this success speaks against tampering lightly with the methodology. Secondly, the dominance of Aristotelian philosophy during the Middle Ages was accompanied by extravagant claims for final causation in nature, so that scientists now are properly suspicious of the oversimple teleological explanations of evolution proposed by some of their critics.[9] No scientist now could attempt, for example, to structure his research on the assumption that acorns yearn to become oak trees or that DNA molecules mutate to help people out of difficult evolutionary situations.

Granted this suspicion of notions of final causation, what about the fact that some modern evolutionists discuss human evolution in terms of the purposes and ideals which guide civilization? In some cases, this sort of language is defended as metaphorical, and it may be used as a convenient shorthand, on the assumption that ultimately it can be (or in principle could be) reduced to concepts that do not rely on the notion of final causation. Nevertheless, we have the impression that these men do use one explanatory model for prehuman evolution and another for human evolution, introducing the concept of purpose as an explanatory agency in the second model. As Whitehead would say, this probably is "a bow to those presumptions, which, in despite of criticism, we still employ for the regulation of our lives."[10] Just for this reason the method will prove unsatisfactory in the long run, because it introduces final causation arbitrarily and fails to show how it has a rational place in scientific thought. In this it reflects the same uneasy ambiguity that we have seen in such early evolutionists as Buffon and Erasmus Darwin, men whose struggle was to reconcile their Newtonian cosmology with an inherited Biblical vision of divine purpose in nature. The ambiguity in each case comes from trying to impress subjective categories on a Newtonian framework that cannot support them.

[9] For a good discussion of problems involved in introducing concepts of final causation into biological theory, written from a Whiteheadian perspective, see W. E. Agar, *A Contribution to the Theory of the Living Organism* (Melbourne: Melbourne University Press, 1943), Ch. I.

[10] *PR* 229.

Modern neovitalists too have begun by accepting the Newtonian view that all events of inanimate nature can be explained fully in terms of efficient causation; but at the level of living organisms, they introduce final causation as an additional explanatory factor that can " suspend " the usual modes of efficient causation.[11] Here also, the problem rests principally in their arbitrary manner of introducing final causation as a metaphysical category to be used in discussing living organisms — teleology appears out of nowhere as a factor disconnected from the rest of nature and not articulated into a rational scheme of ideas. This is the same type of rational disjointedness that we found in suggestions that God at some time introduced the human soul into an already evolved material body — in every case we are not logically a step beyond Descartes, who introduced the idea of God to bridge the disconnectedness of minds and material bodies in his thought.

If we wish to avoid this problem of rational disjointedness in our consideration of final causation, we must begin by considering the nature of scientific understanding, which advances in two complementary ways. Partly it advances by gathering details into already elaborated patterns of thought; this is what engaged Darwin's attention during the laborious years while he assembled his data. But the other side of scientific advance consists of introducing novel patterns of conceptual experience, so that details which previously seemed to be irrelevant or uncoordinated can be lifted into a coherent pattern of thought. This is the aspect of scientific progress that occupied Darwin as he struggled toward a wider theory, one which could unite a host of facts that remained isolated and arbitrary when they were interpreted by the usual theory of divine creation.[12] What we must note here is this: *both modes of advance in evolutionary science so far have fallen within the single overarching Newtonian understanding of reality.* Physicists have for over half a century recognized the limitations of this Newtonian vision, but research in biology still proceeds al-

[11] Hans Driesch, *The History & Theory of Vitalism*, tr. by C. K. Ogden (London: Macmillan & Co., Ltd., 1914), p. 203. For the vitalist argument, see also L. Richmond Wheeler, *Vitalism: Its History and Validity* (London: H. F. & G. Witherby, Ltd., 1939).

[12] See Darwin's own comment, quoted above, Chapter I, note 129.

most entirely in terms of those same conceptions which were so successful in the eighteenth and nineteenth centuries, and in terms of which the idea of final causation is " unscientific." If now we can show that the Newtonian world view is, at least in some respects, not fully adequate for explaining evolution, then the need for *some* broader explanatory base must be granted, and Whitehead's proposal with its notions of final causation can be judged in terms of the wideness of its explanatory capacity.

The Newtonian methodology rests on two cardinal assumptions. There is the assumption that we gain information about the world exclusively by sense experience,[13] and there is the assumption that the entities studied by science are mere objects, devoid of intrinsic value at all times, related to the rest of the world only externally and accidentally.[14] If these related assumptions are allowed, there is no way of thinking that final causation is ontologically real and to be included in scientific thought. Can we avoid this implication?

In the first place, we recognize that the aspect of nature revealed by sense perception *is* utterly devoid of purpose. Our most focused sensory awareness of the external world comes to us through vision, which discloses to us nothing more than external regions that are variously colored, so that we perceive nature with our eyes as a congeries of facts which tell us nothing of purpose, value, or emotional intensity in nature. Deprived of recognizing purpose by our senses, we must admit that the only purposiveness in nature that we can know directly is that within our own personalities, and if we *suppose* that we can recognize purposiveness elsewhere in nature, it is only because we almost inevitably and quite unconsciously live by interpreting nature on the analogy of our own subjective experience. Final causation cannot be demonstrated in the external world so long as demonstration relies solely on sense perceptions — we can never see a purpose, nor can we hear one. Asa Gray was correct: " The word of the actor is not proof." [15]

---

[13] Whitehead calls this the " sensationalist doctrine of perception." *PR* viii.

[14] We have referred to this earlier as the doctrine of " simple location."

[15] See above, p. 93.

But if it is true that sense perception tells us nothing of final causation in nature, it is equally true that it tells us nothing about *efficient* causation. Hume's criticism showed logically that sense impressions depend on a host of quite isolated impulses that in themselves tell us nothing about *any* connectedness in the world, even that of causation.[16] The implications are clear: if our scientific progress really depends exclusively upon information gained from sense impressions, science ought not to tell us anything about causation of any kind; in fact, it should not tell us anything about "law" of any kind, for the notion of law is no more conveyed by sense perceptions than is the notion of causation. Scientists do presently disagree as to the place of causation in modern physical theory,[17] some feeling confirmed in their Humean skepticism by Heisenberg's principle of indeterminacy, but if sense perception by itself reveals no hint of causation in nature, one may recognize this as well by reflecting on the sight of a squirrel's tail as by analyzing the results of Heisenberg's experiment.

The long interval between Hume's criticism and the time when his doctrines made their impact on science, at least hints that scientists live and work in a world where causation and lawful order are real aspects of everyday experience. To expel these notions from thought would require abandoning all scientific claim to an understanding of reality, and while it does appear possible for men to adopt this position intellectually for certain purposes, it seems incredible that anyone could use it consistently as a guide for behavior. Therefore, unless we are honestly willing to abandon

[16] Hume himself was persuaded that the notion of "cause and effect" was essential to any understanding of experience, but he was forced into a disjointed position when he attempted to include the notion in his metaphysics. He appealed to "practice," i.e., to our memory of having viewed previous events in terms of cause and effect. As Whitehead points out, however, nothing about *present* sense impressions conveys to us the notion that we have had *previous* sense impressions, and Hume's appeal to our memory of past causal sequences is a specious argument. See *PR* 204 f.; and David Hume, "An Enquiry Concerning Human Understanding," Sec. VII, Pt. 1, in Edwin A. Burtt, ed., *The English Philosophers from Bacon to Mill* (The Modern Library, 1939), pp. 620–627.

[17] See David Bohm, *Causality and Chance in Modern Physics* (Harper Torchbooks, Harper & Brothers, 1961); Mario Bunge, *Causality: The Place of the Causal Principle in Modern Science* (Meridian Books, Inc., The World Publishing Company, 1963).

serious inquiry, we must refuse to allow the sensationalist assumption of present scientific methodology to set the limits for scientific reflection about evolution.

We turn now to the second assumption of scientific methodology, the assumption of " simple location." It is from visual experience that we derive the abstract conception of nature as composed of bits of matter scurrying through space, but it is just this brilliant abstraction that has proved so fruitful during four hundred years of scientific progress. All through this period, it is true, biologists have rested rather uneasily in the Newtonian world; but as long as the Newtonian model of reality promised to be finally successful in explaining all happenings, it was possible to have faith that the phenomena of biology too could be subsumed within its reigning conceptualities. Even the unrest following Darwin's explicit use of Newtonian concepts in the study of evolution did not shake the confidence of scientists in their metaphysical assumptions, but as the nineteenth century drew to a close, several puzzling facts came to light. For example, physicists were becoming more and more uncertain about their descriptions of electrons — for most purposes, true enough, they functioned like the ideal Newtonian particles, but at other times, they had to be thought of in terms of wave motion. Then early in this century, the quantum theory was advanced to account for other newly discovered phenomena, among them the fact that the path of an electron seemed somehow to be a series of detached positions instead of a continuous line; a moving electron might be imagined as a series of discrete electronic events, but not very well as an ideal Newtonian particle merely moving through empty space.

Clearly the Newtonian cosmology by itself does not prove adequate to explain these facts, and if physicists kept to the notion that the ultimate entities are simply located Newtonian particles, important data would remain utterly mysterious. Admittedly, some philosophers have concluded from all this that human efforts to frame cosmological theory are futile, but at the very least it is now only residual dogmatism for someone to claim that evolution finally will be explained rationally and adequately in terms of a Newtonian conceptual framework that physicists already *know* to be inadequate for understanding well-attested physical phenomena.

Both assumptions of the Newtonian scientific methodology may be challenged, therefore, on the ground that they fail to account for important segments of scientific experience. The conclusion seems unavoidable that science now requires a wider metaphysical base. But this does not mean that the Newtonian conceptions and assumptions are to be merely abandoned. Our task is to recognize their true importance by seeking the explanatory limitations of a methodology based on them, and we must give full expression to the experiences that first led men to the notion of " simple location," while recognizing that this idea needs to be coordinated with other elements of our understanding. Here we may be guided by Whitehead's observation that cosmologies are never merely true or false; they are only more or less adequate to the full variety of experienced facts. Thus when new facts are discovered or when old facts haunt us, cosmologies must be modified; there is real progress, and the usefulness of outmoded concepts is enriched by discovering the limits of their applicability. Therefore, if we wish to rationalize evolutionary theory more fully than the Newtonian cosmology will allow, we must try to show the proper interaction of efficient and final causation, seeking an explanation in which " everything determinable by efficient causation is thereby determined, and . . . everything determinable by final causation is thereby determined. The two spheres of operation should be interwoven and required, each by the other. But neither sphere should arbitrarily limit the scope of the alternative mode." [18] We cannot be content with any attempt to understand purpose in human evolution unless this final causation is related rationally to causal factors in the entire evolutionary process.

2. Whitehead's Philosophy of Organism

Since the time of Descartes, it has been clear that any effort to understand the world must begin somewhere within human experience, because that is all we have. The question is, just *which as-*

[18] *FR* 28.

pects of human experience should serve as the key to an understanding of the external world? Newton and all subsequent empiricists have assumed that we should begin with the clear and distinct deliverances of sense perception, basing our final understanding of nature on ideas that can be derived from this part of our experience. But the fact of evolution has raised a consideration unknown in Newton's time, one that suggested to Whitehead that the empiricist position was too narrow. Specifically, we now know that our own sharply differentiated sense perception is a very recent and quite sophisticated evolutionary development, and creatures existed and evolved adequately for millions of years before sense organs appeared as practical tools for guiding their responses to the increasingly complex outer world. We must think of sense organs somewhat as we do of traffic lights — they are vitally necessary for expediting traffic, but there was traffic before there were lights.

Why, then, should we naïvely take the deliverances of sense perception as our only clue for understanding a world that existed for millions of years before sense perception evolved? Why not begin with the fullness of human experience, including our feelings of purpose, attempting to assign sense perception its proper place in a larger view? This is precisely what Whitehead attempted to do, encouraged by Bergson's belief that philosophy must begin with the concrete totality of experience instead of with the convenient abstractions suggested by sense perception.

As he examined human experience, Whitehead found support in the writings of William James for his belief that human experience grows by tiny bursts or droplets of experience.[19] He took very seriously man's evolutionary continuity with the physical world, and with this in mind, he realized that viewing reality in general as a series of discrete events also illuminated some problems in physics. In particular, quantum theory suggested to him the usefulness of supposing an individual electron to be a connected series of distinct vibratory electronic happenings. This meant giving up the Newtonian habit of imagining the submicroscopic world as a

[19] William James, *Some Problems in Philosophy*, Ch. X, cited in *PR* 105 and 106, note.

mass of enduring particles moving through empty space, but
Whitehead went ahead to develop his cosmology on the assumption that nature in general is a nexus of brief events or processes,
which he called, equivalently, " actual occasions " or " actual entities." [20]

Continuing to use human experience as his model, he suggested
that the actual occasions of which the universe is composed are
all *subjects;* this point he made emphatically by writing, " Apart
from the experiences of subjects there is nothing, nothing, nothing,
bare nothingness." [21] Further, Whitehead proposed that each occasion may be analyzed in terms of categories discoverable somewhere in human experience. Of course, he did not mean that these
categories are of equal weight in every entity, for it would be ab-
surd to suggest that an electron dreams or feels guilty. But he did
propose that even the simplest entities exemplify, if only in a trivial way, all those categories such as feeling, valuing, and purpos-
ing, which are found in human experience. True, it is only a matter of degree, but that makes all the difference.

In reflecting on his experience, Whitehead found some pairs of
contrasts that had to be given expression, among them being repetition and immediacy, endurance and change.[22] We must make
room, he said, for the plain fact that objects around us endure
but that somehow the world changes. Thus, what he set out to understand very broadly is that " *experience* involves a *becoming,*
that *becoming* means that *something becomes,* and that *what becomes* involves *repetition* transformed into *novel immediacy.*" [23]
Hence, his philosophy interprets " experience," whether the experience of a human person or of an electron, to mean ultimately " the self-enjoyment of being one among many, and of
being one arising out of the composition of many." [24] This notion,
that " the many become one, and are increased by one," [25] lies at

[20] *PR* 33, 113.
[21] *PR* 254.
[22] *PR* 206.
[23] *PR* 207. Italics in the original.
[24] *PR* 220.
[25] *PR* 32. Charles Hartshorne refers to this as " Whitehead's novel intuition," in his essay " Whitehead's Novel Intuition," in George L. Kline,

the heart of Whitehead's system, distinguishing it from all other pluralistic philosophies.

Each actual occasion enjoys but a fleeting moment of *subjective* existence, its phase of " subjective immediacy." [26] This is a brief moment of process or " concrescence," [27] during which it becomes what it is by responding to its complex inheritance and narrowing its own possibilities toward that final concrete reality which it becomes. During this phase of subjective immediacy, an occasion is *utterly alone* in the universe, making of itself what it can. The duration of this solitary phase varies, depending on what sort of actual entity we have in mind; Whitehead supposes that an electronic occasion is completed in the space of a single vibration, and that occasions of human personality may be completed in something like a quarter to a tenth of a second.[28]

Passing over, for the moment, the details of concrescence, we note that as soon as an occasion becomes definitely what it is — Whitehead's term for this is " satisfaction " [29] — it remains in the world as an *object* to be felt by subsequent subjects. This is its phase of " objective immortality." [30] Thus a single electronic occasion, when it is completed, remains as a cause whose effect is transmitted forever at the speed of light into the rest of the universe. On the other hand, what we used to imagine as a single enduring electron moving in orbit must be described now as a series of such electronic occasions of experience, succeeding each other in a pattern that we can recognize collectively as an electron. In this fashion, both the wavelike and particlelike aspects of electron behavior may be accounted for.

This quick view of occasions enjoying a brief phase of solitary subjective immediacy before remaining as objects for new subjects immediately suggests that there are two distinct kinds of flu-

---

ed., *Alfred North Whitehead: Essays on His Philosophy* (Spectrum Books, Prentice-Hall, Inc., 1963), p. 23.

[26] *PR* 38.

[27] *PR* 33.

[28] *AI* 183; *MT* 220. Agar, *op. cit.*, p. 70, suggests that the " specious present " for human perception varies from a tenth to a half second.

[29] *PR* 29.

[30] *PR* 44.

ency in the universe. There is first the fluency of internal process as an occasion achieves its final unity, and there is what Whitehead calls the " transition " from a completed entity to every new process that is affected by it.[31] Here we must realize that Whitehead has abandoned the classical Newtonian notion of time, according to which time was a " receptacle " already existing *before* events. He says, instead, that our notion of time grows *from* the happening of events. Specifically, what we call " physical time " is the *transition* from one completed actual occasion to the initial phase of another; apart from such transitions we would have no way of recognizing temporal succession in nature.[32] On the other hand, even though it is enjoyed by the occasion as a real process involving movement toward completion, concrescence itself takes place in utter privacy. Therefore, from the vantage point of an observer able to recognize temporal succession only as transition *between* occasions, this process of subjective immediacy cannot be divided into an " earlier " or " later " phase.[33] Regardless of its duration, each occasion as it moves toward completion or satisfaction defines what is felt by its successors as an indivisible droplet of time. This understanding of temporality will be referred to more than once as our effort to understand evolution as a historical process unfolds.

As Whitehead notes, Hegel failed to take notice of transition in the world.[34] Consequently, he saw world history, we might say, as though it were a single great Whiteheadian process of concrescence. And because any one occasion exhibits no temporal succession *within itself*, Hegel's interpretation of history on the model of a single actual entity introduced a cramp into his desire to explain history in terms of a real temporal succession of events. We shall have occasion later to recall this shortcoming of Hegel's thought.

Let us now turn to consider an actual occasion. To begin with, where does it come *from*, if it has not the character of an enduring Newtonian corpuscle which has existed indefinitely? What Whitehead calls his basic " ontological principle " requires that

[31] *PR* 320, 322.   [33] *PR* 107, 434.
[32] *PR* 107, 126, 196.   [34] *PR* 320.

"the reasons for things are always to be found in the composite nature of definite actual entities . . . no actual entity, then no reason." [35] This means that each occasion arises as a particular way in which the world continuum is focused or "atomized," [36] or to put it another way, every entity springs from its past world.[37] However, according to relativity theory, there is not anything that is simply *the* past for all things alike; an event in the past of one observer may very well *not* be in the past of another observer located in an opposite corner of the universe.[38] This suggests that "pastness," while it does express the definite completedness of occasions, is primarily a function of the ways occasions are *presently effective* in the world. That is, calling an occasion "past" is our way of recognizing that it exists not as its phase of solitary subjective immediacy (which would be unknowable), but as affecting some present occasion of experience. Conversely, we know as "past" only those occasions that are somehow presently effective. Therefore, when Whitehead says that every entity springs from its past world, he means that it springs from all those entities which affect *it*, the whole of what composes *its* inheritance.[39]

This past which is taken account of by a new occasion is called its "actual world," [40] and no two occasions are presented with identical actual worlds, although in practice the difference between the actual worlds of two contemporary occasions may be negligible.[41] Since actual occasions spring from differing past worlds, no two occasions are strictly identical; for most purposes, we may regard all sodium atoms as alike, but there may be times when it is important to look for differences between sodium atoms in a salt mine and sodium atoms circulating in the human bloodstream.

[35] *PR* 28.
[36] *PR* 104.
[37] *PR* 123.
[38] See Milič Čapek, *The Philosophical Impact of Contemporary Physics* (D. Van Nostrand Company, Inc., 1961), Pt. II.
[39] *PR* 124.
[40] *PR* 320.
[41] *PR* 102.

Also, *every* occasion in the past of an entity has its measure of effectiveness on present experience, its " causal efficacy," [42] no matter how distantly removed it may be. Indeed, our very notion of " distance," either temporal or spatial, is basically a measure of the *degree* to which occasions in the actual world of an occasion contribute toward its present experience. Thus, as I write, I may be most effectively influenced by those occasions in my own personality which originated and were completed during the past few moments, but occasions which originated in distant nebulae also have some real, even if trivial, effect on me. This transition from settled past to present immediacy accounts for all the efficient causation of the world, and the notion of efficient causation correctly refers to the heavy hand that is laid upon the present experience of any subject by its past.

In trying to avoid the Newtonian errors against which Whitehead repeatedly warns us, we must bear in mind particularly two aspects of the relationship between an occasion and its past. First, to exist as a subject *is* to embody active reference to the entities that collectively compose its past; there just is no such thing as an entity that exists passively and inert, taking no account of things. Thus the Newtonian intuition of " simple location " finds its proper place as a scientifically convenient abstraction from the fullness of what it means to be actual. Second, the notion of " pastness " or temporal distance between occasions springs from the experience of occasions causally affecting the present; " pastness " is an *explanation* of experience, not a *presupposition* for it.

Also, it is important not to imagine the entities in any occasion's past as being utterly unrelated to each other. Each of them became what it is by synthesizing feelings of its past world, so that the initial data presented to any occasion already bear their own interconnections.[43] We may note in passing that Francis E. Abbot apparently was trying to express a similar notion by proposing his philosophy of relationism.[44] However, he was finally unable to make sense of experience, because he lacked the notion of " transition " by which Whitehead distinguishes the phase of

[42] *PR* 125.   [43] *PR* 173.   [44] See above, p. 99.

subjective immediacy from the phase of objective immortality.

Now, *how* is an actual occasion related to its past world? According to Whitehead, the most basic mode of relationship among actual entities is by *transmission of emotional tone*. Since every occasion enjoys during its phase of subjective immediacy some degree of emotion analogous to our own, Whitehead writes that each occasion begins by " feeling " the " feelings " of all the entities in its past.[45] To emphasize that each occasion responds actively to this inheritance, not passively, he more often uses the coined word " prehension " as equivalent to " feeling." For some purposes, however, this primitive form of experience may even be called " sympathy," [46] and Whitehead compares it at one point with what Quakers call " concern." [47]

In the simplest case, strict conformation of one occasion's feelings to those of another (" physical feeling " [48]) is efficient causation, and to consider occasions merely insofar as they may reproduce the feelings of their actual worlds is to consider abstractly the efficient causation in nature. As a matter of fact, however, there does not seem to be in nature any perfect conformation to the past, any completely determinative efficient causation, for even at the level of electronic events, nature is vibratory, hinting of a limited range of novelty. This provides us with one reason for attributing to electrons some glimmering of mentality, and it is to the question of mentality that we now turn.

We have been discussing the way an occasion prehends the actual entities in its past, and this direct rapport with the environment comprises what Whitehead calls the " physical pole " of the occasion, in which originate simple physical feelings of its world.[49] But there is also a mental pole of each occasion, where there originate " conceptual feelings," introducing into the final synthesis some elements of possibility drawn from a realm of possibilities.[50] These possibilities are called by Whitehead " eternal objects," and they correspond to Plato's forms; [51] they are the pure potentials of the universe, the possibilities of quality, form, and relation that enter into the actual occasions and account for

[45] *PR* 65.   [47] *AI* 178.   [49] *PR* 49, 366.   [51] *PR* 69.
[46] *PR* 246.   [48] *PR* 343.   [50] *PR* 366.

their concrete definiteness.[52] The realm of eternal objects is unbelievably complicated, since it harbors every possibility for every
future occasion in any future universe; also, the eternal objects
vary in complexity and may themselves be analyzed into simpler
and more composite possibilities. A very simple eternal object is
redness, which enters into the concrete reality of molecules in a
skein of yarn; a more complex eternal object is the possibility
that the next occasion of my personality will enjoy a feeling of
affection for an old friend who has telephoned.

Every actual occasion becomes what it is by the selection of
certain possibilities from this realm and the exclusion of others,
as it moves toward its final unity of feeling. When this unity is
reached and nothing about the occasion remains unsettled, the
unity may be described as the realization of some one single complex eternal object which accounts for what the occasion is *in toto*.
In the case of my personality, it is that possibility — immensely
complex — that I will be myself, now, here, enjoying these feelings in this way. Of course, this single complex realized possibility may be analyzed into simpler eternal objects, e.g., the possibility that I will feel the whiteness of the paper on which I write,
or the possibility that I will be distracted by feelings of hunger.
But no matter how far we may analyze an occasion in terms of its
component eternal objects, we remember that its reality as a
single unified complex of feeling can be explained in terms of
some single complex eternal object which is determinative of
its total definiteness.

The physical and mental poles of an occasion originate and
are effective together, so that either considered by itself is an
abstraction. Let us take the simple case of an occasion that feels
another physically, i.e., as a cause in its past. From this feeling,
the mentality of the new occasion derives a purely conceptual
feeling of that eternal object which accounts for the particular
kind of definiteness enjoyed by the entity which is felt.[53] In this
sense, we may say that each actual occasion is objectified by
others in terms of a single eternal object which is the form of its
feeling.[54] In a very low-grade entity, mental activity may be

[52] *PR* 34.   [53] *PR* 39, 379.   [54] *PR* 78.

limited to merely reproducing in conceptual feelings those eternal objects that characterize the physical definiteness of its neighbors, allowing its own process of concrescence to be determined in turn by those same eternal objects. The conceptual feelings enjoyed by any occasion enter into its final unity of feeling along with its physical feelings, so that its mentality, when objectified, becomes part of what is felt by a new occasion; such a prehension by one subject of the mentality in another is called a "hybrid prehension."[55] We shall have occasion to refer to this concept again in explaining the personalities of higher organisms and the way God is related to the world.

We have been discussing the ways physical and mental feelings from one occasion may become aspects of the mentality of another, but the mental pole of an occasion also may introduce into feeling some conceptual novelty that is not derived from its past. That is, it may have conceptual feelings of eternal objects not part of its inheritance; this aspect of mentality serves as the world's escape from mere reproduction, its locus of originality. Thus, the degree to which conceptual novelty is effective in the final determination of an occasion's definiteness reflects its freedom from the heavy hand of its past, and, of course, this varies tremendously. In the rock molecule discussed above, any flashes of conceptual novelty are likely to be eliminated from feeling because they are incompatible with the massive sameness of experience derived from physical feelings of nearby molecules.[56] At the other end of the spectrum, there is human imagination, roaming in far-distant futures and dabbling in endless novelty.

In describing the concrescence of an occasion, Whitehead uses the terms "self-production," "self-constitution," "self-creative," and "self-causation" equivalently to indicate the location of the world's freedom: each occasion in its solitariness achieves its own

[55] *PR* 163.

[56] Only in this sense does Whitehead speak of the "loss" of mentality (*PR* 269; *MT* 230); the mentality of an occasion always contributes toward its process, even though it is not always successful in conveying *novel* conceptual feelings into the final synthesis. The vibratory nature of electromagnetic events suggests a narrow range of novelty even at this level. (*PR* 285.)

synthesis of feelings.[57] In this " self-creation," each actual entity
is guided by *a developing ideal of itself* as becoming just *that*
entity and achieving *that* satisfaction, and it is the enjoyment of
this ideal which is its " subjective aim." [58] The subjective aims
of actual occasions are the locus of the world's purposiveness.

An actual entity thus has a threefold character: it has whatever character is given by its past, it has the subjective character
aimed at, and it has the objective character that will be its effect
on all those occasions which objectify it in the future.[59] Here we
may see the relationship between efficient causation and final
causation in the world: efficient causation refers to the transition
from actual entity to actual entity, while final causation expresses
the purposive internal process whereby the actual entity becomes
itself.[60] Final causation and efficient causation thus require each
other, so that neither is restricted in efficacy because of the other.

At this point we may seek to understand why the intrinsic
value of all things in the world is linked with subjective aim, i.e.,
why value of being is tied to purposiveness. Whitehead uses the
word " beauty " in describing that which accounts for the value
of actual occasions, and " beauty " is " the mutual adaptation of
the several factors in an occasion of experience." [61] Strength of
beauty has two aspects. First, it involves variety of feeling syn-
thesized as contrast, " the absence of painful clash." [62] Whitehead
calls this " massiveness," [63] and, as an example, we may think of
the harmonious massiveness of feeling by which we can prehend
the changing hues of a summer sunset; it is beautiful in its
harmonious variety of color. Second, strength of beauty involves
" intensity proper," which has to do with the *magnitude* of feeling
apart from any reference to its variety.[64] This is seen, for example,
when we find ourselves overwhelmed by powerful feelings of joy
or grief that shut out our awareness of everything else. Thus the
value of an actual occasion revolves around its subjective aim at
beauty, which may vary from massive harmonies of feeling with-

[57] *PR* 342, 373, 75, 443, 135, 238, 339.   [61] *AI* 251.
[58] *PR* 130.   [62] *Ibid.*
[59] *PR* 134.   [63] *AI* 252.
[60] *PR* 228.   [64] *Ibid.*

out much intensity to more intense feelings with slight massiveness. In the sections to follow, we shall speak of this two-sided aim at strength of beauty simply as the aim at "intensity of feeling."

It will be important to bear in mind that subjective aim is always an aim at intensity of feeling (*a*) in the immediate subject, and (*b*) in its relevant future.[65] That is, we must conceive that transition to a future is essential to the nature of an occasion, and that its subjective aim is partly in terms of whatever in that future is relevant to itself. Whitehead writes, "The self-enjoyment of an occasion of experience is initiated by *an enjoyment of itself as alive in the future*,"[66] and the relevant future of an occasion is defined as "those elements in the anticipated future which are felt with effective intensity by the present subject *by reason of the real potentiality for them to be derived from itself*."[67] It is in this sense that entities can influence the initial subjective aims of their successors, and the concept of a relevant future will be essential in clarifying the question of inheritance of acquired characteristics.

No final causes can be effective in the world that are not embodied in the subjective aims of actual entities, and no supposed future goal in evolution can be admitted unless it can be attributed to the subjective aim of some one or more actual entities toward states that they feel as relevant to themselves. Furthermore, the subjective aim of each occasion differs from that of every other occasion, so that there is no ideal of "perfection" common to every existing thing; the ideal for each occasion is for some completion that the givenness of its own past will allow.[68] At another level, we should not suppose that there is some eternal ideal of animal species that members of animal populations approach in differing degrees, nor should we imagine that there is some one ideal for human existence — every future is relevant to its own past.

The "subjective form" of an occasion is *how* that entity prehends its world,[69] and each entity prehends its actual world with a subjective form in harmony with its subjective aim. For example,

---

[65] *PR* 41.   [67] *PR* 41. Italics mine.   [69] *PR* 35.
[66] *AI* 195. Italics mine.   [68] *PR* 128.

I may prehend my small son in the morning with the subjective form of delight, but my wife may well prehend him in the late afternoon with the subjective form of impatience. If my morning delight lasts through breakfast, it is because, in my personality, subjective form is continuous between an immediately past occasion and the new one that originates. Thus the new occasion at least begins with feelings of delight, inherited from the occasion just past, even though modifications may enter into the process.[70] This illustrates the way an entity lays a claim on its relevant future, and it is the primary reason for continuity in nature.

Consciousness is an element in the subjective form of some high-grade occasions, limited so far as we know to animal experience. Specifically, it is *how* we feel the synthesis between physical feelings and conceptual feelings, i.e., the contrast between what *is* and might *not* be, or between what *is not* and what might *be*. Thus consciousness of an apple is the subjective form of a synthesis between a physical feeling of the apple's presence and a conceptual feeling of the apple as absent. Since consciousness depends partly on physical feelings, even at the level of human awareness we are very far from " pure mentality " in experience.

During the droplet of time while an entity is becoming concrete, the subjective aim determines just how there shall be a progressive integration of the many feelings, both physical and conceptual, that must be unified for a final satisfaction. Along the way, various conceptual feelings are felt as more or less valuable to this final sought-after satisfaction, and Whitehead speaks of this as " valuation up " and " valuation down." [71] Feelings that are incompatible with the ideal are rejected from feeling, i.e., they are " prehended negatively." [72] For example, the mentality of a molecule of salt rejects a conceptual feeling that is the possibility of its becoming a molecule of sugar instead. On the other hand, conceptual feelings are admitted to the final synthesis when the mentality of the occasion is able to entertain them as compatible contrasts, and one measure of sophisticated mentality is ability to tolerate widely contrasting feelings. Thus it is characteristic of the more primitive entities that they are, as it were, " narrow-minded."

[70] *AI* 185.   [71] *PR* 368.   [72] *PR* 35.

We have abandoned the notion of enduring substances that undergo change in favor of the notion of occasions of experience that become but do not change. How, then, are we to understand the persistent items of everyday experience, such as books and tables? The answer is that in referring to the actual world we rarely consider an individual occasion. We are conscious of and think almost exclusively of groups of entities, composed of countless individual occasions arranged in spatial or temporal patterns. Whitehead calls any such group of occasions with some sort of connectedness a "nexus." [73] A nexus that exhibits *some trait shared by each member of the nexus in dependence on the others* is called a "society," [74] and the common trait is called the "defining characteristic" of the society; this will be an important concept in our study of evolution. Thus, what we usually call a single enduring electron really is a society of electronic occasions, following each other in temporal order in such a way that each occasion's process of becoming depends upon earlier members of the society, i.e., it becomes *that* electronic occasion largely by virtue of its inheritance from them.

Here we have been speaking of a society in which the genetic relatedness of its members is serial, so that it is an "enduring object." [75] In order to show the analogy between such simple enduring objects and certain higher forms of endurance, Whitehead defines this kind of genetic relatedness as "personally ordered." A molecule is thus an enduring object, i.e., a temporally ordered personal society of molecular occasions, containing its sub-societies of atoms; it hardly needs saying that use of the word "personal" does not imply consciousness. Now, if we recall that each occasion's subjective aim extends to its relevant future, it is not hard to see that by reason of the weight of uniform inheritance derived from its members, any enduring object tends to prolong itself as a demand on the future.[76] In fact, we do observe that inorganic objects of this type endure for millions of years.

Ordinary objects of experience, such as rocks and tables, are composed of many strands of enduring objects; these inclusive

73 *PR* 30.   75 *PR* 52.
74 *PR* 50 f.   76 *PR* 88.

objects are termed "corpuscular societies." [77] A given society may be more or less corpuscular, according to the relative importance of two factors in its composition: (a) the defining characteristics of its various enduring objects, and (b) the importance of whatever characteristic defines the whole nexus.[78] A pile of sand is prehended more in terms of separate strands of personal order, while a chunk of basalt strikes us as a unitary solidness. Of course, evolutionary theory is concerned chiefly with living organisms, which are incomprehensibly complex societies with sub-societies of many sorts, and a cell enjoys kinds of experience that so far transcend our powers of analysis that we are staggered by our ignorance. But in every case, social order depends upon genetic inheritance. On the other hand, there is no reason to suppose that all actual occasions are members of societies, for there are those occasions happening in what we like to call "empty space." To speak of occasions in empty space means only that our instruments cannot detect occasions which are not linked in social order with others so as to perpetuate some pattern of feeling that our sense perception can recognize. A whole universe of such nonsocial entities is conceivable, but (using sense experience as our searchlight) we would not be able to distinguish it from mere nothingness.

There are, of course, many details of Whitehead's cosmology which we have not discussed here, especially those having to do with higher phases of experience. Also, we have not discussed Whitehead's understanding of God's role in the world, since this will be occupying our attention in Chapter V. But the basic concepts required to illuminate evolutionary theory have been mentioned, and we may hope that problems introduced by the extremely condensed nature of these introductory remarks will be resolved somewhat as we come to more concrete applications.

3. Laws of Nature: The Aim at New Forms of Order

"There is an actual world because there is an order of nature," writes Whitehead.[79] How shall we understand this sentence? Recalling that the reasons for things must be sought always in

77 *PR* 301.   78 *PR* 52.   79 *RM* 100.

actual entities, we may understand the order of nature as expressing the characters of the real things to be found in nature.[80] We
stress again that these basic entities are short-lived and internally
related, so that we may view the laws of nature as " communal
customs " which actual occasions mutually impress upon each
other's characters.[81] In a universe filled with electromagnetic
occasions, there are electromagnetic laws; in turn, the capacity
of these occasions to reproduce, so that there may be individual
electrons and protons with long lives, is expressive of the same
laws.[82] In this way, the massively coordinated inheritance from a
vast electromagnetic society maintains the kind of electromagnetic
order that is the background for our lives. In this wide society,
any sporadic flashes of conceptual novelty seem to be thwarted by
the massive sameness of physical prehensions, except insofar as
its entities enjoy the blind conceptual contrast that accounts for
vibration.

The subjective aim of an electronic occasion thus seems ordinarily to be confined very closely to what Whitehead calls a
" physical purpose," [83] the aim to reproduce in itself only those
physical feelings encountered in its environment. In this sense,
both the physical and mental poles of the occasion are blind, and
such blind prehensions are the ultimate bricks of the universe.[84]
Since the subjective immediacy of an occasion is completely private, physical science can have no glimpse into the process of concrescence, and this means that science can investigate only the
characteristics of those simple physical feelings which bind the
world together into a causal nexus. This scientific attention to
modes of transmission of physical feeling accounts for the fact
that the ultimate entities of physical science keep turning out to
be vectors indicating transference.[85] Here we may recall how, in
recent scientific thought, notions of " matter " tend to converge
toward notions of " energy."

Any society is inevitably a mixture of order and disorder,[86] and
the amount of order in a society expresses its degree of success
in impressing characteristics on its members in the form of laws.[87]

80 *AI* 115.   82 *PR* 140.   84 *PR* 370.   86 *PR* 142.
81 *AI* 48.   83 *PR* 280.   85 *PR* 364.   87 *PR* 141.

We have not yet found perfect attainment of order anywhere in the universe, and the notion of law as a social product explains why even the most embracing physical laws are not perfectly " obeyed." For example, along with instances of successful electronic reproduction we find instances of failure; the electromagnetic laws do not apply perfectly, because some individual electronic occasions enjoy subjective aims with a degree of novelty beyond that of mere reproduction, novelty sometimes disruptive of electronic order. Obedience to laws, therefore, must be expressed statistically,[88] and this failure of complete conformity, even at the most basic levels of reality, suggests that we cannot suppose any society to endure indefinitely. At the very peak of order, somewhere the total environmental background is likely to be decaying or in some other way ceasing to encourage the production of members of the society.[89] Forms of order merely have their time and pass away, to be replaced by others.

Because law is a social product, if new kinds of entities appear, or if old kinds of entities change, we must expect new kinds of order and new laws. That is, we must suppose that the laws of nature evolve right along with the organisms that make up the environment.[90] Just so far as there is a significant change in the environment, the character of its organisms is different, and the applicable laws are modified. Conversely, insofar as the identities of organisms are preserved over long periods of time, the laws are stable.[91] This fact lies behind all assumptions that we can predict the behavior of groups of organisms, whether we concern ourselves with electrons or with men — one chief difference between men and electrons is that men are not so reliable!

We have been speaking of societies of electromagnetic occasions, but the notion of law as a social product applies to every nexus that may be defined as a society in our precise sense.[92] It applies to societies of molecules, societies of cells, and to the personally ordered society that is the enduring personality of a human being. True, we usually do not refer to the poorly under-

---

[88] *PR* 150.   [91] *MT* 129.
[89] *PR* 139.   [92] See above, p. 184.
[90] *AI* 116.

stood laws of human personality as "laws of nature," but this is merely because we have chosen to limit the phrase to our discussions of those more widespread and reliable societies which provide the physical environment for the living organisms which interest us.

These high-grade organisms are composed of subordinate, enduring objects (e.g., molecules and cells), and in each case, the pattern of feelings in the whole has its effect upon the feelings of every component organism, influencing their character. For example, in an animal body the individual cells are influenced by the rest of the body, and their molecules, in turn, transmit some feelings from the cells to the electrons within them. In this way, an electron within a living body is a different kind of electron from one outside it, just by reason of the differences in their effective environments. However, Whitehead is anxious to allow the mechanism in the world its proper place, even calling his doctrine, at one point, the theory of " organic mechanism," [93] and he insists that low-grade entities such as electrons and molecules do " run on blindly " [94] in accordance with general statistical laws. We are not to think that molecules in living bodies are somehow resistant to or free from physical causation, and there is no reason to suppose that electrons in living bodies are less law-abiding than those studied in electrical apparatuses. Laws applying to such occasions merely reflect their intrinsic characters, and it is these characters that differ in accordance with the general background against which they find themselves. Although we have not yet discovered the laws describing behavior of electromagnetic occasions in living bodies, the search for such laws should serve as one way of establishing or falsifying the scientific usefulness of Whitehead's cosmology.

Changes in laws themselves very commonly exhibit a law of change. For example, we have discovered lawful ways in which the behavior of radioactive elements is altered during nuclear fission. Also, we are fairly familiar with some laws of embryonic development, and we do not consider the growth of a fetus any the less law-abiding because it exhibits an astonishingly rapid

[93] *SMW* 81.   [94] *Ibid.*

change in its behavior from day to day. A good deal of " social science " is devoted to discovering laws that express aspects of collective human behavior, and such efforts are rewarded with success appropriate to the investigator's skill in recognizing the extent to which human behavior is free and spontaneous. All such laws have precisely the same basis in fact as do electromagnetic laws — they are social products. For example, the orderly managing of a metropolitan transit system depends on knowledge of statistical laws that express the traveling habits of individual commuters. Such laws are liable to be broken, because individual human beings respond to trivial changes in their environment with unpredictable novelty — a sunny day may produce heavy traffic on lines leading to the beaches — but a clever transit planner, considering large numbers of people, will be able to foresee even a number of these changes. Indeed, his job probably depends on his skill at recognizing lawful ways in which the ordinary laws of transit operation change. Probably there are even lawful changes in such laws of change, [95] but commonly such laws are exemplified over periods of time too great for us to observe. Therefore, historians do not agree on the laws concerning the rise and fall of civilizations, and we can only speculate as to the laws that are exemplified by the gradual decay of our electromagnetic universe.

Emergent evolutionists such as Samuel Alexander, C. Lloyd Morgan, and J. C. Smuts were attempting in one aspect of their work to show that some laws applicable to living organisms first applied on earth when these living creatures appeared. For that reason, they believed, these laws could not be reduced to laws concerning the behavior of the lower-grade physical and chemical objects of which living organisms are composed. This doctrine depends on the fact that emergent evolution is concerned with the emergence of real ontological unities, not mere multiplicities.[96] More often we have heard this as the statement " wholes are more than the sum of their parts," and this notion expresses much that is commonplace in our experience. In the sense intended here, its proper ground is the fact that an actual occasion syn-

[95] MT 130.   [96] PR 45.

thesizes a multiplicity of feelings of its actual world into an ontological unity that may be objectified by a single complex eternal object. Each actual occasion achieves its identity as an intensity of feeling by synthesizing its feelings into a multiple contrast, but this is *one* contrast and not a group of dual contrasts.[97] Apart from this it would be impossible (among other things) for human beings to enjoy the unity of personality that we ordinarily experience.

The early emergent evolutionists broke important ground, but critics saw that they did not entirely succeed in clarifying their belief in emergent unities. The problem expressed itself, perhaps most openly, in their inability to explain *why* new laws of nature should emerge along with new entities; Prof. Lloyd Morgan was forced to agree with Alexander that such occurrences must be accepted " with natural piety," [98] i.e., as unexplained facts. From a Whiteheadian perspective, however, it is easier to locate the source of their uncertainty: they were not yet able to use the notion of transition, which is necessary for understanding the temporal difference between the phases of subjective immediacy and objective immortality. For example, what Smuts called " holism " in *Holism and Evolution* [99] bears a striking resemblance to Whitehead's " phase of concrescence," but Smuts was perplexed by his efforts to describe holism in terms that actually required that his entities exhibit *at once* their subjective immediacy and their objective immortality. He was trying to modify the old notion of " simple location " with notions of subjectivity, but in such a way that his entities still endured indefinitely through time. Likewise, Lloyd Morgan spoke of the emergence of a " new kind of relation," [100] by which he seems to describe the process of synthesizing prehensions, but he was forced to suppose that subjective immediacy was an abstraction from this process.[101]

[97] *PR* 349.
[98] C. Lloyd Morgan, *Emergent Evolution* (Henry Holt & Company, Inc., 1923), p. 6.
[99] J. C. Smuts, *Holism and Evolution* (The Macmillan Company, 1926), pp. 238–243.
[100] Morgan, *op. cit.*, p. 65.
[101] *Ibid.*, p. 71.

Consequently, when these men spoke of a whole that was more than its parts, they could not explain precisely in what way the entities that served as parts in a whole differed from analogous entities outside the whole. Without the notion of transition, they were forced to imagine entities that endured as themselves, i.e., as subjects, while they participated in wholes, and they could give no clear explanation of just how these entities were altered by their participation. As a result, their descriptions of wholes never were quite able to escape the stamp of the Newtonian world, where wholes were merely sums of preexisting enduring entities.

Since order in the universe is derived from the characters of actual occasions, we may see why all forms of order ultimately reflect adaptation for the attainment of ends.[102] The character of each occasion is achieved by its subjective aim at intensity of feelings, an aim that specifically involves appetition for its own objective role in its society,[103] and that is heightened by the occasion's own prehensions of previous members. We may summarize in this fashion: the upward surge toward higher organisms and higher forms of order can be traced to the fact that actual occasions enjoy a subjective aim toward increased intensity of feeling. Thus the general purposiveness that pervades nature is exemplified in the growth of complex structured societies,[104] to which we now turn.

4. Life and Mentality in the Physical World

The relationship between "life" and "matter" has perplexed every biologist who ever tried to reconcile his knowledge of living organisms with the Newtonian vision. Maupertuis, the great eighteenth-century French Newtonian, resolved the problem by proposing that God had created the Newtonian particles with a glimmer of mentality, and Diderot spoke of the "self-sufficiency" and "internal activities" of simple substances. The next two hundred years saw repeated such efforts to refashion our concept of matter, but always by modifying the notion of "simple location" in some way that would allow for an understanding of life

[102] *PR* 127.   [103] *PR* 128.   [104] *PR* 153.

on Newtonian principles. The failure of these schemes stems ultimately from the fact that their authors were willing to take the Newtonian abstractions as statements of concrete fact, as an adequate framework on which they could tack their notions of life. Even though modern physicists may visualize ultimate reality in terms of fields of energy instead of in terms of Newtonian corpuscles, the underlying problem remains: how can notions of " life " be reconciled with notions of " physical nature " in such a way that no important intuitions are abridged or omitted?

To begin with, we have noted that physical laws are not perfectly obeyed, and we know that the widest backgrounds of physical order are decaying in slow but definite fashion. The speed of this decay does not concern us, only the fact that, be it ever so slow, physical reality runs downward. At the same time, the facts of evolution point to upward impulses, counter to this slow decay of levels of order; even the origination of systems of electronic and stellar order must have required some urge for " matter " to run upward.[105] Recalling these facts, Whitehead says that " life is an offensive, directed against the repetitious mechanism of the Universe . . . an aim at that perfection which the conditions of its environment allow." [106]

Apparently, this notion bears a resemblance to Bergson's belief that " life " and " matter " are engaged in a struggle,[107] with life seeking to explode upward and matter resisting its vital impulse.[108] Whitehead's thought does owe a good deal to Bergson, as he himself declares,[109] but his discussion of life differs from Bergson's in a way that illuminates the important differences between the two men. Bergson, like other early emergent evolutionists, lacked the notion of transition in his thought, and this deficiency appears throughout his works in the form of belief that the discrete objects studied by science are mere abstractions

105 *FR* 24.
106 *AI* 87.
107 Henri Bergson, *Creative Evolution*, tr. by Arthur Mitchell (Modern Library, Inc., 1944), p. 270.
108 *Ibid.*, p. 109.
109 *PR* vii.

from a single process of becoming. For him the life of separate organisms was merely a convenient practical abstraction from the " universal vital compulsion " [110] that accounted for the richness and diversity of organic forms. He wrote about evolution in a way that resembles strikingly the way Whitehead describes a single concrescent occasion, and indeed Bergson did seem to envision the entire evolutionary process as a single happening.[111] Consequently, he could deal with efficient causation only awkwardly, since efficient causation expresses the transition from one real entity to another. Likewise, his vision of nature as a single entity deprived him of any very plausible way of attributing teleology in nature to anything less than evolution as a whole. Just as Whitehead attributes a unfied subjective aim to each concrescent occasion, Bergson spoke of the purposiveness of nature as " including the whole of life in a single indivisible embrace." [112] He did not believe that God determined the entire evolutionary process from without, since this sort of divine predestination struck him as nothing more than an inverted mechanism; but he was unable logically to attribute purposiveness to any creature within the evolutionary process, since he viewed them all as abstractions from the real entity, nature. It is not surprising, then, that the *élan vital* appears in Bergson's writing as a blind force, a river that splashes unpredictably down its channel with no destination.

Whitehead's intention, on the other hand, is to explain the life of the world in terms of discrete actual occasions and discrete individual organisms, which are the realities of nature; the difference between the two men at this point could hardly be greater. Bergson made room for " life " by denying (implicitly) the ontological reality of the entities discussed by science in terms of " matter " and efficient causation, while Whitehead took " matter " and efficient causation with utter seriousness and introduced " life " as an agency of modification, traceable to the sub-

---

[110] Bergson, *op. cit.*, p. 57.

[111] For example, " The truth is that there is one indivisible act." *Ibid.*, p. 105.

[112] *Ibid.*, p. 50.

jective aims of real things. In spite of invaluable contributions, then, Bergson presented only the flux at the heart of things and did not give adequate expression to the permanences.

From Whitehead's viewpoint, the problem for nature is the production of societies that are structured with a high complexity, thus encouraging the existence of actual occasions which enjoy increased intensities of feeling.[113] For evolutionary "success," however, any such increased intensity of process must be balanced by a power to perpetuate the society's patterns of feeling, and Whitehead notes two ways in which nature has solved this problem. Material bodies, such as rocks and stars, are aggregates of structured societies that persist for millions of years by means of massive average objectifications of their environment. In the occasions of such societies, mentality is only vanishingly effective, serving merely to eliminate from feeling whatever vagrant conceptual feelings are passed on by previous occasions that have failed to obey the appropriate physical laws completely.[114] These structured societies are called "inorganic," and we recognize them as being dominated by patterns of physical feeling that can stimulate our sense organs.

The second way of solving nature's problem is by an initiative in conceptual feelings. Whitehead says the world advances into novelty along a road paved with "propositions," [115] a proposition being the possibility that some specific entity or entities will, in fact, be characterized by some specific set of eternal objects.[116] Therefore, novelty enters the world whenever some actual occasion admits into conceptual feeling a proposition that does not merely conform to past matter of fact; in the case at point, occasions in the society aim to admit some novelty from the environment as a contrast that is reconciled with feelings already characteristic of the society in question.[117] In this manner, the dominant characteristics of social order are preserved, but a greater intensity of feeling has been achieved: *by means of final causation the society has adapted itself to the environment.* Structured societies in which this second solution is important are termed by Whitehead "living societies." [118]

113 *PR* 154.   115 *PR* 284.   117 *PR* 155.
114 *Ibid.*   116 *PR* 282.   118 *PR* 156.

In the lowest-grade living societies, of course, this purposive adaptation occurs quite without the kind of conscious mentality that we know by introspection; the mentality involved need not even approach in complexity the rather limited kind of imaginative entertaining of alternatives that we may attribute to an ant.[119] We note, then, that " aliveness " may be attributed to any society of occasions or organisms whose reactions cannot be fully explained by some one or more traditions of pure physical inheritance. " Life " is the escape from physical routine, the answer to the question: how can there be originality? [120]

All the life in any society can be traced finally to individual living occasions,[121] those occasions which aim to introduce some novelty, some feelings not merely gained by inheritance. At this point, we must introduce a notion that at first glance seems startling, but which will help us understand exactly why " life " continues to elude the gaze of scientists — life is a characteristic of " empty space." [122] Let us try to clarify this notion. To begin with, we have observed that inorganic societies, such as rock molecules, endure by repeating their patterns of physical feeling, and it is the spatiotemporal endurance achieved by such canalized physical inheritance that makes possible our study of these enduring objects by sense perception, using scientific instruments to detect them. Now it is precisely a freedom from such domination by the physical past that characterizes those occasions we have called " living "; [123] since by their very nature they are dominated by novelty and do not participate in any strand of physical order, science cannot detect them by means of sense perception. This explains why they enjoy their brief existence in what to us is " empty space." A scientist studying a living cell, for example, can detect only its atoms and molecules, which are strands of physical inheritance; the life of the cell occurs now here, now there, as fleet-

---

[119] In *MT* 230, Whitehead speaks of mentality as being " merely latent " in electrons and atoms, but it is clear from the context that he means *complex* mentality, so there is no contradiction with his intention to ascribe a mental pole to every occasion.

[120] *PR* 158.

[121] *PR* 156–164.

[122] *PR* 161.

[123] We should note that an occasion may be more or less alive, depending on the importance of novel feelings in its satisfaction. *PR* 156.

ing bursts of novelty in the " empty space " between the molecules.

In the empty space of cells, influenced by the originalities of living occasions, the transmission of physical feelings is altered; chemical changes take place that otherwise would not occur. This accounts for the fact that laws applying to the behavior of atoms and molecules within living bodies differ slightly from the laws that apply to analogous inorganic societies outside the body. Also, it explains why all living organisms require food — the supporting physical structure is continually breaking down, and it must be repaired, using complex societies from outside the body.[124]

We have noted as a major evolutionary trend the move toward central unified mentality in the higher creatures: worms appear to be little more than coordinated cells, but insects demonstrate some central control, and men possess (during periods of psychical health) a unified personality that can exercise far-reaching control over their bodies. Clearly, any explanation of life must account for this centralized coordination in living creatures. But we are reminded that all the *life* of an animal body is located in the empty spaces of its myriad cells.[125] How then, in a body composed of millions or billions of cellular centers of life, can we account for the existence of a unifying mental control that transcends the individual cells? Finally, how can we explain the appearance of what Whitehead calls " presiding " or " dominant " occasions in the bodies of higher animals?

Whitehead begins by defining a living society as one that is dominated by one or more " entirely living " nexūs,[126] such a nexus being one in which the mental pole of each member introduces some novelty. He suggests that although a living nexus of occasions must depend on inorganic societies for its persistence, even in the lowest forms of life the mentality in an entirely living nexus is " canalized into some faint form of mutual conformity." [127] Thus, a living nexus can support a thread of personal order along some historical route of its members, allowing for stead-

---

[124] *PR* 162.
[125] *PR* 165.
[126] *PR* 157. Whitehead uses the word " nexūs " as a plural for " nexus."
[127] *PR* 164. The term " canalized " is borrowed from Bergson.

iness of purpose in addition to isolated flashes of novelty.[128] Such
an enduring entity is a " living person," [129] and like all strands of
personal order it has its defining characteristic. In this case, the
defining characteristic is mental, a hybrid prehension by which
each occasion in the route receives a depth and character to its
mental originality by feeling the conceptual novelty of its predecessors.[130] In this way, the originality of succeeding occasions can
be canalized so that the route does not exhibit chaotic and contra-
dictory flashes of novelty which might destroy even the underlying physical order. As nearly as we can tell, the higher organisms all contain at least one such " living person." The human
living person is that which is known to us through introspection
as " I " and which is popularly called the soul.

Many arguments about " Lamarckian inheritance " are muddled
by imagining the life of an animal as though it were somehow one
process of concrescence, with a single subjective aim determining
the whole process. We must studiously avoid this error by remembering that an animal body is a structured society of occasions,
not a single actual occasion.[131] It contains some entirely living
nexus which is the reason it is alive, but in addition it harbors a
complex system of inorganic societies. Thus a living cell, the simplest example of what Whitehead calls an " animal body," [132] is
an intricate pattern of intertwining nexūs with varying defining
characteristics, its living nexus functioning by protecting the sub-
servient societies while at the same time depending on them. The
cell serves as the major environment for all its sub-societies, just
as the human body is the most important part of the total environment for all its sub-societies, both living and nonliving.

The overall picture, then, is one of life as a passage from mere
physical order to mental novelty and from mental novelty to coordinated inheritance of mental novelty.[133] The evolution of " living persons " made possible the appearance of personal mentality,
an evolutionary breakthrough that rivals in importance the first
appearance of cells on earth, for it, too, apparently has set the direction for all future evolution on our planet. Once organisms

---

[128] *PR* 163; *AI* 209.   [130] *Ibid.*   [132] *Ibid.*
[129] *PR* 163.   [131] *PR* 157.   [133] *PR* 164.

with personal mentality appeared on earth, the general upward surge toward novelty could flower in a multitude of new ways, and continued evolutionary advance has been located more and more in those animal groups that have achieved personal mentality.

5. ORGANISMS AND ENVIRONMENTS

Modern evolutionary theory is addressed rather explicitly to the problem as stated by Whitehead: to explain the evolution of complex societies of higher value. Thus it deals chiefly with the ways whole animal populations evolve, using a definition of species that expresses the ability of groups of organisms to reproduce themselves over long periods of time, often in the face of an increasingly complex environment. Of course, it is individual organisms that are produced, for they are the units of emergent value in terms of what they are for themselves,[134] but it is only when we consider their collective effect in the evolutionary process that we can apply the recently developed statistical laws of population genetics. In this sense, these laws are exactly analogous to the laws of physics, for an animal population is not a " superorganism " any more than an electromagnetic field is; it can be studied as a unit only by abstracting from the behavior of its individual members.

Whitehead points out that the key in understanding evolution is to understand how favorable environments are evolved along with the evolution of particular kinds of organisms.[135] This is exemplified if the relationship of an organism to its environment favors the endurance of other analogous organisms; if, in addition, the organism favors the production of subsequent analogous organisms, we approach the situation where the species automatically develops along with the environment, and the environment with the species.[136] Perhaps the primordial example here is a society of molecular occasions in the inorganic realm, displaying astonishing powers of survival that are based on just such a comfortable relationship between individual organism and environment — each occasion transmits to its successors just those physical feel-

[134] *SMW* 110.   [135] *SMW* 112.   [136] *Ibid.*

ings which perpetuate both the species of occasion and its molecular environment. But no matter which organisms or societies we study, we find this mechanism of evolution. Thus in the case of those living things which we can observe most easily, there is genetic reproduction of individual organisms from other organisms of the same species. And there is the provision of a favorable environment — peach seeds are surrounded by fruit, chicken embryos grow within eggs, and human infants are raised in families. In addition, species of creatures quite commonly provide favorable environments for each other. Whitehead suggests that electrons and hydrogen nuclei provide the simplest example of two species of creatures apparently free of competition with each other,[137] and we have all enjoyed the picture of African tickbirds tidying the hide of a hippopotamus.

Ordinarily we think of any species or society in terms of its more immediate environment, e.g., salmon in a river or human beings in families and cities. But in each case the society and its environment are themselves only part of a wider, supporting social background. Both salmon and man depend on the inorganic societies of the earth, and the planets of our solar system in their turn inhabit a wider electromagnetic environment. Therefore, in considering any society we must remember what Whitehead calls its " layers of social order," [138] which have wider and wider general characteristics as the background broadens. It is useful in a laboratory to consider fruit flies apart from the men whose melon rinds they inhabit, but we should remember that evolutionary theory does make this kind of abstraction in its search for new and illuminating simplicities in the relationships of animal societies to their environments. The theory always presupposes that certain wide layers of social order in the background are constant, and, of course, this assumption is only relatively correct. In particular, the statements of population genetics purposely neglect many aspects of the background, including any possible changes in the subjective aim of occasions in the various sub-societies that compose the population in question.

We have traced the upward surge of evolution to the subjective

[137] *SMW* 114. [138] *PR* 138.

aims of actual occasions, and if in this way we can locate final causation *in nature,* the term " natural selection " may be broadened very simply so as to apply quite adequately to the whole evolutionary process. Evolution toward adaptation thus involves the natural selection of societies in terms of the degree to which their members achieve intensities of feeling that are sufficient to combine the contraries of the environment into contrasts of feeling without destroying the type of social order involved.[139] Also, except for the possible case of wholesale catastrophe, such natural selection cannot be an either/or situation, since it involves the persistence or dissipation of forms of order that only gradually come into existence and vanish.

But at this point we may sense a gulf between a discussion of electronic and atomic societies and our desire to explain the evolution of complex higher organisms. Obviously, we cannot merely assume that a description of events at the level of individual actual occasions applies without modification to events at the level of trees and men, complex organisms composed of societies of societies. Let us try to fill this gulf. If we are to avoid serious logical errors, we must distinguish carefully between the several grades of actual occasions discussed by Whitehead and the several grades of *aggregations* of occasions. We shall examine nature in each way, pausing here to note that we are describing only grades of entities and aggregates that seem to occur in nature; they are not all required by Whitehead's cosmology.

There are four discernible grades of actual occasions, not sharply distinguished from each other.[140] First, there are the occasions in empty space, those occasions which we cannot detect with sense perception. Second, there are the actual occasions in historic routes that we have called inorganic enduring objects, such as electrons and rock molecules. Third, there are the actual occasions that are moments in the life histories of enduring living objects, occasions which exhibit some conceptual originality by which they lift into particular relevance certain aspects of the diffuse message from their worlds. Sense perception is the climax of this urge to deal more effectively with the environment by a selec-

[139] *PR* 248.   [140] *PR* 269.

tive attention to parts of it. Fourth, there are the actual occasions that are moments of the life histories of enduring objects with conscious knowledge. Such occasions, found in human personality and probably also in the higher animals, are able to compare inherited experience with conceptual possibility.[141]

All the above are grades of single actual entities, but we also find in nature four main types of *aggregates* of entities. First, there are the inorganic things whose parts merely transmit an average experience and that are able in this way to persist for long periods of time. Second, there is the vegetable grade, most impressive as a democracy of cells in which subjective aims are limited to the survival of the cells and possibly of the individual organism. Here there is a coordinated expressiveness that goes beyond the merely average expression typical of inorganic nature, even though the total organism imposes a limit on the amount of conceptual novelty which can be enjoyed by occasions within it. As Whitehead says, " A tree sticks to its business of mere survival." [142] Third, there is the animal grade, in which is found at least some faint striving to " live better." [143] All animals entertain aims that transcend the mere aim at survival, although an oyster may enjoy only rather trivial aims beyond those we have attributed to a tree's occasions. Fourth, there is the human grade of animal life, which reveals an immense enlargement of capacity for novel conceptuality.

Combining both modes of analysis, we have roughly five types of occurrences in nature, all shading off into each other. There is the inframolecular activity studied by physics. There is the large-scale inorganic realm of molecules, persisting for millions of years. There is cell life with its complexly organized structured society of molecules. There is vegetable life with its more highly organized republic of cells. And there is animal life, exhibiting in its higher forms some central direction of a society of cells; here we find human existence, a body with its presiding personality.[144]

In *Modes of Thought*, Whitehead suggests that animal life always includes a " central actuality," [145] but his more consistent

---

141 *PR* 270.   143 *FR* 18.   145 *MT* 39.
142 *MT* 43.   144 *MT* 215.

view is that taken in *Process and Reality*, where he says that we have no grounds for attributing central control to many lower forms of life.[146] Also in *Adventures of Ideas*, he attributes a dominant personal society merely to " most animals, including all the vertebrates." [147] The ambiguity in his expression probably indicates only his own belief that there is no sharp distinction between kinds of organisms, once we push our observations beyond certain arbitrary limits,[148] and he observed that even in human beings central personal dominance is fleeting and apt to vanish.[149] But the question may now be asked: why should there be a dominant occasion or society in some animals and not in others?

The existence of central control depends on coordination of the various paths of inheritance through an animal body,[150] so that some one occasion occupies a standpoint at which it is presented with a peculiar richness of bodily experience. Now, any actual occasion exists as the enjoyment of some definite quantum of the temporospatial continuum, some " region " that defines the actual world available to it for prehension. The standpoint of an occasion is defined *for* it, not *by* it, and in this sense an occasion is the *outcome* of its region. Therefore, the presiding occasion in an animal body (if any) depends for its very existence on a given region of intensive bodily experience. And, in fact, the nervous systems of animals do provide for just such a focused richness of experience, by transmitting vivid impulses from relatively remote parts of the body. Thus central direction of animal bodies is most closely related to the possession of a complex central nervous system, and animals without central nervous systems resemble vegetables in their limited ability to make novel and coordinated responses.

We may suppose, finally, with some confidence gained from anatomical and physiological study, that the higher organisms most commonly studied by evolutionists contain ordered sub-societies

---

[146] *PR* 164. Agar, *op. cit.*, p. 66, suspects that all animal life above the sponges may generate a " central agent."
[147] *AI* 207.
[148] *MT* 21.
[149] *PR* 167.
[150] *PR* 166.

which may be described somewhat as follows. In some animals, a society of presiding occasions is the "intersection" [151] of the complex supporting structure of enduring objects. Then there are societies of cells, forming organs and tissues; in some cases these societies are widely dispersed, as in the case of societies of blood cells. Indeed, a single red blood cell, in circulation, seems to lose its social relationship to other analogous cells, although in its beginnings it inhabits a blood-forming organ where social relationships obtain. Within the cells and in the body fluids there are societies of molecules and even societies of atoms, and metabolism is expressive of the delicately balanced forms of molecular and atomic order that prevail. Also, there are societies of electrons, and there are the occasions in the empty spaces of the body that account for its life. Apparently, the complex effects of these various societies on each other are utterly beyond our powers to analyze, and so far we have only the most fragmentary understanding of how, e.g., the physical laws governing behavior of glycogen molecules must be modified if we are studying molecules that are affected by the living nexūs within liver cells.

6. The Problem of Lamarckian Inheritance

We can clarify the problem of Lamarckian inheritance, i.e., inheritance of characteristics acquired in response to need, by examining the ways in which we might expect transmission of influence among the levels of social order just proposed. As usually considered, the problem involves a consideration of whether environmental factors may lead to bodily responses that are transmitted to the level of societies of cells, in particular to the societies of sexual cells which play a major role in the succession of generations. We shall begin by considering a general case.

"Adaptation," as we have seen, is a process of increasing the intensity of feeling by a width of contrast in which potentially destructive contrary feelings are felt as compatible. Also, we have seen that each occasion is guided partly by its ideal of itself as "transcendent creator," i.e., as having its effect on the future, and

[151] *Ibid.*

every historic route of occasions tends to perpetuate itself.[152] Now, what is a "need imposed by the environment"? This must be some contrary feeling inherent in the environment, one which threatens to destroy a level of order in the relevant future of some actual occasion or society of occasions. In this light, we may guess that the least-complex "relevant future" is that for one occasion in an enduring electron, whose subjective aim may be limited to passing on its defining characteristic to a single succeeding actual entity. There is no reason to suppose that an electronic occasion entertains any aims which concern the future of a wider society of electrons. But for occasions within higher-grade societies, the relevant future is correspondingly more extensive, and it may, in some cases, extend to the future of entities in other societies that are significantly related to them. Thus the subjective aim of a DNA molecular occasion may include an aim to perpetuate the existence of analogous molecular societies, and an aim to perpetuate the existence of its own atomic sub-societies. At this very low level of events, a "need" imposed by the environment upon a molecular society will be prehended in terms of its potentiality to disrupt this relevant future; any novel response by a given molecular occasion can then be described as the aim to "save" that relevant future by an increased width of feeling. Obviously, the conceptual novelty required is far below consciousness, for we are speaking of events at the level of chemical combination.

When we consider the complex structured society of a living cell with its living nexus, the subjective aims involve concern for the futures of a multiplicity of intertwining societies. For example, liver cells inhabit an environment dominated by their fellows, so that the subjective aims expressed in these structured societies may well include aims to preserve the immediate future integrity of adjoining cellular societies. But even here it is doubtful that the subjective aims expressed include any aim for the future of the whole liver; aim for a relevant future probably does not extend much beyond an urge to perpetuate the molecular sub-societies that are supportive of the life of the cell and its immediate neighbors. This conjecture is in line with our actual observations of liver

[152] *PR* 88.

cells, for pathologists know that although they exhibit a remarkable plasticity of response to insult, this response has its definite limits. For example, the occasions within liver cells are not able to synthesize compatible contrasts from their feelings of molecular carbon tetrachloride occasions in their actual worlds, and in the presence of carbon tetrachloride the order of the cells is disrupted. As a corollary of the above sketch, we see the impossibility of thinking that the liver " intends " to store glycogen " in order that " the body and ultimately a society of presiding occasions may be benefited. Carbohydrate metabolism in the liver is merely expressive of the complexly evolved ways in which sub-societies within liver cells can adapt themselves to changes in their immediate environment. For most purposes, we are not seriously in error if we regard these processes as dominated by efficient causation, and medical science is based largely on knowledge of laws expressing the scope and mode of these elementary processes. Biochemists are well aware of how fantastically complicated are the routes of physical causation in even the simplest living cells, a fact that testifies to the very complex experience enjoyed by the occasions within cells. But we have only just begun to trace these causal sequences in cells, and there is every reason to expect that future research will disclose the machinery of living cells to be more intricate than we can yet imagine.

As research continually turns up these new sequences of physical causation, there is a sense in which the possible role of final causation seems ever more vanishingly small.[153] How shall we explain the proper relation of efficient causation and final causation in such cases? In the first place, we must admit that although present biochemical and cellular reactions may seem purposive, scientists are correct in claiming that final causation is negligible. It is not absent, since all actual entities have subjective aims; but it is negligible. Here the key is to recall that conceptual novelty en-

---

[153] See, e.g., B. F. Skinner, "Freedom and the Control of Men," *American Scholar*, 25 (1955–56), pp. 47–65, where he writes: " Every discovery of an event which has a part in shaping a man's behavior seems to leave so much the less to be credited to the man himself; and as such explanations become more and more comprehensive, the contribution which may be claimed by the individual himself appears to approach zero."

ters feeling and contributes to satisfaction in such a way that the objectified occasion becomes a part of the actual world which then is felt *physically* by succeeding occasions. This means that patterns of response may originate by a display of conceptual originality and then be passed on as physical feelings without repeated novelty of mentality; subsequent occasions *inherit* the patterns from the past but do not *introduce* them.

Thus final causation passes over into efficient causation, and during millions of years unbelievably complicated patterns of efficient causation have developed. The peach tree blindly produces seeds embedded in fruit, and the ovum blindly divides when it is fertilized. But these events have not evolved mechanically or by chance; in every case, such patterns of efficient causation can be traced ultimately to the subjective aims of past actual occasions, In turn, the world advances by fresh responses to its inherited forms of order. *The inheritance of acquired characteristics of feeling is fundamental to evolution.*

In his sparkling Gifford Lectures of 1963–1964, published as *The Living Stream*, Sir Alister Hardy develops at length a theory of evolutionary change that leans heavily on just such a mode of passage from subjective aim to efficient causation.[154] For this reason, its general form is remarkably similar to the interpretation we have been making in this chapter, although Hardy limits himself mainly to description. His thesis is that an " internal selective force," the behavioral habits of animals, is extremely important in evolution. Although he speaks of this occasionally as " the ' psychic life ' of animals," he tries not to define its metaphysical status, giving us instead an impressive group of examples that suggest the role of animal habits in evolutionary adaptation. Baldwin and Lloyd Morgan were correct, he says, in proposing organic selection as an explanatory mechanism in addition to natural selection,[155] and he gives their theory a modern expression that allows for the immense variability in a population gene pool.

According to Hardy, if a population of animals changes its hab-

---

[154] Sir Alister Hardy, *The Living Stream: Evolution & Man* (London: William Collins Sons & Co., Ltd., 1965).
[155] See above, p. 142.

its, random variations in the population gene pool will produce, sooner or later, small changes that make the animals more efficient in their adopted habits. As an example, he cites Darwin's finches, which exhibit an astonishing variety of beaks, all directly adapted to different feeding habits. Hardy suggests that we should call in the usual factors of natural selection in explaining this situation, but in addition we may think that competition for food led the birds to adopt new feeding habits that spread through the population. Finally, there was natural selection of whatever random changes in beak form turned out to be helpful in the new ways of feeding.[156] In a way which echoes our own suggestion above, Hardy proposes that the complex instinctual actions of creatures like spiders and bees have arisen " by new habits being subsequently passed into the instinctive equipment." [157] He traces the inward factor as far back as protozoa in this regard, noting that some Foraminifera (one-celled marine animals) build extremely complicated " houses " from spicules of sponge.[158] But he does not believe that plant evolution is much affected by habit, since it seems to be almost completely determined by the usual " external " selective forces. Even in this case, however, the habits of insects seem to have a striking effect on the evolution of flower patterns.

Hardy leans over backward to avoid any suggestion that his " internal selective force " somehow *replaces* the well-established forces of natural selection, so we may hope that his viewpoint is received with sympathy in the continuing scientific discussion. It should be enhanced in explanatory value by the kind of analysis we are attempting, specifically when it comes to the question of analyzing the actual routes of transmission of feeling; it is to this that we now turn.

" Inheritance " in the Whiteheadian sense clearly is conditioned by routes of transmission and depends upon the standpoint of the occasions concerned. Since there is no direct physical connection between changes in a total animal body and changes in a single cell or society of cells, there is no reason to suppose that any

[156] Hardy, *op. cit.*, p. 174.   [158] *Ibid.*, p. 231.
[157] *Ibid.*, p. 198.

molecule in a living body is much affected by aspects of the pattern of feelings of the *whole* organism which may be reflected in it.[159] It is only credulous to believe that Lamarckian inheritance can be explained in this way. What we should expect is that any modification in the body's total pattern of feeling will be transmitted through a series of modifications in descending societies. In this way, there will be, finally, some modification of every cell, and the smaller entities within the cells will be altered in turn.[160] But even a large change in the pattern of feeling of the total body will not produce any notable change in the physical inheritance of its cellular occasions, except insofar as there are peculiar routes of transmission such as are provided by the nervous and circulatory systems.

Mutations can be produced by irradiation, which indicates that occasionally some DNA molecular occasions are modified by including in their patterns of contrast the pulse of emotion from an X-ray particle; statistical statements about mutation may express the laws that apply to such changes. Now the relevant future for such occasions in the DNA molecule does not, so far as we suspect, include any state of the total animal body. It seems unlikely that it includes even the immediate future state of the cell in whose structured society it participates as member of a sub-society, for such aims (if any) would be located in the occasions of the cell's living nexus. Precisely in this sense, gene mutations are random with regard to the future of the total organism. The subjective aim of genetic occasions neglects that part of its world which is the whole animal, analogously to the way that our human subjective aims are oblivious to the future of possible societies of organisms beyond the range of our radio telescopes. For this reason, further scientific discoveries about the causes of genetic mutation cannot illuminate the *ascending* course of evolution, and knowing these causes will help us only in understanding the future of DNA molecules, not the future of man, except as genetic research may aid us in controlling such diseases as diabetes mellitus.

But, we may ask, can the purposes of higher-grade occasions in an animal body " trickle down " to the molecular level? Can a

[159] *SMW* 149.   [160] *SMW* 150.

DNA molecule in a man's body be affected by the conscious desire of the man's personality? Here we must be cautious. According to Whitehead, the *mental* poles of occasions are prehended immediately, i.e., they are not separated by any spatial or temporal distance from the process which is a new occasion. He cites as evidence for this belief the occurrence of telepathy, and he proposes it as the "doctrine of immediate objectification" for the mental poles of occasions.[161] This is in contrast, we may note, with the requirement that the physical poles of occasions be prehended by mediation through contiguous occasions.[162] In principle, therefore, it is possible that the mentality of a human personality can immediately affect the entities in bodily sub-societies, both in one's own body and in the bodies of others; modern psychosomatic medicine attempts to investigate the first of these theoretical possibilities, whereas the second has remained, up to now, largely the province of psychical research. However, two considerations speak against the plausibility of believing that the conscious or unconscious aims of presiding occasions ordinarily exert any directly effective influence on, e.g., the DNA molecules of body cells. First, as Whitehead points out, direct objectification of mental poles usually is rendered insignificant because such prehensions are hopelessly intermixed with and weakened by routes of mediate objectification.[163] Thus the subjective aim of a human personality cannot be expected to have much pure impact on a DNA molecular occasion. Second, we have supposed that the mentality of DNA molecules is much too limited to accept into feeling the kind of complex eternal object that would be involved in this case, e.g., the possibility of a certain future modification in total bodily form.

In a fascinating section (Chapter IX), Sir Alister Hardy discusses telepathy in human beings, giving evidence for his own belief in it and then speculating as to the possibility that some analogous phenomenon among lower animals may help explain the development and stabilization of group behavior patterns and organic forms. He wonders whether, in this case, there may be two parallel "streams of information" available to an animal population — a shared gene pool and "the psychic stream of shared ex-

[161] *PR* 469.   [162] *PR* 468.   [163] *PR* 469.

perience." [164] If so, he notes, traditional intuitions of " types " or
" archetypes " of organisms may not be quite so outmoded as we
suppose, for there *would* be a pattern or form existing independently of any one organism.[165] This possibility deserves much
more attention than it has received, although we must be careful
in drawing analogies from human telepathic experience. The pattern of bodily form of an animal (even that of a one-celled animal) would be a very complex eternal object, and we must be
cautious about suggesting that there are occasions in animal bodies that enjoy a mentality sufficiently rich to include such an eternal object in feeling. On the other hand, we have seen that transmission of emotional tone is the primary mode of relationship
among entities, and we may well speculate that there is, for every
level of real society, a corresponding level of complexity of mentality that is shared immediately by members of the society. What
remains to be done is to assess these typical levels of mentality
and discover the ways in which they may be widened in excep-
tional cases.

The conclusion is that Lamarckian inheritance is expressive of
the ways in which feelings are transmitted from occasion to occasion, but it is strictly limited in scope by the available routes of
transmission between occasions and their environments. My desire
to stand up is transmitted effectively by physical feelings to a
vast society of nervous and muscular cells, but my desire to have
a son with blue eyes is ineffective, thwarted by lack of an effective
route of transmission to the society of reproductive cells some distance from my brain; his blue eyes are to be explained genetically. The proper interpretation of Lamarckian notions in genetics is that all new patterns of efficient causation in animal bodies
can be traced to *some* reaction influenced by final causation. But
locating *which* actual occasions were involved, and *when*, makes
all the difference in the world. Neo-Lamarckians are correct if they
affirm, e.g., that the giraffe's long neck is the result of teleological
factors in evolution; but they are wrong if they suppose that the
teleology can be traced to the subjective aims of presiding occasions that inhabited the bodies of past giraffes. Instead, the

---

[164] Hardy, *op. cit.*, p. 258.   [165] *Ibid.*, p. 260.

" need " for and development of long necks is expressive of complexly related changes of subjective aim in innumerable sub-societies of past giraffe bodies. Description of the detailed steps involved is quite beyond our powers, but the discussion need not be fruitless if we will remember to distinguish the relevant levels of occasions, environments, and routes of transmission.

7. GOALS IN EVOLUTIONARY CHANGE

Considerations of evolution are only handicapped by the idealistic notion that we should be able to demonstrate some single goal for the whole process, and any appeal to the evidence must result in admitting that there are and have been *many* directions of evolutionary change. Therefore, whenever we devote our attention to the ways evolution has culminated in human personality, we must remember that we are limiting our attention to but one of nature's many " experimental pathways." Our real problem, however, is to *understand* and *explain* these diverging directions of evolution, and to do this in the light of our view that nature's general upward surge occurs because individual occasions enjoy subjective aims toward greater intensities of feeling.

Viewed in this way, evolution appears as *a general movement toward societies of organisms with more complex mentality*, even though the movement has been sporadic and never has had any one type of organism as its goal. This points us to the really important discovery incorporated in the modern theory of evolution by its notions of inheritance and natural selection: evolution is a historical process. There are always new possibilities, but they depend on what has happened before; as Whitehead says, successful progress " creeps from point to point, testing each step." [166] Nature is through and through historical, and all her cyclical phenomena appear capricious and arbitrary unless they are understood in the context of the irreversible temporal progression that characterizes our universe. Thus what we observe is that the general upward surge of nature has been channeled by the concrete facts of history into countless divergent streams, and Bergson cap-

[166] *AI* 28.

tured this facet of evolution in his vision of the *élan vital* as a river that splashes down the mountain, endlessly diverted into fresh and unexpected rivulets.

Whitehead also insists that the detailed happenings of evolutionary history could not have been predicted,[167] but for him this fact derives from the absolute independence of each occasion's share of final causation during its moment of concrescence. The freedom of the universe is located in actual occasions, and their subjective aims cannot be foretold in detail. The only goals in nature, then, are the goals of actual occasions, goals always limited to the relevant futures of the occasions involved. This helps explain why we should not think of evolution as a single stream moving toward the day when *Homo sapiens* would appear, for nowhere in the past have there been creatures harboring occasions whose relevant futures included such a future course of evolution. Even such a high-grade organism as a dog seems to enjoy aims that fall far short of envisioning the future of his own species; probably when dogs mate they are oblivious even to the possibilities of reproduction.

It is not until we consider man that we find occasions of personality able to entertain aims that much transcend the future states of their own immediate organisms, and even here we differ from animals only in degree. In fact, only sporadically do any of our aims comprise states of the distant future, essential as these long-range goals may be in setting the tone for our lives. Ordinarily, our aims are quite modest — to open a door, to eat, to sleep, to wake. Our own sexual aims only occasionally extend to the aim for reproduction, and even at such times the relevant future does not extend much beyond our enjoyment of possible future relationships with our children. Not many of us can testify that our sexual actions were undertaken with an aim to perpetuate the species *Homo sapiens!*

In any case, we cannot understand the history of evolution as a teleological process except as we specify just which actual occasions are entertaining the aims. No fish ever intended that his descendants should be reptiles, no reptile ever thought of generating

[167] *PR* 74.

birds, and no primitive " ape-man " suspected that he would give
rise, eventually, to modern man. Of course, man *is* the present
high point of that general upward surge that we find everywhere,
and in this sense the purposiveness of nature finds its fullest expression in *Homo sapiens*. But from this we are justified in con-
cluding only that man is historical like the rest of nature, the result of an unimaginably tortuous route of evolution. When the earliest living organisms inhabited our planet, it was impossible to
know that this intricate process, combining efficient and final causation, would issue in man a billion years hence. Thus we cannot
say that nature intended man from the beginning, nor can we
agree with Hegel that all of history was leading up to the human
spirit.

In trying to understand the complexly related diverging directions of evolution, we may follow Whitehead's suggestion that organisms exhibit an urge " to live, to live well, to live better." [168]
In this sense, we may regard the appearance of a new species as
the discovery of some new methodology of life, some new mode
of existence in an environment, some novelty that transcends the
established order. If a happy choice is made, then evolution has
moved upward. If not, eventual extinction may testify to the limitations of the new mode of existence. But note that we are speaking
only of the *limitations* of a mode of life, not of its achievement in
terms of richness of mentality, for a species may well find itself
limited in ways that bear little or no relationship to its possibilities
for advance in mentality. The dinosaurs appear to have been limited by their size and need for an aqueous environment, factors
that alone may account for their final extinction after millions of
years of evolutionary success; even though dinosaur brains were
quite small, there is no particular reason to attribute their extinction solely or even mainly to mental sluggishness. Such a judgment
overestimates the significance of mentality in prehuman evolution,
and for all we know, dinosaurs might eventually have developed
a very complex mentality if climatic conditions had remained
favorable. History is pliable beyond our expectations!

Here we may introduce Whitehead's definition of evil as " in-

[168] *FR* 18.

sistence on birth at the wrong season." [169] Nature teeters continually on the brink of novelty, but this is also the brink of disorder, and a novel fact may throw back or inhibit the already existing forms of order. In the long run, however, such evil always is self-defeating, for it promotes its own elimination; this occurs through destruction, degradation, or elevation of the kinds of evolutionary order that exist.[170] Thus, a species whose members are continually in pain either ceases to exist, or it loses its sensitivity to pain, or it develops some more harmonious relationship among its body parts, overcoming the pain. In this way, the evil in evolution repeatedly eliminates itself by inducing the disappearance of the kind of order in which it appears. Recognizing the really evil aspects of any event, therefore, depends on making a comparison with what *might* have been, i.e., deciding which possible future has been thwarted. A hog is not evil, and a man reduced to the level of a hog's behavior is no more evil than the hog; but there *is* evil in his failure to realize a human future instead of a hoggish future.[171] On this basis, much of what we might view from an absolute standpoint as evil loses some of its poignant quality; it is only abstractly sentimental to mourn the fact that piranha fish have become carnivorous or that human beings traffic in the flesh of innocent cattle. The relevant question is always: what were the other real possibilities that were thwarted? On this basis, evil can be distinguished from mere matter of fact, and the actual sources of evil can be illuminated.

The evolutionary phase of adaptive radiation indicates that in general new methodologies of life spread quickly, responding to the inherent possibilities for diversity. Then there is a prolonged middle phase, which is the " good life " for that mode, a period during which novel possibilities are explored. But gradually the freshness of novelty weakens into repetition of pattern and solidification of instinct; there is what Whitehead calls " relapse into the well-attested patterns of mere life." [172] If, at that point, a new adventure into novelty is not begun, the species begins to enter old age. Also at that point, unless there is external interference, a species may exhibit great survival power, for the downhill course of

[169] *PR* 341.   [170] *RM* 93.   [171] *RM* 94.   [172] *FR* 19.

physical patterns is exceedingly slow. Lungfishes continue to grope their way along the ocean floor, oblivious of man and his ventures into space.

Whitehead suggests three ways, not sharply distinguishable, in which a species may achieve stability at the price of abandoning progress. There is, first, the " way of blindness," or relapse into mere instinct. Here, operations that originated by means of conceptual novelty are carried on routinely through inherited patterns of feeling. Thus ants do not contrive their complex society anew with each generation; they inherit its pattern blindly in the form of physical feelings. Human society also exhibits its share of blindly felt pattern in the form of uncriticized custom and the deadening weight of " common sense." Second, there is the " way of transience," which characterizes species in which a continual round of short-lived individuals has evolved to protect the species against fatigue in its individual members. Transience is a kind of blindness, merely providing novel individuals to encounter the old routine of experience. Third, there is the " way of rhythm," which pervades all nature; rhythm is essentially a means to introduce experiential novelty in an orderly way, by a cycle that repeats itself. Elsewhere we have commented that this fact of rhythm at the most primitive electronic level is one reason for supposing that the basic principles of life are exemplified in all physical events.[173]

In the previous paragraph, we have hinted at the relationship between " instinct " and " intelligence," and we must now deal explicitly with this point. Instinct, says Whitehead, comprises the accumulated urges of inheritance.[174] Thus we wake to discover ourselves living out a largely unrationalized inheritance from the past, and our lives remain orderly only so long as most of what we do secures for us instinctively a harmonious relation with our environment. All such habitual routine is established by the reproducing of forms of order first attained by the spark of conceptual novelty, the final causation in actual occasions. Then this final causation passes over into efficient causation, so that once a routine is established, it requires no further originality; but this relationship between final and efficient causation accounts for the

[173] *FR* 21. [174] *AI* 53.

purposive appearance of many purely instinctual patterns of behavior.

In actual fact, most of the " purposive " activities of lower organisms seem to be carried out quite automatically.[175] Thus bees have developed elaborate routines that embody the attainment of complex " goals," but it is foolish to suppose that a bee understands why it gathers pollen from clover blossoms or constructs a hive. Only when we disturb the routine of an anthill are the ants forced to respond in novel ways, and we observe in this case that they display signs of chaotic disorder before relapsing into the performance of their duties, modified by whatever new factors we have introduced. In such societies, dominated by routine, novelty has become trivial in importance by comparison with mere repetition of instinctual pattern. It is an error, therefore, to suppose that elaborate social systems are indicative of high-grade intelligence — they may as well be the result of low-grade intelligence applied for a long time, repeatedly introducing small changes in routine. Even at the level of human inventiveness, the element of novelty appears as an agency modifying order, e.g., the earliest automobiles bore a striking resemblance to the horse-drawn vehicles that they replaced.

E. W. Sinnott has devoted a great deal of attention to the problem of organic form, impressed by the intricate developmental patterns of plants and animals, and in a series of books [176] he has taken the " quality of directive self-regulation " that characterizes these patterns as a clue to the nature of life.[177] Thus he sees in an embryo's steady growth toward adulthood a primitive sort of goal-seeking that points to a " biological origin of psychical activities." [178] He stresses that his " concept of organic purposefulness " is an alternative to the organismic approach of men such

---

[175] Many fascinating examples are given by E. S. Russell, *The Directiveness of Organic Activities* (Cambridge University Press, 1945).

[176] E. W. Sinnott, *Cell & Psyche: The Biology of Purpose* (Harper Torchbooks, Harper & Brothers, 1961) ; *The Biology of the Spirit* (Compass Books, The Viking Press, Inc., 1957) ; *Matter, Mind and Man: The Biology of Human Nature* (Atheneum Publishers, 1962) ; *The Problem of Organic Form* (Yale University Press, 1963).

[177] Sinnott, *Matter, Mind and Man*, p. 39.

[178] Sinnott, *The Biology of the Spirit*, p. viii.

as Von Bertalanffy, who are content with merely drawing attention to the scientific usefulness of organismic concepts without focusing on the notion of purpose.[179] However, in the light of our previous discussion, it would appear that Sinnott's examples of organic purposiveness [180] really are elaborate patterns of physical feeling, efficient causation, which have developed gradually down through evolutionary history. As we have seen, once such intricate patterns have evolved, we need not suppose that novelty of subjective aim plays an important role in their repetition. On the other hand, because novel aims ultimately explain the *origins* of such physical patterns, Sinnott is correct in supposing that whatever accounts for these biological developmental patterns also accounts for human purposiveness. But instead of hoping that " a study of developmental processes in the laboratory may throw light on the nature of mental processes," [181] we should recognize that it is the ever-repeated transition from final causation to efficient causation between actual occasions that finally throws light on the nature of developmental processes.

Apparently, it is an oversimplification to suppose that the behavior of organisms is *either* directed by ideal aims *or* automatic, since patterns that arose through final causation are inherited through the efficient causation which physiologists can study; hints of some such relationship between final and efficient causation in organisms appear in the writings of several authors. Samuel Butler, for example, observed that the most efficient bodily processes were those which went on automatically, and this prompted him to postulate an " unconscious memory " by which young animals could " remember " patterns of behavior from their parents.[182] E. D. Cope tried to clarify the same fact, as we have noted earlier.

Every occasion enjoys its modicum of purpose, but *conscious*

---

179 *Ibid.*, pp. 128, 110.
180 Sinnott, *Matter, Mind and Man*, p. 45.
181 Sinnott, *The Biology of the Spirit*, p. 50.
182 See Samuel Butler, *Unconscious Memory* (1880), and the discussion in Basil Willey, *Darwin & Butler: Two Versions of Evolution* (London: Chatto & Windus, 1960). Darlington also discusses Butler's views in *Darwin's Place in History*, Ch. 7.

purpose is a fleeting element even in our own experience, and " absentmindedness " is ever a reminder of this fact; I intend to change my shoes, but a few moments later I discover that I have, in fact, initiated a much longer chain of physical causation and have mistakenly undressed for bed! Also, it is well known that complicated bodily movements are carried out most effectively when conscious control is at a minimum. Athletic training is largely an attempt to establish physical habits, and the high jumper's personality merely triggers a complex sequence of physical reactions; our applause is not for today's aim to high jump seven feet, but for yesterday's endless practice. Only unskilled divers consciously try to keep their feet together, and piano students struggling to learn a piece of music " by heart " testify that the merest flicker of conscious attention at a critical point may result in failure, requiring that they start over from the very beginning in a renewed effort to let the freshly established physical routine run its course. The enjoyment of *any* skill comes from conscious experience of some physical routine that flows smoothly with a minimum of direction — it is achievement without unnecessary attention. Just for this reason animals and children are delighted with repetitive games, and we all seek ways in which the need for conscious direction of our activities can be transcended.[183] It is

---

[183] In an effort to show that goal-directed behavior (what Sinnott calls " organic purposiveness ") may be carried on quite without consciousness, Agar suggests that we reserve the word " purposeful " for acts with consciously conceived ends, using " purposive " for goal-directed behavior when we are uncertain as to the presence of consciousness. (Agar, *op. cit.*, p. 23.) However, this proposal tends to focus our attention on the fuzzy borderline between consciousness and unconsciousness, instead of on that transition from final causation to efficient causation which is found in every entity, including those which never enjoy conscious mentality. Ralph Stayner Lillie also discusses this in *General Biology and Philosophy of Organism* (The University of Chicago Press, 1945), pp. 49, 96, 113, 173. Lillie's book also reflects his enthusiasm for Whitehead, but he is inclined to believe that final causation must be effective only in intra-atomic events (cf. pp. 23, 131, 206), so that he proposes a teleological factor in gene mutations (p. 167). A similar proposal is made by J. M. Burgers, *Experience and Conceptual Activity: A Philosophical Essay Based Upon the Writings of A. N. Whitehead* (The M.I.T. Press, 1965), pp. 124, 170 f. We have seen, however, that this avenue is not fruitful in widening our understanding of the trends in evolution.

for this reason that computers offer such immense possibilities for the enrichment of human existence.

8. MAN IN AN EVOLVING NATURE

" When we come to mankind, nature seems to have burst through another of its boundaries." [184] In this way Whitehead expresses an intuition shared by all and strongly suggested by the evidence: astonishing growth of the human brain during the past million years surely must be taken as indicating the methodology that this genus was developing, i.e., an increasing reliance on focused central mentality. It is true that human beings differ from animals only in degree, for we pass our days very largely in animal-like routine, and there is no " soul " in man that does not have its analogy in those higher animals which contain a personally ordered dominant society of occasions. But our reflective ability makes all the difference, and Whitehead notes three related features of human reflective experience that help to indicate the great gulf separating occasions of human personality from those in animal personalities.[185] First, we have the experience of spatial relationship, of being jointly associated with other entities. Second, we experience ourselves as originating from a past and being determined toward a future; this provides the basis of whatever memory and sense of history we enjoy. Third, we experience ideals — entertained, achieved, compromised, or lost. Samuel Alexander sought to explain these same three aspects of human reflective experience in *Space, Time, and Deity*,[186] and

[184] *MT* 36.
[185] *MT* 141.
[186] Samuel Alexander, *Space, Time, and Deity* (2 vols.; London: Macmillan & Co., Ltd., 1920). In these Gifford Lectures of 1916–1918, Alexander combined the notion of emergence with a radically evolutionary metaphysics, developing the conception of God as the ideal toward which the universe evolves. Therefore, " We are responsible for our acts, seeing that on the issue of them depends in their measure the character of God." (II, p. 400.) He attempted to solve the problem of relating subjectivity and objectivity by following the same path as Francis E. Abbot, i.e., equating them, so he identified God's subjectivity (God as ideal) with God's objectivity (God as actual), failing to make clear how God could in any sense transcend the world ontologically. He wrote, " It is, properly

Whitehead acknowledges his debt to Alexander, suggesting that our awareness of existing in terms of unrealized possibilities provides us with our best reason for believing in a world outside our own personalities.[187]

In this vein, Whitehead defines man as that genus of animals in which " the central activity has been developed on the side of its relationship to novelty." [188] It is the outrageous novelty of human expression, he notes, that is sometimes beatified, sometimes damned, and sometimes even protected by copyright. This relationship to novelty is twofold for occasions of human personality. First, they receive novelty from various parts of the body, synthesizing these feelings into compatible contrasts. Second, and of greater significance, they introduce novelty themselves by entertaining various unrealized possibilities; at its highest development, this function is the aim for what we call ideals.[189]

Consciousness arose very late in evolutionary history, as a refinement of experience; in particular, it had to wait upon the evolution of sense perception, which serves consciousness by abstracting some clear and distinct elements from the vague mass of feelings presented to the body. Consciousness *always* occurs secondarily to experience, for it appears uncertainly as an aspect of subjective form in the process of concrescence.[190] This relationship between experience and consciousness has some important implications for our study. In the first place, thought is mainly concerned with justifying or modifying *already existing* conditions.[191] This " justifying role " of thought suggests that human civilization began with the slow and imperfect introduction of ideas which were explanatory of patterns of behavior and emotion *al-*

---

speaking, Space-Time itself which is the creator and not God." (II, p. 397.) Charles Peirce developed a similar metaphysical evolutionism in which the forms of thought and the laws of nature evolve, and in which God is the end of being, a growing creature of evolution. See Charles Hartshorne and Paul Weiss, eds., *Collected Papers of Charles Sanders Peirce* (Harvard University Press, 1931–1935), I. par. 487.

[187] *MT* 141.
[188] *MT* 36.
[189] *MT* 37.
[190] *PR* 83, 249–251.
[191] *AI* 114.

ready enjoyed by the peoples concerned, and this observation should illuminate the origins of Biblical understandings of creation. As far as the " modifying role " of thought is concerned, its success is limited. Human existence can be understood as a vast pattern of habits, only slowly modified by the force of ideas, and this accounts for our belief that " actions speak louder than words." As long as a man's actions betray some pattern of settled instinct, Whitehead observes, it does not much matter what he says.[192]

Second, it is clear that we cannot understand human mentality apart from its environment; in spite of immense capacity for imaginative voyages beyond nature, the mind grew out of nature and is in nature, not over against it. For this reason we must assume that every mode of human consciousness is largely historically produced, reflecting in its measure the influence of some effective background. Here the power of our physical environment to condition consciousness is immense, as enthusiasts for LSD testify; and the poet in quest of novel conscious experience seeks it by wandering in the woods. Still, it is the human environment that is most effective in producing modes of consciousness which become characteristic of wide human societies, and no human mentality can be understood apart from the defining characteristics of the society that nourishes it and is in turn nourished by it. Consequently, we never can hope to discover or define any mode of consciousness that is merely " normal," " natural," or " basically human." History will not so rudely be torn away. Indeed, *consciousness* of the way prehended data bear their relationships in themselves, which makes possible what Asa Gray called " the sense that there is a *reason why* " for events in nature, probably appears as a defining characteristic of mentality only in certain human societies. Some social ideals will enter into the defining characteristics of every mode of consciousness, but human beings are fickle in their ideals, and we cannot suppose that any particular mode of consciousness is bound to endure indefinitely.

The physical and mental environment for human thought has reached in our time a fantastic richness, as Whitehead notes:

[192] *SMW* 4.

"modes of communication, physical and mental, writing, preservation of documents, variety of modes of literature, critical thought, systematic thought, constructive thought, history, comparison of diverse languages, mathematical symbolism, improved technology providing physical ease." [193] To these words, written in 1933, we could add the newer vistas of jet travel, communications satellites and space rocketry, nuclear energy and computers. Teilhard de Chardin expresses the richness of this environment for human consciousness when he speaks almost poetically of a "new layer, the 'thinking layer,'" which since the end of the Tertiary period has spread over and above the world of plants and animals. "In other words," he writes, "outside and above the biosphere there is the noosphere." [194] Man's behavior in this new "layer" of his environment is uncertainly experimental, balanced between hope and despair, still part of an evolutionary history that teeters precariously between order and novelty.

The subjective aims of human occasions require expression into a relevant future, and the basic fact of expression is transmission of feeling into the environment. Here the human body itself is the primary field of expression for the mental novelty in occasions of human personality, and language has arisen in man as the highest vehicle of this expression. Language is a very high-grade form of what Whitehead calls "symbolic reference," [195] i.e., certain aspects of our experience symbolize conscious meanings to us, meanings that in turn are symbolized by the words expressed. It is hard to overestimate the importance of language in enriching and perpetuating modes of human mentality, and Whitehead even writes of a sense in which "the souls of men are the gift from language to mankind." [196] But there are also those human modes of expression which avoid language, and we often experience the peaks of human existence through the medium of these feelings: the loving embrace, the welcoming smile, the com-

[193] *AI* 55.
[194] Pierre Teilhard de Chardin, *The Phenomenon of Man*, tr. by Bernard Wall, with an introduction by Julian Huxley (Harper Torchbooks, Harper & Brothers, 1961), p. 182.
[195] *S* 8.
[196] *MT* 56.

passionate tear. Thus it is only approximately correct to identify human history with expressions of language, and any such definition must be undertaken cautiously, remembering that the fullness of history concerns *all* expressions of human feeling.

A brief consideration of human ethics and morals in terms of Whiteheadian evolutionary thought seems justified, since the internal relations of actual occasions account ultimately for the relationship between individual organisms and their societies. Morality consists in maximizing the conditions that lead to the best achievements of value for individual organisms,[197] and moral codes in human society are attempts to focus attention on such modes of behavior as encourage both individual worth and social harmony; the attainable levels of individual worth provide us with our chief means of judging various codes. Such codes always express the dominant characteristics of the society involved, and any move toward higher forms of social order begins on some platform of already accepted morality. But there are no absolute moral codes, for morals always concern behavior that will produce value at some specific point in history. Our notion of absolute values depends on the persistence of some kind of order over a long period of time, but any such kind of order is liable to change, outmoding previous moral codes. No one admonishes a queen bee by saying, " Do not commit adultery."

Organisms can modify their environment effectively only by acting collectively, and cooperative feelings are essential to any group that is self-sustaining.[198] Certainly, ferocity is a minor note in the nonhuman parts of nature; rocks do not grumble among themselves, and, in general, animals are peaceable unless they are hungry or physically disturbed. The gentler features of human relations have roots that are lost in the history of animal behavior, and Darwin observed correctly that emotions of respect and friendliness characterize the higher animal groups.[199] Whitehead even speculates that ferocity may have been a rather recent development; [200] perhaps man's exaggerated aggressiveness arose when he became able to imagine himself as possessor of his neighbor's

[197] *MT* 19.
[198] *AI* 44.
[199] See above, p. 80.
[200] *AI* 76.

goods and to suspect his neighbor of the same imaginings. Certainly human beings appear to be the only creatures capable of enraged hostility stemming from imagined threats to their security, and this observation implies that we should abandon all hope for a peaceful future which comes by " evolving away from our animal instincts," as Lyman Abbott fondly hoped.[201] Quite the opposite! Indeed, we may find a germ of truth in ancient stories of an Age of Innocence — we may speculate, for example, that Neanderthal man was a peaceful creature who fell victim to a more highly evolved (and fiercer) Cro-Magnon race.

What may we say of man as the guide for future evolution? Whitehead writes, " Senseless agencies and formulated aspirations cooperate in the work of driving mankind from its old anchorage. Sometimes the period of change is an age of hope, sometimes it is an age of despair." [202] Certainly there is a sense in which Julian Huxley was correct in writing, " We, mankind, contain the possibilities of the earth's immense future." [203] But the immense problem is to estimate the actual content of human subjective aims and how their expression will affect the world. In this vein we may draw three conclusions from Whitehead's thought. First, since nature is historical, the future will be built on the foundations of the present, not on the basis of some imaginary or idealized history. Second, the ideals that finally will prove effective in guiding human history will be those which are cherished by human societies for their individuals, and by which, in their turn, individuals explicitly nourish society. Since there is no reason internal to history why the ideals entertained by human beings will be lofty, things can get better or worse; nature's upward surge toward higher levels of feeling has been diverted time and again into blindness and extinction. As long as human consciousness is dominated by abstractions that grow out of and enrich concrete experience, there can be upward evolution,[204] but men do not confine their abstractions to possibilities that encourage beauty, and

[201] Abbott, op. cit., p. 46.

[202] AI 14.

[203] In his introduction to Teilhard de Chardin, The Phenomenon of Man, p. 28.

[204] MT 168.

humanity is plunged to the brink of destruction when society becomes dominated by ideas that are separated from the depths of those experiences on which it is built.

Third, and perhaps most important, human existence is so complex, and our understanding of it so fragmentary, that any exhaustive plans for future societies are not worth the paper to write them on. Every such plan is the product of human mentality, focused by neglecting wide areas of experience and unable to express with adequate generality the values it seeks. The best-laid plans of mice and men will always go astray, and we can only advance uncertainly from point to point, critically examining each new order by testing it against the liveliness of our experience. Everything depends on the appeal to experience, and in a century of frantic change, we struggle to admit to consciousness those aspects of our experience which in the long run exalt society instead of debasing it.

9. The Evolutionary Cosmology of Teilhard de Chardin

When the evolutionary writings of the late French Jesuit paleontologist Pierre Teilhard de Chardin began to be published posthumously in 1955, they quickly became the focus of widespread interest in both scientific and theological circles, and the appearance of his works in English (beginning with *The Phenomenon of Man* in 1959) has served to continue and widen the critical study of his thought. Consequently, any present discussion of evolution that approaches it both from the side of science and the side of theology would be incomplete without some comment on Teilhard's thought. For this reason, we shall evaluate his evolutionary cosmology briefly, trying to discuss the more clearly scientific aspects of his thought here and reserving comment on his theological vision until the next chapter.

Anyone familiar with Whitehead's thought must be struck, as he reads Teilhard's books, by the many fascinating parallels between the basic vision of the two men. Of course, this is not merely accidental, for each man in his way was indebted to Bergson, and there are aspects of Bergson's evolutionary thought in the background of both the Whiteheadian and the Teilhardian discussions of evolution. Perhaps most important as a parallel with Whitehead, Teilhard's whole interpretation depends on his belief in " the within of things," and he devotes a whole chapter in *The Phenomenon of Man* (Chapter II) to an elaboration of this notion. Here he attributes to every entity a private inwardness, " their reserve, one might say," [205] which is the site of nature's purposiveness and which he very loosely calls " consciousness." This notion appears to express precisely the same situation that Whitehead discusses as the phase of subjective immediacy. Clearly, both men wanted to make a place for subjectivity and final causation among the real agencies in evolution, and Teilhard, likewise, speaks of an upward surge toward higher kinds of mentality on our planet, writing in a way that closely resembles the intent of our own effort of a few pages back. In this he writes of a " law of complexification " [206] that is exemplified most completely in man, " the axis and leading shoot of evolution." [207]

Calling attention to the spherical shape of our planet, which is responsible for the fact that man finds no isolated places wherein he might diverge into two species, Teilhard speaks of " man, the species which converges." [208] Again like Whitehead, he insists on the social nature of modes of human consciousness, and he refers repeatedly to the way in which our planet forces an " ever-tightening compression " [209] of man's mentality. This " psychically convergent structure of the world " plays a major role in Teilhard's thought, and he speaks of the twentieth century as a time in evolutionary history when the power of ideals forces man headlong into a novel future where his diverging ideals finally will coalesce.[210] For such reasons as these, anyone who is moved by Whitehead's vision of nature is bound to find Teilhard's thought refreshing and suggestive.

But with this said, we must point to one major assumption by

---

[205] Teilhard de Chardin, *The Phenomenon of Man*, p. 54.
[206] *Ibid.*, p. 50.
[207] *Ibid.*, p. 36.
[208] Pierre Teilhard de Chardin, *The Future of Man*, tr. by Norman Denny (Harper & Row, Publishers, Inc., 1964), p. 301.
[209] *Ibid.*, p. 275.
[210] *Ibid.*, p. 276.

Teilhard that seriously restricts his ability to make rational sense of his basic vision of inwardness as the moving finger of evolution. Where Whitehead successfully delineates the reciprocal relationship of final and efficient causation by recognizing a temporal transition between the short-lived phase of subjective immediacy and the phase of objectivity, Teilhard's vision very clearly implies that natural entities are *simultaneously subjective and objective.* Like Hegel, Bergson, and the early emergent evolutionists, he has not been able to use the notion of transition to indicate a temporal difference between the isolated moment of subjectivity and the later objectified entity that can be recognized by sense perception. For example, in discussing atoms he writes, " The radius of action proper to each cosmic element must be prolonged in a straight line to the utmost limits of the world itself." [211] Then, by assuming (as Whitehead does not) that the inwardness of an atom endures through time, he supposes that this " radius of action " (i.e., the way an objectified atomic occasion is prehended everywhere) is equivalent to the " within " of an atom (i.e., its subjective immediacy). Accordingly, he goes on to conclude that the subjectivity of the atom encompasses the universe: " The volume of each of them is the volume of the universe." [212]

This identification of subjectivity and objectivity in nature is chiefly responsible for the offense that most scientists have taken at Teilhard's initial claim that *The Phenomenon of Man* should be read " purely and simply as a scientific treatise." [213] We have described the reasons for believing that no subjectivity in nature can be detected by a scientist, using sense perception as his vehicle for knowledge, and Teilhard's use of the word " phenomenon " in reference to the " within " of man stretches the word beyond any recognizable scientific definition. In what must have been the most pointed response by a scientist, the British biologist P. B. Medawar insisted that Teilhard " does not even preserve the common decencies of scientific writing," [214] and even though we may be less offended than Dr. Medawar, we must agree that

[211] Teilhard de Chardin, *The Phenomenon of Man,* p. 45.
[212] *Ibid.*
[213] *Ibid.,* p. 29.
[214] P. B. Medawar, in his review of *The Phenomenon of Man* in *Mind,* LXX, No. 277, pp. 99–106.

Teilhard, like many brilliant predecessors, was mistaken when he tried to impress his vision of subjectivity in nature on a scientific methodology based ultimately on sense perception. Scientists can study only the " without " of things, never their " within," which is isolated from the entire universe.

Further resembling Hegel and Bergson, Teilhard seems to envision the whole evolutionary process as though it were *a single slowly culminating event*, and his language often resembles the way Whitehead describes the process of concrescence in a single occasion. Where Whitehead emphasizes that the past is objectively real apart from its participation in any *particular* occasion, Teilhard appears driven by his vision of nature as a single (the only!) event to see the past as real only insofar as it is caught up into the present of this event. Thus he writes of past evolutionary happenings, " I do not pretend to describe them as they really were, but rather as we must picture them to ourselves *so that the world may be true for us at this moment*." [215] Likewise, in a way that reminds us of how the subjective aim of an occasion is unified, the evolutionary process appears to Teilhard as a single movement leading toward the appearance of man. He writes, " This ' orthogenetic ' view of animal evolution . . . only achieves full validity, in terms of my argument, to the extent that it implies a continuous psychic ' chain ' going back to the beginning of life." [216] Here the notion of a " continuous psychic chain " corresponds most closely to the developing mentality that in Whitehead's view is characteristic of the process of each actual occasion. Teilhard, however, interprets it as applying to evolution as a whole, so that we are presented with the image of a single mentality which gradually approaches fullness as the centuries pass.

Teilhard's evolutionary thought has plumbed the depths, raising immensely important intuitions to our attention, but his feeling for subjectivity at the heart of nature is obscured by his ac-

---

[215] Teilhard de Chardin, *The Phenomenon of Man*, p. 35. Italics mine. This tendency in Teilhard to depreciate the objective reality of the past may account for some judgments that he fails to recognize adequately the reality of evil. See, e.g., Benz, *Schöpfungsglaube und Endzeiterwartung*, pp. 249 ff.

[216] Teilhard de Chardin, *The Future of Man*, p. 282.

ceptance of the old Newtonian doctrine of enduring substances. In the end he is not able to show the important difference between subjectivity and objectivity in nature, and his language becomes poetic when we seek clarity, mystical when we hope for precision. What he has left for us is most valuable when seen as " vision," not as " explanation."

V

EVOLUTION AND THE CHRISTIAN DOCTRINE OF CREATION

1. JEWISH UNDERSTANDINGS OF CREATION

During the past generation, scholarship has been deeply formed and immeasurably enriched by the existential approach to theology and tradition. This approach, with its penetrating insights into human subjectivity, has helped us to see and remember, among other things, that theological doctrines do not spring full-blown into the world from some great doctrinal reservoir; instead, they are, in their way, like evolving animal species, particular conceptual expressions generated by very complex historical situations. Doctrines are efforts to state objective truth, but we recognize that they spring, first of all, out of the subjectivity of men, reflecting the inward responses of human beings to the wideness and unfathomable depths of their experience. I do not mean that theology is " merely subjective " or that it cannot hope to reach truth; the point is merely that all human thinking begins in human experience and that the elements of mentality which fleetingly reach consciousness are derived, every one, from outside the particular occasion of personality that at any moment is the locus of human subjectivity.

This fact accounts for the truth of claims that Old Testament understandings of Creation arose as Jewish men tried to understand their own existence in the world, seeking to clarify the meaning of those elements of experience which persistently rose to awareness. If this be the case, it becomes important to ask after the nature of the experiences for which Jewish understandings of Creation were explanatory. Here we are informed by recent Old Testament study that the literature of Jewish society expresses a gradually focusing vision of themselves as a people living a *meaningful historical existence,* one in which the overriding principle of meaning, the root source of historical continuity, was felt to be *the effectiveness of divine purpose in the world.*[1] This sense of living in a unified strand of history appears as one principal defining characteristic of Jewish society as it became differentiated from the general background of the ancient Near East.

Records from this ancient world indicate that its peoples felt the reality of their world in an active sense, so that it appeared to their consciousness as a constellation of *happenings,* not as mere fact. Their feeling for *time* grew out of this primordial sense of living in a nexus of events, so that they did not have our modern sense of "time like a mighty river" which flows on independently of events.[2] In this sense their feeling for the priority of events over temporality was much the same as that proposed by Whitehead. However, they felt the series of events amid which they lived to be like the simply located Newtonian particles of our earlier chapters, merely side by side in sequence, like pearls on a strand. They had little or no sense that these events were internally connected, and their feeling of existing amid a capriciously ordered sequence of happenings led them to speak of their lives in terms of a series of "times." There were good times, bad times, times of flood, times of drought, following each other mainly without intelligible pattern; some early efforts to fathom a pattern for the sequence of times can be found in the Babylonian concern for chronologies, which was principally an effort to predict the future by analogy with patterns of events known to have occurred in the past.[3]

---

[1] See, e.g., Wolfhart Pannenberg, "Redemptive Event and History," and Hans Walter Wolff, "The Understanding of History in the Old Testament Prophets," in *Essays on Old Testament Hermeneutics,* ed. by Claus Westermann, ET ed. by James Luther Mays (John Knox Press, 1963).

[2] Hartmut Gese, "Geschichtliches Denken im Alten Orient und im Alten Testament," *Zeitschrift für Theologie und Kirche,* Bd. 55 (1958), Heft 2, pp. 127–145.

[3] *Ibid.,* p. 132.

In this Near Eastern world, where the times were chronically "out of joint," the Jews crystallized a quite novel persuasion that the events of their own existence (both past and future) were not meaninglessly isolated but were, in fact, chapters in a single story. It was the persuasion that they lived in *history*, that the events of their national experience were purposefully connected. This self-understanding developed hand in hand with belief that behind their often surprising history as its source and sustainer there lay a saving reality, a locus of novel and purposeful response to the agonies and dangers that beset their fitful movement toward national identity. They expressed this element of their experience as belief in a purposefully redemptive God whose effectiveness in the world guided them through apparently hopeless situations toward goals that he envisioned.

The Jews had this feeling of divine purpose in their history not in terms of some overarching divine plan that automatically ran off, but as *God's personal responsiveness to the concrete details of life.* What they felt was a free and lordly aim that responded directly and appropriately to whatever historical impasse they found themselves in. Thus Gen. 29:31, " When the Lord saw that Leah was hated, he opened her womb." Sometimes the fulfillment of God's purposes was seen in very unlikely or unexpected events, as when Joseph's brothers set out to kill him and, in the long run, he saved them. Joseph then said, " As for you, you meant evil against me; but God meant it for good " (Gen. 50:20). In either case, the primary intuition was of a divine personality that realized its purposes by a never-ending series of freshly responsive acts.

These divine responses were not felt as capricious, however. They appeared to the Jewish people as signs of *a divine constancy* that linked the happenings of Jewish existence into a single history, as the work of " the faithful God who keeps covenant and steadfast love with those who love him and keep his commandments, to a thousand generations " (Deut. 7:9). Intuitions of divine stability thus began as a persuasion that God was faithful in keeping his promises, continually catching up the already decided events of the past into his novel fulfillments: " Behold,

the former things have come to pass, and new things I now declare." (Isa. 42:9.) God was thought to be able to accomplish
his purposes in many different ways, even to the point of abandoning one direction of action in favor of another if concrete
circumstances on earth so warranted: " If that nation, concerning
which I have spoken, turns from its evil, I will repent of the evil
that I intended to do to it." (Jer. 18:8.) Clearly the Jewish intuitions of divine constancy at the heart of reality were not expressed
in terms of belief that God was metaphysically beyond change.

The increasing persuasion of the Jews that divine purposiveness lay at the heart of reality, uniting all its objective elements
into a value-laden whole, was paralleled by the gradual uniting
of what began as quite separate tribal traditions into a single
story of Israel's escape from Egypt, its covenant with God on
Sinai, and the establishment of a kingdom in Canaan. As von
Rad observes, the literary remains of this move toward historicity
appear as a single historical theme in the first six books of the
Old Testament: " God . . . called the patriarchs and promised
them the Land of Canaan. When Israel became numerous in
Egypt, God led the people through the wilderness with wonderful
demonstrations of grace; then after their lengthy wanderings he
gave them under Joshua the Promised Land." [4] The surprising
thing about this process is that groups of people whose ancestors
never had been in Egypt began to adopt the escape from Pharaoh
as part of their own history, so that their attitudes toward life
and the future were shaped by that past. Of course, this adoption
of a new past was a precarious and never completely successful
venture, judging from the frequency of prophetic rebuke when
people allowed the general Near Eastern religious climate to
usurp the place of loyalty to Israel's traditional covenant on Sinai:
" ' Woe to the rebellious children,' says the Lord, ' who carry out
a plan, but not mine.' " (Isa. 30:1.) But this prophetic attitude
expresses a persuasion that among the elements of God's purposes for Israel was his aim for them to enjoy some kind of

---

[4] Gerhard von Rad, *Genesis: A Commentary*, tr. by John A. Marks
(The Westminster Press, 1961), p. 14. Cf. Deut. 6:20-24; 26:5-9; Josh.
24:2-13.

future which could be entered only if they were willing to allow present and future experience to be shaped by a particular strand of the past. That is, openness to the future could not be divorced from a certain openness to the past, and God was felt to be the lord of past happenings as well as present and future ones. Thus the psalmist's expression of faith is a reflection on past events as well as an attitude toward the future: " But I trust in thee, O Lord, I say, ' Thou art my God.' My times are in thy hand." (Ps. 31:14 f.)

The Greeks were to develop a deep sensitivity to the orderly sequence of natural causes and the unswerving course of what they called fate, but Jewish consciousness of a saving reality at the heart of human experience remained vivid enough so that the Jews felt even ordinary events in their history as being almost entirely determined by divine purpose. Their literature is sprinkled with allusions to God's decisive role in the outcome of all kinds of events, and this sense led them toward persuasion that they existed, first of all, as *creatures of God's purposes*, not as entities subject to natural forces. Thus for the Jewish man there was no feeling of natural law to be violated, and he did not find it incredible that God had parted the waters of the Red Sea or that God had given the Israelites victory over their foes in battle.

We may be astonished that Jewish consciousness was so little shaped by the weight of that natural causation which so impressed Aristotle and which is the object of modern scientific study. But, in any case, centuries of living in a world whose events were felt chiefly as expressions of divine purpose led the Jews on beyond the belief that only their own personal and national experiences happened in the light of divine purpose. They began to apprehend wider and wider areas of the world in terms of that same divine aim which unified their own history, until they extended their own experience to the whole creation, affirming that the whole world appeared above all else as a locus of saving divine responsiveness. They became persuaded that the whole of nature lay beneath God's creative hand, and in the long run they arrived at belief that God created everything, " the heavens and the earth."

Jewish understandings of Creation thus grew out of their own experience of being saved in particular situations, ending in the belief that the same divine purposes which had created their history also had created that larger history which was the whole world. They were not, like Plato or Aristotle, trying to fathom the basic principles of nature by asking the question, " Under what circumstances did or does the world come into existence? " For if one proceeds in this fashion, he asks, " Is there one causal agent for creation? or more than one? is creation temporal or eternal? must we postulate some eternal ' matter ' or potentiality for a world to exist? " And it is in this vein that he may ask, " Who is the creator? " and answer by saying, " *God* is the creator," or, " The demiurge." Jewish writers arrived at their faith in divine creation not as a result of such rational speculation but out of historical experiences. So we should not imagine that they followed a line of questioning at all, rather that they felt almost as an intrusion into awareness the feeling of God's providential response when Israel was oppressed by very worldly troubles, widening to a dawning realization of God's creative power in the world. We may use the passive tense to indicate this: they *found themselves persuaded* by their experience in history that God creates the stars (Isa. 40:26), the wind (Amos 4:13), a man's clean heart (Ps. 51:10), the heavens and the earth (Gen. 1:1).

It is in this sense that the two Creation stories of Genesis (Gen. 1:1 to 2:4a and 2:4b-25) were part of a carefully worded attempt by Jewish writers to link their historical theme with primeval history. The editor of the older J story in Gen., ch. 2, collecting his society's traditions and cultic stories at the time of Solomon or a little later, gave the Hexateuch its basic form as a unified theological expression of Jewish life. Most of the stories he compiled had a long history before Solomon's time,[5] but the Yahwist editor was telling a single story of divine guidance, in which God's providence was revealed in every area of human existence as well

[5] Elsewhere von Rad notes that much is to be said for the assumption that the J account of Creation (where human life is created from the waterless steppe) is derived from very old pre-Palestinian traditions. See Gerhard von Rad, *Old Testament Theology*, Vol. I: *The Theology of Israel's Historical Traditions*, tr. by D. M. G. Stalker (Harper & Brothers, 1962), p. 28.

as in nature. It was a story of God's promises to the Jewish people, promises of land [6] and blessing,[7] sometimes even wrested from God by force.[8] And it was a story of the fulfillment of God's promises, even though men betrayed him.[9] Evidently the stories of primeval history were included because they provided an explanatory background for the kind of historical existence that Jews in Solomon's time already were enjoying, an existence felt in terms of movement toward the fulfillment of divine purposes. As von Rad says, the basic position of the writers of Gen., chs. 1 and 2, is " faith in salvation and election," testifying to Jewish belief that the same God who made his covenant with Abraham and at Sinai was also the creator of the world.[10]

Let us now examine the affirmations of the Genesis stories. The older J story, beginning with Gen. 2:4b, proceeds immediately to discuss man, plainly reflecting the way in which faith in divine creation grew out of human feelings of divine purpose. We note that God created man (ch. 2:7) and only then planted a garden (ch. 2:8) to set him in, and that man is instructed regarding good and evil (ch. 2:17) before the birds and beasts are created (ch. 2:19). It could hardly be plainer that the Yahwist was more interested in human history, sin and grace, than in what was to become known much later as " natural history "! His main purpose was to link the beginnings of human history with Israel's experience of God's grace to a rebellious people, and the story of the Fall in Gen., ch. 3, serves as background for the call of Israel as it was personified in Abraham (Gen. 12:1-3). Still, the Yahwist's account of how the animals were named may well reflect very early recollections about human mentality; also the story of man's fall from innocence may have its germ of historical truth, as we suggested elsewhere in this book.

Genesis 1:1 to 2:4a is Priestly doctrine, carefully developed and pruned over centuries of growth, and nothing is there either by

[6] Von Rad, *Genesis*, p. 21. Cf. Gen. 12:7; 13:14 f.; 15:18; 24:7; 26:2 f.; 28:13; 50:24.

[7] Gen. 12:2; 17:16, 20; 26:3; Ex. 20:24; Deut. 7:13.

[8] Gen. 18:22-33.

[9] Gen., chs. 12; 20; 26; Ex. 23:26; Num. 23:19; I Kings 8:15.

[10] Von Rad, *Genesis*, p. 44.

chance or merely because it was part of the world of Near Eastern thought. It is intended to be taken literally for what it is, the product of sophisticated theological thought. Von Rad says, " To write out these thirty-five verses, Israel's faith required centuries of carefully collected reflection." [11] Thus we find in this story the orderly description of earth's history that provided Scriptural geologists with their data: the heavens appeared first, followed by the earth with its seas and continents, and only then did living things make their bow. First there were vegetables (created, awkwardly for Scriptural geologists, before the sun!) ; then, sea creatures and birds, and, finally, land animals and man. Obviously the Priestly thinkers had made some commonplace observations about the large classifications of nature and living forms, observations that they meant to integrate with their theological viewpoint. The modern theory of evolution begins with these same naïve observations and merely tries to explain them in terms of a larger causal background, avoiding the sharp distinctions between classes.

Certain features of this first Creation story stand out. To begin with, God is shown as the One who establishes the beginnings of everything actual, " heaven and earth," but he does not do this all at once. If we recall that faith in Creation grew out of Israel's experience of God in her history, the Genesis story of Creation as a succession of divine acts apparently reflects Israel's understanding of her own history as a series of creative acts by God.[12] Also, the world is seen as real, not illusory. Creation is not merely an emanation of God but is his product, with a reality distinguishable from his own. This sense of God's otherness lay very near the center of Jewish intuitions of divinity, so that in Israel's faith, God is the hidden one: " Truly, thou art a God who hidest thyself, O God of Israel, the Savior." (Isa. 45:15.) He was felt in some way to be utterly different from the world he

---

[11] *Ibid.*, p. 61.

[12] Here it is significant that the Priestly account ends with the summary, " These are the generations (*tōlᵉdōth*) of the heavens and the earth when they were created." (Gen. 2:4a.) Later on, *tōlᵉdōth* are real genealogies, forming Israel's prehistory. (Gen. 5:1; 6:9; 10:1 ff.) Just as there was later a history of Israel, so there was formerly a history of creation.

created, and this intuition produced the notion of "holiness" as applying to God alone: "To whom then will you compare me, that I should be like him? says the Holy One." (Isa. 40:25.)

However, though God was felt as being utterly different — "other" is a better word — he was not felt to be isolated from the world. Just as the continuation of Israel's history always depended on God's ever new keeping of the Covenant, so did the whole Creation rest in his hand; there was no suggestion that it could continue to happen for a moment apart from his sustaining care for it. This meant that the Creation mattered to God, that what happened on earth had a real effect on him and was felt in terms of his purposes. We recall the psalmist's cry, "May the Lord rejoice in his works" (Ps. 104:31b), and Amos' sense of God's response to Israel's unfaithfulness: "'I hate, I despise your feasts, and I take no delight in your solemn assemblies.'" (Amos 5:21.)

The Jews conceived of a three-story universe,[13] naïvely following the testimony of sense perception, so that heaven was believed to be a great vault arching over the earth. The earth itself was seen as a flat disc resting on pillars (I Sam. 2:8), with waters above the heavens (Gen. 1:7; Ps. 148:4) and waters below (Ps. 24:2), so that during the Flood "the fountains of the great deep burst forth, and the windows of the heavens were opened" (Gen. 7:11). We now properly reject this understanding of Jewish experience, but what we should recall is that they felt these large structures of reality not as evidence of a self-sustaining "order of nature" but as the continually new effects of God's purposeful activity in the events of his world. The constancy of nature is a sign that God continues to show forbearance to his Creation, just as he showed forbearance to Israel and saved it from the perils which threatened it. The order of nature is therefore not that of the Greek *kosmos*, maintained by its own indwelling rationality, and we hear nothing of "natural law." Instead, the regularities of nature are based entirely on God's faithful keeping of his covenant promise to Noah. (Gen. 8:22; cf. 9:13-17.) Everything depends directly on God, and every created thing is an

[13] Ex. 20:4; Ps. 115:15-17.

agency of his purposes; even the stars serve him as means to divide time for man.

As the concrete effects of God's saving purposes, the Creation is value laden: " and behold, it was very good." For both the Priestly writer and the Yahwist, the divine purposes embodied in the Creation are good, and there is no room for a metaphysical dualism that supposes the world to be evil. Evil must be recognized and dealt with, but it is not created by God. Finally, earth and its creatures are summoned to participate in the divine plan, and as its climax, man appears, created " in the image of God " (Gen. 1:27).

The doctrine thus stresses the complete dependence of the whole creation on God, man's special place of honor and responsibility, and the purposes of God that lie beneath and continually respond to concrete events in nature and human history. God has created the world to be a habitation for man, in whom his ultimate purposes could be fulfilled (Isa. 45:18), so that the world of nature is essential to human history as the place where man is to serve God joyfully, exercising sovereignty as God's responsible representative (Gen. 1:28; cf. Ps. 8:3-8).

For a long while, Old Testament scholars have recognized that the texts that deal extensively with Creation are rather late in origin, consisting mainly of Deutero-Isaiah, the Priestly document, and a few psalms. On the other hand, the religious atmosphere of Canaan was filled with " creation " myths, so that Jewish thinkers almost certainly connected their faith in God with the idea of creation long before these explicit Biblical statements appeared. Why was an Old Testament doctrine of creation so long in appearing? Von Rad suggests that it took Israel a long time to link the idea of Creation carefully with its saving history,[14] for the story of Creation had to be made the beginning of Jewish history instead of merely a timeless myth telling of cycles of rebirth and dissolution, to be repeated in connection with the worship of nature gods. This was a long and difficult task, but when it was accomplished, the idea of Creation was fused in Jewish consciousness with those notions of a saving history which

14 Von Rad, *Old Testament Theology*, Vol. I, p. 136.

expressed the core of Jewish experience.

Since Israel's faith in Creation grew out of Israel's own historical experiences of salvation, it is not surprising that Old Testament writers so closely linked the notions of creation and salvation and often spoke of salvation as a new creation by God. Thus the prophets spoke of God in terms of his making a new beginning or a new covenant with his people after judging them (cf. Ezek. 36:26-28; Jer. 31:31-34; Hos. 2:18-23), and this theme of a new creation is especially prominent in Deutero-Isaiah (e.g., Isa. 44:21-28; 51:9-11). The events of history were seen as a continuation or renewal of God's original creative act.

In this long process of clarifying their own belief in divine creation, Jewish thinkers found ways to synthesize the intuitions of other nearby peoples with their own major feeling of divine purposiveness at the heart of reality. For one thing, recurring intuitions of some negativity at the heart of experience haunted the ancient Near East, and the mental climate of those times was continually clouded by a sense of the nothingness that lurks at the borders of human existence. There was something about their experience that people felt inwardly as a threat of disruption, and this feeling was given mythological expression in stories of a primeval battle between forces of order and forces of chaos. A number of Old Testament passages speak of Creation using such more or less demythologized motifs from Canaanite thought.[15] One such idea is that Creation was God's struggle against an opposing chaos, often depicted as a dragon.[16] Thus Deutero-Isaiah writes, " Was it not thou that didst cut Rahab in pieces, that didst pierce the dragon? " (Isa. 51:9b; cf. Ezek. 32:2-8.) Likewise, Ps. 46:3 and 89:9 reflect the hostility of mythical

---

[15] Some of these ideas were not altered significantly or reduced in importance even by centuries of Jahwism, as we discover by noting the appearance of a female consort for Jahweh in the isolated Jewish colony of Elephantine, as late as the sixth century B.C. See *Altorientalische Texte zum Alten Testament*, ed. by H. Gressmann (2d ed.; Berlin and Leipzig, 1916).

[16] Werner Schmidt has shown in detail how the Canaanite Baal was opposed by a dragon, in *Königtum Gottes in Ugarit und Israel* (Bonn, 1961).

primeval waters toward God, who rebukes them (Ps. 104:7; cf. 93:4) and smites the dragon of chaos (Ps. 74:13), fixing the boundaries of the earth (Ps. 74:17; cf. Job 38:8-11; Ps. 33:7; Prov. 8:27-29; Jer. 5:22). Although the dragon of chaos might be roused again (Job 3:8), we are told that God has set a guard over it (Job 7:12).

Now, what role do these mythical ideas play in Jewish faith? It is the poets, we note, who make use of these vivid images from mythology, sometimes painting a picture that suggests cosmological dualism. But God's sovereign and purposive power over Creation is always the major theme of the poets, just as it is for the Priestly and Yahwistic writers; we find the mythological images serving them only as vivid illustration, never as central motif. Thus Deutero-Isaiah's reference to Rahab appears incidentally in the midst of his plea for God to ransom Israel by showing forth his strength as in generations long past.

The Priestly account of Creation does depict a watery chaos (Gen. 1:2) and a separation of the waters (Gen. 1:9-19), but in the light of the above we should not infer that the writer believed that God struggled against the chaos. Here the stress is entirely on God's effortless freedom and spontaneous initiative in Creation: "God said . . . and it was so." The same complete power over his world, which God was felt to exercise in Israel's history, is here expressed in his act of creation, and the chaos appears only as a vaguely defined opposite of creation. God raised the world up out of formlessness by his Word and guards it faithfully against any lapse into chaos (cf. Ps. 104:29-30), but the chaos is no real opponent. Clearly the Babylonian and Canaanite intuitions of some negativity haunting human existence were taken up and related to Jewish intuitions of divine purposiveness in a way that leaves no doubt that the Jews felt God's purposes to be decisive in settling the outcome of events.

We have noted that Near Eastern peoples felt their world primarily as *happenings*, and that their notion of a sequence of "times" grew out of their sense for the external relationships of the happenings to each other. So in Jewish thought, there was no idea of time as a Newtonian receptacle existing prior to the happening of events. Reality *was* events, and the Jews had become persuaded that God was lord of every single event in their history. Since there were no *events* at all apart from God's purposive activity, there was no *time* in their history when God was not lord and creator. Consequently, we may suppose that they did not conceive of any time before Creation, and the phrase " in the beginning " probably indicates their assumption that time (i.e., history) began when Creation began.

In a similar vein we may presume that the Jews did not reflect over the abstract notion of any unformed matter that might have preexisted Creation. The verb *bara* (to create) as used in the Old Testament always has God as its subject, and though it is not used with reference to preexisting material,[17] it seems unlikely that Jewish writers were anxious to stress the point that God's creative power is devoid of prior conditions. This seems the more probable, considering that their faith in divine creation was itself an extension of faith that God saved them out of what were sometimes grievously concrete circumstances! Probably it was not until the Jewish faith in Creation was confronted with Hellenistic notions of a demiurge that much attention was given to God's absolute freedom from prior conditions. Thus when the Pentateuch was translated into Greek about 300–200 B.C., its translators steadfastly avoided the Greek verb *demiourgein* in speaking of God's creative action, lest they suggest the Platonic notion of a creator limited by his material.[18]

In the Jewish Wisdom Literature an approach to Creation is found that differs both from the careful reflection of Genesis and from the vivid imagery of poets and prophets. Here there is real interest in explaining *how* the world was created and how the phenomena of nature are related to Israel's saving history. Where the writer of Gen., ch. 1, began with Israel's history and saw Creation as its prelude, the Wisdom Literature begins with faith in Creation and speaks of Israel's history in order to rationalize this faith.[19] Quite possibly this effort at explanation

---

[17] Von Rad, *Old Testament Theology*, Vol. I, p. 142.

[18] B. W. Anderson, " Creation," *The Interpreter's Dictionary of the Bible*, ed. by G. A. Buttrick (Abingdon Press, 1962), I, p. 731.

[19] Von Rad, *Old Testament Theology*, Vol. I, p. 450.

reflects contact with Hellenistic thought, for in Prov. 8:22-31 we read that "wisdom" was created by God in the beginning, encompassing the world and man. The word which calls man to salvation in Israel's history is here identified with the rationality already present at Creation (e.g., Prov. 8:35), and we are given a more sophisticated explanation of *how* God's purposes goven both nature and human history.

2. Earlier Christian Understandings of Creation

The New Testament references to Creation are deeply shaped by these Old Testament views, and the New Testament writers echo Jewish affirmations that God created the world by his Word and determines it by his purposes from beginning to end. Frequently they refer to the original Creation,[20] or to what has taken place since the "foundation of the world." [21] Jesus was seen in various ways as the fulfillment of God's purposes in Israel's history,[22] purposes "which he set forth in Christ as a plan for the fulness of time." [23] Jesus is the beginning of a New Covenant,[24] and through him we are to inherit a kingdom "prepared for you from the foundation of the world." [25] Most interestingly of all, Jesus is seen as a revelation of the same divine purposes that support the whole creation, for in Christ "all things hold together." [26] God even created the world *through* Christ.[27] By the central event of the resurrection, God's purposes in Christ are clearly identified with his purposes in creation, and Paul writes accordingly of the God "who gives life to the dead and calls into existence the things that do not exist." [28] Significantly, in Rev. 22:13 we read of Christ as "the Alpha and the Omega, the first and the last, the beginning and the end," titles which were used originally by

20 Mark 10:6; 13:19; Rom. 1:20; 8:19 ff.; II Peter 3:4.
21 Matt. 13:35; 25:34; Luke 11:50; John 17:24; Eph. 1:4; Heb. 4:3; 9:26; I Peter 1:20; Rev. 13:8; 17:8.
22 Matt. 1:22; Mark 1:15; John 12:38; Rom. 8:4; etc.
23 Eph. 1:9 f.
24 Luke 22:20; II Cor. 3:6.
25 Matt. 25:34.
26 Col. 1:17.
27 John 1:1-18; I Cor. 8:6; Col. 1:15-16.
28 Rom. 4:17.

Deutero-Isaiah to speak of God.[29] Not only do writers of the New Testament agree with Jewish faith that God creates the world with divine purposes which determine its beginning and end, but they add to this Old Testament doctrine of creation a new affirmation: everything is focused in Christ, through whom God creates, sustains, and saves his world.

Reading the New Testament, we have the impression that very little attention was paid to faith in Creation except at those points where the New Testament gospel expressly confronted the world of Hellenistic-Roman thought, to which the idea of divine creation was a stumbling block. So long as Christians were among Jews, even Hellenized Jews, faith in Creation could be assumed, and the only dispute concerned the role of Jesus in the divine plan of salvation. But the speeches attributed to Paul in The Acts show that he was among people for whom divine creation was far from obvious. Replying to the crowds who mistook him for Zeus in Lystra, Paul objects that God does not walk around in the world, because he is its creator and sustainer: " You should turn from these vain things to a living God who made the heaven and the earth and the sea and all that is in them. . . . Yet he did not leave himself without witness, for he did good and gave you from heaven rains and fruitful seasons, satisfying your hearts with food and gladness " (Acts 14:15-17). Again in Athens, Paul stands on the Areopagus, attempting to persuade his Greek audience that God is not to be thought of pantheistically as a principle hidden in nature, but is instead personally related to the world: " What therefore you worship as unknown, this I proclaim to you. The God who made the world and everything in it, being Lord of heaven and earth, does not live in shrines made by man, nor is he served by human hands, as though he needed anything, since he himself gives to all men life and breath and everything. . . . He is not far from each one of us, for ' In him we live and move and have our being'; as even some of your poets have said, ' For we are indeed his offspring ' " (Acts 17:23b-28).

Biblical intuitions of God's saving relationship to the world

[29] Isa. 44:6; 48:12.

arose among people for whom rigorous philosophic reflection and the search for a coherent metaphysical system played virtually no role in experience, but the missionary efforts of the early Christian church were carried out chiefly among peoples long shaped by just such a tradition of Hellenistic thought and its search for the rational principles behind human experience. Therefore, if the Biblical intuitions of God's continuous creative relationship to the world were to survive in this atmophere, they had to be clarified intellectually; and there simply was no alternative to Hellenistic thought as the vehicle for theological reflection. Also, and in terms of the mission of the church, of greater evangelical concern, the intellectual side of Gentile civilization was part of the world that the gospel had to " overcome " and incorporate within itself if Christians were to be faithful to the Biblical notion that their God was the God of *all* people. There had to be an effort to show how the personal categories of Biblical thought could illuminate and fulfill the insights of Greek philosophy. Consequently, Christian theology has, from the first century, borne both the fruits and the scars of its encounter with Greek thought, and much of our discussion of evolutionary theory is prompted by the need to pull strands of Biblical thought from their hiding places among certain Greek metaphysical intuitions.

Classical Greek reflection over the nature of God had its roots in Olympian religion, whose gods were felt to enjoy their reality entirely within the natural order of the world. There the characteristic function of divinity was to serve as an underlying source or principle of the normal course of events, and the Olympian gods were not felt to transcend the world in the sense of existing somehow apart from it. It was but a step from this vision of divinity as the ground of natural order to a philosophic search for the nature of this divinity, based on a persuasion that divinity must be precisely that principle required to explain the existing circumstances of nature. Thus pre-Socratic philosophers began their study of nature not as a prelude to modern natural science but as the obvious avenue for a quest after the true essence of divinity, and all Greek thought after them has been stamped by the assumption that man can discover the nature of divinity by inference from the observable details of reality.[30]

As far back as Anaximander, Greek philosophers sought to reduce the number of philosophic principles to one, and their rational quest for the true ground of objects at hand gradually led toward the notion that God is One. Along with this, there was a pressure to conceive of the one ultimate source of natural order as being radically different from the objects of nature, a pressure that led Greek thinkers to contrast the apparent corporeality of natural objects with a supposed " spirituality " or " rationality " as the essence of divinity. In this same vein, they contrasted the transience and change in nature with a presumed divine permanence and immutability that lay behind it. And because every object that is composed of several elements seems subject to change by decomposition, they supposed that an unchanging divinity must, therefore, be perfectly simple.

It is true that scattered in Plato's writings there were hints that God changed and responded to the world (e.g., *Sophist* 249), and in the *Timaeus*, Plato speaks of divinity that realizes its designs as a persuasive agency within the universe.[31] But Aristotle's immense work of analyzing and refining Plato's vagrant intuitions eliminated such notions effectively from Greek theological thought, so that the Greek notion of God that existed to greet Christian faith was typically an understanding of God as one, simple, invisible, incomprehensible, eternal, immutable spirit. To speak of God was to speak of a realm of pure being, removed from the earthly realm of becoming which men knew so well in everyday experience, and the problem posed to Christian theologians was to find means of reconciling this metaphysical vision with their own historical experience.

In general, Christian thinkers in the early centuries carried on the discussion with Greek philosophy by trying to show that the God of the Bible was precisely that divinity which philosophy

---

[30] Werner Jaeger, *The Theology of the Early Greek Philosophers* (Oxford: At the Clarendon Press, 1947), Ch. I. See also Wolfhart Pannenberg, "Die Aufnahme des philosophischen Gottesbegriffs als dogmatisches Problem der frühchristlichen Theologie," *Zeitschrift für Kirchengeschichte*, Vierte Folge VIII, 70. Band (1959), pp. 4–6.

[31] Plato, *Timaeus* 42d, 45a.

sought to understand. Paul provides our first example, for in Rom. 1:18-32 he takes over some prevalent Stoic ideas about divinity (that God is invisible and eternal), then turns them to his advantage by viewing them in the light of his faith in a God who acts in history.[32] The work of relating Christian theology to Greek philosophy finally began in earnest with the work of the second-century Apologists, and every systematic theology since then has been, in some fashion, a continuation of their work. Let us now quickly trace this aspect of Christian thought, with an eye to how it affected the doctrine of creation up until the rise of evolutionary thought.

In Greek thought the divine spirit always remains bound up with a material principle, and this duality is rooted in the method of reasoning from a given world to divinity as its source. That is, if one thinks his way back from the world to Plato's demiurge by inferring him as the ground of the world order, it is quite irrational to discard the notion of world once the notion of a creator has been arrived at — his existence was postulated in the first place only as an explanation for the world. Of course the writers of the Old Testament were not dealing with such philosophic refinements when they devised their doctrine of creation, and in fact it was not until the first century A.D. that Jewish or Christian thinkers explicitly claimed that God had created the world from nothing. In Jewish literature this idea appears first in II Macc. 7:28, and we find it twice in the New Testament — once, as we have seen, in Rom. 4:17, and again in Heb. 11:3. But belief in creation from nothing was by no means an obvious part of early Christian faith, and in the second century, Justin (ca. 100–ca. 165) agreed almost in passing that God had created the world by rearranging unformed matter.[33]

We have seen that Biblical peoples derived their sense of time from their feeling for a sequence of events, and that their notion of God as creator grew out of their persuasion that he was pur-

---

[32] Günther Bornkamm, " Die Offenbarung des Zornes Gottes," in *Das Ende des Gesetzes: Paulusstudien* (Munich: Chr. Kaiser Verlag, 1958), pp. 18 ff.

[33] Justin, *Apology* I. 67.

posefully effective *in all times.* Given this, the notion of a timeless creation from eternal matter was a stumbling block to
Christians in two ways: it postulated a second principle in creation, and it removed creation from the sphere of history. The
Middle Platonism known by Christian Apologists of the second
century had focused attention on this opposition of God and
matter,[34] so in spite of the example of Justin, other theologians
responded by insisting on creation *ex nihilo.* This was, of course,
primarily a response to the first of the two stumbling blocks, an
attempt to defend the idea of God's freedom and uniqueness in
creation. But the Greek notion of divine eternality as separation
from all times focused the attention of Christian writers on circumstances " in the beginning," i.e., outside of history, so that
their ardent defense of *creatio ex nihilo* tended to foster interest
in divine creation as the original source of the world. Thus it
was that the basic Biblical intuition of God's creative presence
in all temporal events slipped gradually out of focus.

The first church father who insisted explicitly on the notion of
creatio ex nihilo was Theophilus of Antioch, arguing that if
matter were eternal then it would be on a par with God.[35] Tertullian (ca. 160–ca. 240), whose writing in Latin did so much to
shape the vocabulary and the ideas of the Western church,
insisted vigorously in a full-scale treatise that the Biblical notion
of divine creation meant *creatio ex nihilo.* Even though the Bible
writers had not said expressly that creation was from nothing, he
wrote, they certainly would have made it clear if God had used
preexisting matter.[36] It was Tertullian who coined the phrase
" God of the philosophers," [37] describing the way in which Greek
thinkers thought of God as unapproachable and beyond entering
the world in Christ. Likewise, Irenaeus (ca. 126–ca. 200) took the
notion of creation from nothing as essential to faith in- God's
freedom: " He did Himself make all things freely, and as He
pleased." [38]

[34] Pannenberg, " Die Aufnahme des philosophischen Gottesbegriffs,"
p. 18.
[35] Theophilus, *To Autolycus* II. 4; cf. I. 8; II. 10; II. 13.
[36] Tertullian, *Against Hermogenes* XIV.
[37] Tertullian, *Against Marcion* II. 27.
[38] Irenaeus, *Against Heresies* III. 8. 3.

Origen (ca. 185–ca. 254), who introduced a wide stream of Platonic ideas into Christian theology, tried to protect the notion of divine freedom by showing that to believe in eternal matter was less rational than believing God created it. But he combined this with Greek ideas, claiming that the created world is itself eternal. Since God is eternal and unchanging, he said,[39] a creation in time is impossible, because it would have meant change for God. Accepting also the Greek notion that God is utterly simple and without diversity, he reasoned that God must have created all his creatures as spirits equal and similar to one another.[40] Then, in order to explain the obvious differences among existing creatures, he proposed that these bodily historical inequities reflected the degree of the spirits' free and sinful rebellion against God in the realm of eternality.[41] This forced effort to combine notions of eternality and history appeared again when Origen tried to express the Biblical sense of God as the creator of successive events. Here he wrote, " When God made this world that we see about us, that was not the beginning of his activity. There will be another world after this one, and our belief is that in the same way there were others before this one." [42] Likewise, trying to reconcile the Greek notion of divine immutability with the Biblical notion of a God who repeatedly enters history with saving novelty, he observed that God always had wanted men to know him, but he only revealed as much of his eternal nature as they could stand from time to time.[43]

Augustine's reflections over the doctrine of creation assumed also that God is eternal and unchanging Being, and this Greek idea of God was so central in his thought that even in the Middle

[39] Replying to the Stoics, who supposed God to be a material body, he wrote, " The doctrine of the Jews and Christians, which preserves the immutability and unalterableness of the divine nature, is stigmatized . . . because it says in the supplication addressed to the Divinity, ' Thou art the same,' it being, moreover, an article of faith that God has said, ' I change not.' " Origen, *Against Celsus* I. 21.

[40] Origen, *De Principiis* 2. 9. 6.

[41] Origen, *De Principiis* 1. 8. 1.

[42] Origen, *De Principiis* 3. 5. 3. Here we are reminded of Bonnet's idea of palingenesis.

[43] Origen, *Against Celsus* IV. 7.

Ages, Augustinians could be recognized by their readiness to admit that the highest name for God was that of eternal and immutable Being.[44] With God as eternal, Augustine (354–430) had to conceive of creation as being somehow eternal, too, and he did this by proposing that God instantaneously created creatures in such a manner that the germs of later creatures were contained in the original creation.[45] He took the words "the earth was without form" (Gen. 1:2) to mean that God had created unformed matter, from which he fashioned the world: "For Thou, O Lord, hast made the world of a formless matter, which matter, out of nothing." [46] Also, said Augustine, God created time and space along with the creatures. Therefore, those who ask what God was doing before Creation should see that "there could be no time without a created being . . . let them cease to speak that vanity." [47] Again we see the tension between the philosophic notion of divine eternality and the Biblical sense of history as a series of events created by God.

Thomas Aquinas (ca. 1225–1274) continued the tradition of trying to reconcile notions of God as eternal and immutable Being with Biblical notions of history. For him this took the form of an immense effort to modify some aspects of the newly popular Aristotelian philosophy according to the light of Christian faith. This he sought to do in such a way that his modifications of Aristotle would appear not merely arbitrary, but rationally necessary; that is, he hoped to bring metaphysics into harmony with faith in a way that seemed reasonable to philosophers. Accordingly, he accepted as valid nearly everything Aristotle wrote about nature, and he intended to write theologically about creatures "only so far as they are referable to God as their beginning and end." [48] Thus he used the Greek method of reasoning from the world (God's effects) back to God as the orig-

[44] Etienne Gilson, *History of Christian Philosophy in the Middle Ages* (Random House, Inc., 1955), p. 71.

[45] Augustine, *De Genesi ad litteram* IV. 33. 51; VI. 6. 10; V. 7. 20. Cited in Gilson, *op. cit.*, p. 73, note 22.

[46] Augustine, *Confessions* XII. 8.

[47] *Ibid.*, XI. 30.

[48] Thomas Aquinas, *Summa Theologica* I. 1. 3.

inal cause of the world,[49] focusing his attention on creation as the origin of the world. He realized that by this method he could not come rationally to the Biblical idea that the world had a beginning, so in order to protect belief in God's freedom in creation, he insisted that we know of the world's beginning only through faith.[50] He then proposed that in the beginning God simultaneously created a hierarchy of creatures, ordered according to their degree of perfection.[51] Since the original creation, Thomas said, God keeps things in existence by a " continuation of that action whereby He gives being, which action is without either motion or time." [52] That is, from God's viewpoint both original creation and subsequent conservation of the world is a single eternal act. Likewise, God's providence is eternal, and every creature exists in terms of a proper end derived timelessly from God.[53] Here we see that it was easy for Thomas, within Aristotle's thought, to recognize the subjectivity in nature, but it was not by any means so easy to show just how the creative divine purpose was related to a historical world; the intuition of God's novel responsiveness in new events was clouded by attention to the divine power in an original and eternal creation.

Luther and Calvin did not add any basically new ideas to the doctrine of creation that they inherited from Thomas Aquinas and the scholastic theologians, but their great interest in the uniqueness of God's act in Jesus tended to separate further the notions of divine creation and salvation. Reformation thought was eager to establish that God's saving act in Jesus was not continually repeated in the Mass, and this effort to focus divine salvation in a single event made it easy to suppose by analogy that divine creation had been completed in a single original ordering of the universe.[54] Thus Calvin wrote of " the Artificer who sta-

---

[49] *Ibid.*, I. 2. 3.
[50] *Ibid.*, I. 46. 2.
[51] *Ibid.*, I. 47. 1.
[52] *Ibid.*, I. 104. 2.
[53] *Ibid.*, I. 22. 2.
[54] Jaroslav Pelikan, " Creation and Causality in the History of Christian Thought," in Sol Tax and Charles Callender, eds., *Evolution After Darwin*, Vol. III (University of Chicago Press, 1960), p. 37.

tioned, arranged, and fitted together the starry host of heaven in such wonderful order," [55] clearly referring to creation as an event long past.

As modern science rushed toward its climax in Sir Isaac New-ton during the following century, this theological focus on the beginning of the world was sharpened even further by scientists. In the face of widening confidence that God was not presently active in nature, men like Newton found that belief in an orig-inal divine creation was the only plausible way of voicing their intuitions of divine purpose in the world, and Deism arose in the seventeenth century as the ultimate expression of faith in God as a Great First Cause. In this way the Greek vision of God as an ultimate metaphysical principle obscured the Biblical sense of a God creatively present at all times and in all events. It was this quite unbiblical understanding of God that became, as we have seen, part of the theological common sense of many Chris-tians during the years they had to respond to evolutionary thought.

3. CONTEMPORARY CHRISTIAN UNDERSTANDINGS OF CREATION

In earlier chapters we have discussed the impact of evolutionary thought on modern theology, in some cases carrying the discussion purposely into the twentieth century. In this way we have already discussed the present Roman Catholic viewpoint and the kind of natural theology represented in the British and American tra-ditions of rational religion. Likewise, we have considered Amer-ican fundamentalism and the development of a Kantian style in nineteenth-century German theology. But at this point we must mention some other contemporary understandings of creation that raise points important to our Whiteheadian view which will follow.

Emil Brunner's doctrine of creation hinges on his persuasion that theology no longer can operate in terms of the separation of subjectivity and objectivity that we have traced to Kant and which has characterized much German thought for two hundred years. To illustrate the impotence of theology that begins by

[55] Calvin, *Institutes* I. xiv. 21.

accepting this cleavage in reality, he points to the thought of Schleiermacher. After aptly describing Christian faith as the feeling of absolute dependence, Schleiermacher then said this experience entitles us to " postulate the feeling of absolute dependence as valid for everything without exception . . . [so that] we conceive each and every thing as completely conditioned by the interdependence of nature." [56] In terms of his own philosophic assumptions, Schleiermacher here moved unjustifiably from the realm of human subjectivity to the realm of nature's objectivity, and Brunner objects that he confused the feeling of absolute dependence with " the causality which runs through Nature, with which it has nothing at all to do." [57] Trying to anchor theological thought somewhere else than in the philosophic tradition that has produced this schism between subjectivity and objectivity, Brunner turns to the New Testament for the discovery that truth is found neither in isolated subjectivity nor in pure objectivity, but in *encounter*. In the event of Jesus, he says, we have a subject-to-subject encounter with God. Therefore it is here and only here that we know ourselves as living in terms of a " loving Creator who as a Thou calls us to himself." [58]

No philosophic reflection about the origin of the world can ever bring us to the Biblical view of a God who freely creates it, he notes, for the very idea of creation is irrational and cannot be imagined.[59] In fact, the notion of *contingency* has emerged into philosophy only as an expression of Biblical faith in creation.[60] Therefore, we must realize that Christian belief in *creatio ex nihilo* arises not as the fruit of reflection, but because " truth comes to man as a personal summons." [61] Calling our attention to the fact that Israel knew God first as lord of history and only then as creator,[62] he very pointedly draws a parallel for Christians: " The

---

[56] Schleiermacher, *Glaubenslehre*, §46.

[57] Emil Brunner, *The Christian Doctrine of Creation and Redemption: Dogmatics*, Vol. II (London: Lutterworth Press, 1952), p. 9.

[58] Emil Brunner, *Truth as Encounter* (The Westminster Press, 1963), p. 19.

[59] Brunner, *The Christian Doctrine of Creation and Redemption*, p. 11.

[60] *Ibid.*, p. 12.

[61] *Ibid.*, p. 8.

[62] *Ibid.*

Christian belief in Creation arises at the point where all Christian faith arises, namely, in the revelation of God in Jesus Christ." [63] That is, just as Old Testament faith in divine creation expressed the discovery of the Jews that they lived in a purposeful history, Christian belief in Creation arises out of that point in history where the divine purposes are most fully disclosed — Jesus Christ. We are referred to Heb. 1:2, " but in these last days he has spoken to us by a Son, . . . through whom also he created the world." In Jesus Christ, God's final reason for creating the world is revealed,[64] and " from Him alone . . . can we understand what God's creation of the world really means." [65]

Brunner recognizes the validity of scientific thought about nature, and he says it is merely " this dirty trick of a lazy apologetic " [66] to deny the fact of evolution, although we need not accept the current neo-Darwinian explanation.[67] However, it is only *after* we are illuminated by God's Word in Jesus Christ that we can recognize the divine revelation in this evolving world and see the laws of nature as part of God's creative order.[68] Only in this restricted sense of recognizing in nature the same God who *already* is known through Jesus Christ, may we speak of a true " natural knowledge " of God or of a " Christian natural theology." [69] Knowledge of God gotten merely from reflection about the world apart from Jesus Christ, Brunner warns, is " inevitably a mixture of true knowledge and the deification of the creature." [70] It is precisely this danger of deifying the creature that we must guard against in our reflection about evolution, by distinguishing clearly between divine creation and divine preservation of the world. " To preserve that which has been created does not mean continually to create it anew," [71] Brunner cautions, because the notion that things require continual re-creation suggests that they do not have any real existence apart from God. The Biblical doctrine, on the other hand, makes clear that the created world is real over against God; what is once created does not need to be created again, but kept " by a divine thread of preservation above

63 *Ibid.*   66 *Ibid.*, p. 33.   69 *Ibid.*, p. 25.
64 *Ibid.*, p. 13.   67 *Ibid.*, p. 42.   70 *Ibid.*, p. 23.
65 *Ibid.*, p. 14.   68 *Ibid.*, pp. 25, 40.   71 *Ibid.*, p. 34.

the abyss of nothingness." [72] In this sense, maintains Brunner, each human being is both an expression of God's preservation and his creation: the inherited forms of bodily order are *preserved* by God, but the unique human person is *created*, and therefore related directly to God as its creator. [73] It is from the viewpoint of faith, then, that the emergence of the human spirit may be recognized as a "'discontinuity'" not explained in terms of natural causes; [74] this distinction is reminiscent of the two Kantian realms, with their discontinuity bridged by faith.

Karl Barth agrees with Brunner that we cannot think our way from the existing world to belief in God as creator. If we seek merely to explain the world, he says, a number of plausible suggestions could be made regarding its origin — it might be eternal, or self-creating, or a happenstance, or even the whim of a cosmic monster. [75] The notion that God created the world is, by the criteria of reason, no more or less plausible than these others. And that is just the problem, for, as Christians, we cannot stake our lives on God the Creator if he is only a plausible human hypothesis. Schleiermacher's disciples were mistaken, observes Barth, when they tried to explain faith in creation as a discovery coming out of human piousness, for " no very solid structure can be built on the feeling of dependence." [76] We must pray that our faith in creation is more than this, that it is " an answer to the divine self-witness." [77] And since God's full self-witness happens only in Jesus Christ, it is only there that we can know God as creator of heaven and earth. [78] Here Barth and Brunner agree, appealing to revelation in Jesus Christ as the source of our belief in creation. However, where Brunner says that the Christian may recognize God in the evolving world, Barth rejects this notion. He strictly avoids any suggestion of " natural theology," claim-

[72] *Ibid.*
[73] *Ibid.*, p. 35.
[74] *Ibid.*, p. 40.
[75] Karl Barth, *Church Dogmatics*, Vol. III, Part 1, ed. by G. W. Bromiley and T. F. Torrance (Edinburgh: T. & T. Clark, 1958), p. 7.
[76] *Ibid.*, p. 9.
[77] *Ibid.*, p. 8.
[78] *Ibid.*, p. 28.

ing that the world of nature never reveals God truly, even to the man of faith.

"The aim of creation is history," says Barth, the history of salvation "which encloses all other history and to which in some way all other history belongs to the extent that it reflects and illustrates the history of salvation." [79] Thus to say that we can know God as creator only through Jesus Christ means specifically that we know God as creator only in knowing him as lord of that history which is Israel's, and which reaches its goal in the appearance, death, and resurrection of Jesus. [80] Therefore, faith in creation can take place only in the context of historical promise and fulfillment, [81] and to say things are "of God" is to affirm that they were called into being by the lord of this history. [82] Faith in Jesus Christ is life in the presence of the creator, so it can be "an absolute new beginning brought about by God." [83]

Barth develops quite explicitly this notion that God is lord of all history. In the first place, because the creator and the deliverer are one and the same, to be created at all *means* to be given a place in the saving history. That is, God's creative power *is* his power to bring things into existence with a particular history. "My own standpoint, my existence," writes Barth, "has been given to me by the One who in this history has already dealt with me, so that even as I exist I find myself at the center of this history." [84] It is quite unbiblical to suppose that God creates anything so that it merely exists, for in coming into existence each creature is predestined to participate in the saving history. [85] This means that God has control over the past of each creature as well as over its present and future, [86] and Barth further emphasizes this divine lordship over the past where he says that God created time. He agrees with Augustine that there was no time prior to creation, [87] but then he objects to Augustine's idea that creation is eternal. Our sense of temporality, he observes, involves a feeling of transition from the past as well as toward the future; therefore, time "in its very beginning, as it is created . . . is

---

79 *Ibid.*, pp. 59 f.   82 *Ibid.*, p. 44.   85 *Ibid.*, p. 46.
80 *Ibid.*, pp. 13, 27.   83 *Ibid.*, p. 32.   86 *Ibid.*, p. 32.
81 *Ibid.*, p. 11.   84 *Ibid.*, p. 45.   87 *Ibid.*, p. 70.

not only present and future but also past." [88] In other words, creation was from the beginning the creation of things with a past determined by God. Barth insists that even God's inwardness is historical, " for being triune it is not non-historical but historical even in its eternity." [89] The divine eternality is not timelessness, but the immediate unity of present, past, and future.[90]

Rudolf Bultmann's approach to a doctrine of creation appears as one aspect of his lifelong effort to point out the infinite gap that separates God from his world, the gap that Barth once recognized by saying, " God is in heaven and you are on earth." [91] But this magnificent effort comes to us also as a theological labor very deeply shaped by the Kantian tradition and its sharp cleavage between the realms of subjectivity and objectivity. We recognize this Kantian heritage especially in Bultmann's discussion of how God is related to the world. The inmost locus of human responsiveness and decision stands quite outside the entire objective world, claims Bultmann,[92] and it is this heart of man's existence that Bultmann believes Heidegger has successfully analyzed. Likewise, God stands outside of what we call nature, and the objectivity that can be studied by scientists and historians is " a closed continum . . . connected by the succession of cause and effect. . . . [It] cannot be rent by the interference of supernatural, transcendent powers." [93] Therefore, we cannot suppose that God acts as a cause of this-worldly events; in fact, to make such a claim is to speak mythologically, and it is Bultmann's belief that faith should not be tied down to the imagery of mythology which has led to his passionate concern for demythologizing

[88] *Ibid.*, p. 71.

[89] *Ibid.*, p. 66.

[90] *Ibid.*, p. 67.

[91] Schubert Ogden uses this quotation from the preface to the second edition of Karl Barth's *Epistle to the Romans*, in his Introduction to *Existence and Faith: Shorter Writings of Rudolf Bultmann*, selected and tr. by Schubert Ogden (Living Age Books, Meridian Books, Inc., 1960), p. 14.

[92] Rudolf Bultmann, *Primitive Christianity in its Contemporary Setting*, tr. by R. H. Fuller (Living Age Books, Meridian Books, Inc., 1957), p. 20. Cf. *Jesus Christ and Mythology* (Charles Scribner's Sons, 1958), p. 65.

[93] Rudolf Bultmann, " Exegesis without Presuppositions? " in *Existence and Faith*, pp. 291 f.

the New Testament gospel.[94] To say that God " acts " means for Bultmann not that God is involved in historical events in any way that can produce recognizable effects, but that in the midst of the world we discover our own most deeply inward locus of decision " addressed by God here and now . . . questioned, judged, and blessed by him." [95] " To every eye but the eye of faith," writes Bultmann, " the action of God is hidden." [96]

This means that the doctrine of creation is not speaking of this-worldly events.[97] Bultmann agrees that Genesis employs mythic images,[98] but he makes it clear that the Old Testament doctrine of creation witnesses centrally to God's transcendence and " man's sense of utter dependence on God." [99] Likewise, the Christian idea of God as creator means that God stands beyond and outside all powers of nature and history.[100] " Here in *this* realm," insists Bultmann, " God is not to be found. . . . He is beyond them. He is their source; for from him are all things." [101] Belief in creation, therefore, expresses our faith in the radical qualitative difference between God and the objective world — but it is precisely this difference that makes possible our decision for faith, since faith is recognition that we too, in our inmost selfhood, can be free of the objective forces of the past and freely open to the future.[102] Just as nothing from the natural world of objectivity, no evidence available to a historian, can point to God as creator, likewise our decision for faith does not depend on any this-worldly event. Our own free decision is at the same time given to us by God, but this total divine-human

94 Rudolf Bultmann, " New Testament and Mythology," in Hans Werner Bartsch, ed., *Kerygma and Myth: A Theological Debate*, tr. by Reginald H. Fuller (London: S.P.C.K., 1957), pp. 10 f.

95 Rudolf Bultmann, " Bultmann Replies to His Critics," in *ibid.*, pp. 196 f.

96 *Ibid.*, p. 197.

97 Bultmann, *Jesus Christ and Mythology*, p. 69.

98 Bultmann, *Primitive Christianity*, p. 16.

99 *Ibid.*, p. 18.

100 Bultmann, " Faith in God the Creator," in *Existence and Faith*, p. 174.

101 *Ibid.*, pp. 174 f.

102 Rudolf Bultmann, *Theology of the New Testament*, tr. by Kendrick Grobel (Charles Scribner's Sons, 1951), I, p. 315.

event occurs wholly apart from the realm of objectivity.

Paul Tillich shares with Bultmann the approach to Christian faith through existentialist insights. But in sharp contrast to Barth and Brunner, who seek to avoid philosophic assumptions in devising their doctrines of creation, Tillich bases his understanding of creation upon his assumption that we live in a world whose basic ontological structure is the subject-object relationship. " The self having a world to which it belongs precedes all other structures," [103] he observes, and from this he concludes that all existing things participate in the same sort of subject-object polarity. Therefore, whatever is able to enter human experience is *by definition* an object,[104] and our language has developed to express this relationship between subjects and objects. But God is not a subject, nor is he an object standing over against other existing things. He is rather the ground of being,[105] the power of resisting nonbeing.[106] Since God is not any particular being, we are quite unable to speak literally of him using our human language, and we must speak symbolically. " God is being-itself," claims Tillich, and " nothing else can be said about God as God which is not symbolic." [107]

This understanding of the limitations of human language means for Tillich that all traditional theological terms must be reinterpreted symbolically, and the idea of creation is no exception. Again beginning with human existence as he did in seeking the ontological structures, he says, " The doctrine of creation is not the story of an event which took place ' once upon a time.' It is the basic description of the relation between God and the world." [108] More precisely, it is the answer to the question raised by man's discovery that he is finite,[109] and the doctrine basically symbolizes man's relation to the ground of being. Thus it has

[103] Paul Tillich, *Systematic Theology*, Vol. I (The University of Chicago Press, 1951), p. 164.

[104] *Ibid.*, p. 172.

[105] *Ibid.*, p. 156.

[106] *Ibid.*, p. 236.

[107] *Ibid.*, p. 239.

[108] *Ibid.*, p. 252.

[109] *Ibid.*

nothing to do with how creation may be related to time, the question that so intrigued both Augustine and Barth.[110]

Man is the purpose of creation, its *telos*, since he is the creature most able to actualize his freedom. But the very fact of this ontological freedom carries with it the implication that man will fail to realize his essence fully and find himself unavoidably estranged from it. " Creaturely freedom," says Tillich, " is the point at which creation and the fall coincide." [111] In this situation, the notion of *creatio ex nihilo* symbolizes two aspects of man's finite existence, i.e., that while we always experience ourselves against a background which somehow threatens us anxiously with nonbeing, still as Christians we do not trace the tragedy in our lives to God as the ground of being.[112] Indeed, it is because the ground of being continually holds back the threat of nonbeing that we have spoken of God's preservation of the world,[113] experiencing also his continuous creative preservation in the order of nature. Besides this, we have experience of being moved to realize a transcendent ideal in our lives, and this experience is symbolized by the notion of divine providence; [114] as Christians we live in faith that this providence is a permanent activity of God. Not only that, but the symbol of providence " carries the warmth of belief in loving protection and personal guidance." [115]

In a way that resembles Barth's efforts to depict some kind of inward process in God, Tillich speaks of " a creative process of the divine life," [116] claiming that we may call God a living God, and affirm that he includes temporality.[117] God recreates the past as he creates the future, says Tillich, so that " from the point of view of eternity, both past and future are open." [118] But we are warned not to take these images literally, for to speak of God as the " cause " of earthly temporality is to speak symbolically,[119] and if we say that God is in relation to the world as a causal agency, " this statement is as symbolic as the statement that God is a living God." [120]

John Macquarrie's recent *Principles of Christian Theology* pre-

---

110 *Ibid.*, p. 257.
111 *Ibid.*, p. 256.
112 *Ibid.*, p. 254.
113 *Ibid.*, p. 261.

114 *Ibid.*, p. 264.
115 *Ibid.*, p. 268.
116 *Ibid.*, p. 255.
117 *Ibid.*, p. 274.

118 *Ibid.*, p. 276.
119 *Ibid.*, p. 238.
120 *Ibid.*, p. 271.

sents very clearly his " existential-ontological theism," [121] in which God is called " holy being," that before which we take up the " faith-attitude of acceptance and commitment." [122] Macquarrie acknowledges his indebtedness to Heidegger's philosophy, viewing it as a basis for a " viable twentieth-century philosophical ('natural') theology," [123] but his view of creation also reflects a deep admiration for Bultmann's thought. Macquarrie agrees with Bultmann that the Christian doctrine of creation does not concern the coming-into-existence of the world; instead, it is an answer to the question, " What does it mean to be a creature? " [124] Here we begin with the fact of human existential dependence, and then we recognize God as the " letting-be " that precedes all our is-ness.[125] It is therefore this " letting-be-ness " in which God's goodness is founded,[126] and when we interpret the rest of nature on the model of our own experience we recognize that it, too, is part of God's creation.[127]

At times Macquarrie seems to draw the Kantian line between human subjectivity and natural objectivity, for he claims that all subhuman nature lacks man's subjective " answerability " for its existence and is characterized instead by " sheer dependence and contingency." [128] Also in describing levels in the hierarchy of existing things, he notes that inanimate objects exhibit mere " material being." [129] However, he refers approvingly to the work of C. Lloyd Morgan and Teilhard de Chardin,[130] men who have tried to express the notion of emergence, in which higher levels of being appear as previously existing elements are gathered up and transformed. Thus animals exhibit not only material being but organic being,[131] and at the pinnacle of being we find men, of all

---

[121] John Macquarrie, *Principles of Christian Theology* (Charles Scribner's Sons, 1966), p. 106.
[122] *Ibid.*, p. 105.
[123] *Ibid.*, p. ix.
[124] *Ibid.*, p. 195.
[125] *Ibid.*, p. 194.
[126] *Ibid.*, p. 209.
[127] *Ibid.*, p. 197.
[128] *Ibid.*
[129] *Ibid.*, p. 131.
[130] *Ibid.*, p. 206.
[131] *Ibid.*, p. 131.

creatures able to " display in their kind of being the widest diversity in unity " by uniting both these lower levels of being into the new unity of personal being.[132] More precisely theologically, since God's essence is " letting-be," Macquarrie sees the hierarchy of creatures in terms of their creaturely capacity to imitate or participate in God's letting-be-ness. Man stands at the pinnacle of creation as that creature which brings this " to an altogether new level, that of free cooperation in letting-be." [133] And in reference to Rom. 8:22, he locates even the material entities in the hierarchy around this notion, writing of an " inarticulate, unconscious ' travail ' of the lower levels of creation . . . striving toward a goal." [134] Here it seems that Macquarrie does want to attribute some flickering subjectivity to what he elsewhere calls " material being."

He refers to God the Father as " primordial Being," an expression that points to " the ultimate act or energy of letting-be, the condition that there should be anything whatsoever, the source not only of whatever is but of all possibilities of being." [135] This notion protects our intuition of divine transcendence, but it is an abstraction apart from " expressive Being," the second person of the Trinity, through whom the energy of primordial being pours out and gives rise to particular things.[136] It is this expressive being that we discover above all in the finite being of Jesus, " in such a way that his being is caught up into Being itself." [137] Also, since the Biblical God is involved in history, we must speak of a " risk " taken by Being when it moves out to manifest itself in a world of concrete beings, because " in this process Being could become split, fragmented, and torn within itself." [138] There is always within creaturely being a twofold possibility, to advance into fuller being, or to slip back into nothingness,[139] and God's willingness to risk becoming fragmented within himself is precisely what calls forth our allegiance.[140] The third person of the Trinity is called " unitive Being," expressing the function of the Spirit to maintain and restore creatures in their being so that they fulfill their po-

---

132 *Ibid.*, p. 207.   135 *Ibid.*, p. 182.   138 *Ibid.*
133 *Ibid.*, p. 208.   136 *Ibid.*   139 *Ibid.*, p. 198.
134 *Ibid.*, p. 205.   137 *Ibid.*, p. 183.   140 *Ibid.*, p. 183.

tentialities instead of slipping toward nonbeing.[141]

By calling God " holy being," Macquarrie intentionally locates himself in the long theological tradition that associates God with being, a tradition which he traces to the Bible itself.[142] However, he is eager to avoid any suggestion that God is mere static being. This would be indistinguishable from nothingness, as Hegel observed,[143] and to be intelligible being must include becoming. Likewise, " becoming is unintelligible apart from some conception of being, in which the becoming is included." [144] Here Macquarrie clearly intends to make his concept of " holy being " adequate to the fullness of historical experience,[145] but he does not go on to clarify just *how* divine becoming is included within divine being. We find what seems to be a similar willingness to stop at the level of affirmation where he discusses the two models that have been used in the past to speak of divine creation. The model of " making," he observes, successfully expresses God's transcendent freedom over the world, and the model of " emanation " expresses the divine immanence. We need both notions, says Macquarrie, and " perhaps this is best done by holding side by side in their tension with one another the models of making and emanation." [146]

In closing our brief discussion of contemporary doctrines of creation we must comment on Langdon Gilkey's book *Maker of Heaven and Earth*, because of his several explicit references to Whitehead, even though in general his work reflects many of the same existentialist assumptions that we have found in Bultmann, Tillich, and Macquarrie. Gilkey distinguishes quite sharply between subjectivity and objectivity, even tracing the conflict between science and religion to our habit of supposing that these spheres overlap. Speaking of the doctrine of creation, he says,

[141] *Ibid.*, p. 141.

[142] *Ibid.*, p. 107.

[143] *Ibid.*, p. 101. The reference is to Hegel's *Encyclopedia of the Philosophical Sciences*, Logic, Section 87.

[144] *Ibid.*, p. 101.

[145] He writes, " This would seem to be a sufficient answer to the complaints of those who say that a philosophy or theology which makes basic the idea of being results in a static, abstract system that cannot do justice to concrete dynamic experience." *Ibid.*, p. 101.

[146] *Ibid.*, p. 202.

" Because they have reference to two events on two entirely different levels of being, the inquiries of science and the theological doctrine cannot conflict." [147] He agrees with Bultmann that " all language about God and His relation to the world must be in terms of analogy," [148] since to speak of God using the language appropriate to our ordinary experience of a cause and effect world is to speak mythologically.[149]

Observing that the idea of *creatio ex nihilo* arose as an effort to combat dualism, he then comments that dualism appears " in our time in perhaps its most impressive form in the philosophy of Whitehead." [150] Creation is the act that sets God apart as God, claims Gilkey,[151] so that " both the simple God of popular religion and the esoteric God of process philosophy, by their essential lack of ontological transcendence, are never holy enough to be objects of genuine religious concern." [152] Thus the " ultimate irrationality " discussed by Whitehead can never be the God whom we find at the heart of our Christian experience.[153] This suggests to Gilkey that the problem of relating theology to philosophy can be

[147] Langdon Gilkey, *Maker of Heaven and Earth: A Study of the Christian Doctrine of Creation* (Doubleday & Company, Inc., 1959), p. 55.

[148] *Ibid.*, p. 64. Elsewhere Gilkey says that we desperately need " a theological ontology that will put intelligible and credible meanings into our analogical categories of divine deeds and of divine self-manifestation through events." See " Cosmology, Ontology, and the Travail of Biblical Language," *Journal of Religion*, Vol. XLI, No. 3 (1961), p. 203.

[149] Gilkey, *Maker of Heaven and Earth*, p. 259.

[150] *Ibid.*, p. 49.

[151] *Ibid.*, p. 79.

[152] *Ibid.*, p. 89. Ian Barbour, in *Issues in Science and Religion*, proposes the idea of continuing creation as most adequate to the Biblical intuitions of God's action. Although he bases much of his thought on Whitehead's cosmology, Barbour is eager both to ensure that our language about God is not merely abstract and metaphysical (p. 386), and to preserve the notions of divine freedom and transcendence that spring from religious experience (pp. 418, 458). He wonders, e.g., whether Whitehead's God may be "*too powerless* to inspire worship" (p. 448). Beginning from within the Biblical perspective of " judgement and redemption in Christ " (p. 459), he suggests, we may use process metaphysics to aid in developing a doctrine of revelation in history that would allow God's initiative a larger role than was given to it by Whitehead himself (p. 458).

[153] *Ibid.*, p. 200.

resolved only by " conducting a philosophical inquiry capable of expressing that attitude toward existence characteristic of Christian men." [154] These bases of a Christian philosophy he believes to be our intuitions of a " dependent, contingent, and yet real finitude, and a transcended order." [155] Finally, objecting to the notion of evil that we have discussed in Chapter IV, Gilkey writes, " It is a denial of God's care to say, whether with Plotinus, Augustine, Thomas, Bradley, or Whitehead, that . . . for God, or at least from His perspective, evil as experienced by finite creatures is not real, but only an error due to a finite point of view." [156]

4. GOD AND EVOLUTION: A WHITEHEADIAN VIEW

At this point we must interrupt the theological discussion in order to return to our Whiteheadian interpretation of evolutionary theory, moving now to consider the relation of God to evolution. Already we have discussed the laws of nature and the general course of evolution as a process combining efficient causation with the final causation that is effective through the subjective aims of actual entities. And we have seen that because of this, nature is characterized by novel responses to a settled past. However, up to this point we have avoided any reference to God in our Whiteheadian sections, and three questions now remain: (a) within Whitehead's thought, what is the relationship of God to this evolving nature? (b) is this Whiteheadian view compatible as it stands with Biblical understandings of creation? (c) if not, can the philosophic system be modified so as to allow for the plausibility of Biblical insights, without jeopardizing the rational coherence of the philosophical system itself?

At the outset we should realize that we are not at liberty to introduce the idea of God as a *deus ex machina,* a " God of the gaps " who appears over the horizon just in time to drive off the gathering ambiguities of our scientific understanding. If the existence of God is to be credible, it must be because " the general character of things requires that there be such an entity." [157] That

---

154 *Ibid.*, p. 124.   156 *Ibid.*, p. 181, note 2.
155 *Ibid.*, p. 138, note 17.   157 *SMW* 174.

is, if the cosmological system up to this point appears to provide a reliable and persuasive description of an evolving nature, and if this system itself requires God for its completion, we are justified rationally in bringing in the idea of God. At this point Whitehead sought to emulate Aristotle, who introduced his notion of the Unmoved Mover only as a requirement of his general metaphysical system.[158] Of course, the notion of God as a completion of the cosmological system implies that we must be able to explain in some detail *how* God is related to the world, if we are to escape the accusation of introducing God for merely religious reasons — and Whitehead objected strenuously to any device by which the idea of God is grafted artificially onto a philosophic system merely to satisfy unrationalized religious emotion.[159] This does not mean that Whitehead rejected religious affirmations about God, for he regarded religious experience as a uniquely important aspect of human experience. But it does mean that religious feelings or the occurrence of " revelation " *by themselves* do not justify introducing the idea of God into a cosmology that seeks to describe a good deal more than religious experience. God's *existence* must be required by the whole philosophic scheme, not just by religious experience or special revelation, although our insight into God's *nature* may well be broadened through such experiences.

Returning to our Whiteheadian description of nature, we may begin by observing that several earlier affirmations were left dangling, unexplained in terms of other Whiteheadian notions, so

---

[158] *SMW* 173. Burgers' discussion of evolution omits reference to the notion of God, because " it would lead to difficulties to refer to it as a means for explanation." (*Experience and Conceptual Activity*, p. 33.) Of course, this is directly opposite to Whitehead's intention to include God within the explanatory scheme of ideas.

[159] *AI* 94. This may be an appropriate point to mention what is, so far as I know, the only effort by a biologist to reconcile a Whiteheadian understanding of nature with Christian faith in Creation. This is L. Charles Birch, *Nature and God* (London: SCM Press, Ltd., 1965). At first glance, Birch appears to be introducing the idea of God in the arbitrary way that Whitehead deplores, but to accuse him of this is to miss his point. He writes primarily as a testimony to the way a Whiteheadian approach to evolutionary biology and Christian faith in a God of persuasive love (p. 75) illuminate each other, and he organizes his thought around a Christological center.

that up to this point our discussion suffers from the same kind of rational disjointedness which we found, say, in the arbitrary proposal that subjective categories appeared in nature when man appeared. In particular, we have said that the subjective aim of an actual occasion is toward increased intensity of feeling, and that the laws of nature are expressive of an upward movement toward higher forms of order. But we have not said *why* these things are so. Should we now rest content with these conditions, accepting them " with natural piety " as the given? Are they the ultimate irrationalities, i.e., those facts behind which reason cannot penetrate, for which there just is no explanation? If so, we need not — cannot — introduce the idea of God as an agency in evolution. We have seen that a good many modern scientists and philosophers of science *are* content to stop at this point, pressing explanation only to some analogous given, e.g., that matter exists in motion, or that chemical compounds display a certain instability.

But if we seek to be rigorously coherent in our thinking, we are driven to ask the reason for any such basic conditions that we discover. What we require is some explanatory insight, a statement of *how* and *why* things are coordinated; this demand for rational coherence is just what Whitehead says Bergson evaded by failing to explain *why* there should be an *élan vital* calling forth the advance of life against the relapsing tendencies of matter.[160] Further, in line with our principle of tracing the reasons for anything to the natures of actual entities, we must seek the reason for this basic coordination in some actual entity, not in abstract principles. This quest for full explanation led Whitehead to postulate the existence of God; thus the fact of God's existence, not the above mentioned conditions, turns out to be the ultimate irrationality when our quest for understanding is pushed to its limit.[161]

In earlier writings Whitehead did not entirely avoid the note of

---

[160] *FR* 29.

[161] *SMW* 179. It is important to recognize what this statement does *not* mean, since it seems to be so frequently misunderstood, e.g., by Gilkey, *op. cit.*, p. 200. Whitehead means that the *fact* of God's existence cannot be explained, i.e., it is irrational. But *what* God is may very well be explained, at least in principle; in any case, we should not take the notion to mean that God himself is or acts irrational.

arbitrariness in his discussion of God,[162] but his main reason for introducing God is clear: the evolutionary order of nature points to a source of order. Some entity must be postulated to explain why the ongoingness of nature ("creativity"[163]) results in *something* instead of the mere nothingness of chaos. That is, something must account for the fact that each process of concrescence culminates in a concrete entity instead of remaining merely an undifferentiated aspect of a confused universe of mutually thwarting feelings. The actual entity that accounts for this fact can only be God, acting as the source of order, and Whitehead thus refers to God as "the principle of concretion,"[164] and "the principle of limitation."[165]

But now, how does God do this? Since so much of our last chapter hinged on the notion that all actual occasions enjoy subjective aims, let us begin our effort to explain God's relationship to the evolving world at this point. We may start by asking, how is it that entities have subjective aims at all? It *might* be that they produce their own subjective aims out of nothing, selecting their standpoints in the universe at random. But if entities merely enjoyed subjective aims randomly, what reason would there be for a rock molecule to endure in the same place for a billion years? Why is it that aims are such as to produce not only much order but an increase of order? We must conclude that if actual entities provided their own subjective aims at random, an ordered universe would be quite out of the question. Therefore, some source of restriction of aims and standpoints is required to explain the order in the world. This source is God, and apart from the fact that God sets certain limits to the aims of occasions, the laws of nature would relapse into chaos.[166] This limitation by

---

[162] See the discussion in John B. Cobb, Jr., *A Christian Natural Theology, Based on the Thought of Alfred North Whitehead* (The Westminster Press, 1965), pp. 137–150.

[163] *PR* 11, 30, and *passim*.

[164] *SMW* 174; *PR* 374.

[165] *SMW* 178.

[166] *AI* 119; *PR* 377. Agar interprets Whitehead erroneously to mean that "it is part of the metaphysical nature of the world that completed actual occasions give rise to other actual occasions." (Agar, *op. cit.*, pp. 77 ff.) On the basis of this error, he then finds the notion of God to be an

God is the reason that physical laws can express the statistical probability of some particular outcome in events that involve large numbers of entities,[167] as it is the source of intuitions that God is the sustainer of nature.

Since each entity is utterly alone in the universe *during* its concrescence, God's restriction of subjective aim must be traced to the initial phase, that aim with which the process begins.[168] That is, God supplies to each new occasion the *initial aim* with which its own self-causation starts. Thus it is as provider of initial aims that God can be understood as related to the world, at this point in our argument. Further, if we are to think of God literally (not symbolically or analogically) as creator, sustainer, and provider for an evolving world, we must be able to base such notions on an understanding of how God does in fact provide initial aims. To this we now address ourselves.

In Whitehead's view, God has foreseen every possible concrete state of the universe, and he has eternally ordered the eternal objects so that for *any* future which may become concrete, God has eternally his ideal purposes.[169] No matter which occasion we mention — be it an occasion in a snow crystal that may fall in the Sahara twenty-five thousand years from now, or an occasion that might have existed in the personality of a brother I do not have — God knows eternally just which ordering of the eternal objects he would hold out as a " lure "[170] for its initial phase of feeling. This aspect of God, in which God has his aims eternally settled for any and every possible course of history in the universe, is God's " primordial nature."[171] Here is the aspect of God that we feel as the intuition of God's unlimited foresight and unswerving faithfulness of purpose, no matter what the course of events.

---

arbitrary addition to the philosophical scheme (p. 201). Burgers' exclusion of the notion of God from his discussion results in a similar error, e.g., " A society is the cause of its own persistence." (Burgers, *op. cit.*, p. 51.)

[167] PR 315.
[168] PR 374.
[169] PR 18, 46, 134.
[170] PR 131.
[171] PR 46.

From the fact that occasions enjoy a degree of freedom in their subjective immediacies, we know that God does not determine the actual state of the world in advance. He envisions every possibility for what *may* happen, but he does not know in advance what *will* happen, for each occasion is liable to modify its divinely ordered initial aim into a somewhat different final subjective aim of its own. Thus before *this* detailed state of the universe became a concrete fact, God's purposes for its actual occasions had no preference in his primordial nature over his purposes for some other particular state of affairs that might have developed but did not. For this reason, history is not the unrolling of a divinely determined scroll, and we cannot say that there is a single direction for evolution. God's singleness of purpose for evolution is settled eternally, but it is a complex purpose that considers every possible course of history, not merely the one which does, in fact, become concrete.

Thus the initial aim given by God to an entity is always an aim for some specific ideal possibility, that maximum value which in God's judgment is possible for it in the light of its own settled past and its relevant future. " The initial aim," writes Whitehead, " is the best for that *impasse*." [172] God's purpose in the world is always " embodied in the particular ideals relevant to the actual state of the world." [173] Here we see an important correspondence between the manner in which God provides initial aims and our conclusion that evolution is to be understood as an open-ended historical process, characterized by novel responses to a settled past. Also it is the reason for all theological doctrines of special providence, the main intent of which is to express faith that God's overall purposes do not exclude his attention to the particular situations on earth.

If God is to respond in this fashion to concrete details of the world, evidently he must know about them, and this can happen only if he is affected by the world. This takes place as God's immediate and everlasting conscious prehension of every objectified actual occasion, so that his provision of initial aims always reflects his continually new consciousness of events in the world.

[172] *PR* 373. Cf. *PR* 134 f., 343.   [173] *RM* 152.

This responsiveness to the world Whitehead calls God's "consequent nature," [174] and, of course, it develops in relationship to the evolving universe.[175] "The truth itself is nothing else than how the composite natures of the organic actualities of the world obtain adequate representation in the divine nature," writes Whitehead.[176] God's complete conscious knowledge of every happening allows him, we must presume, to predict the future within certain rather narrow limits in the case of details and within wider limits in the case of historical trends, but never completely.

Besides reflecting the adjustment of divine purposes to details of history, the initial aim provided by God defines both the spatial and temporal standpoint of a new occasion in the universe,[177] and this is equivalent to defining what kind of entity it will be, as well as where and when it will occur. Although the world continuum is potentially divisible in any number of ways, Whitehead notes, nothing about the past settles just how the continuum will be "atomized" into new occasions,[178] and God determines this by deciding for each new occasion just which actual occasions will compose its causal past.[179] Thereby he determines which feelings each new occasion must take account of. For example, why should a just completed occasion in my personality be followed by a new occasion which then becomes — of all things — another occasion in my personality, instead of an occasion in a cup of tea in China or a flash of experience in the far reaches of space? God determines this by defining the actual world of this new occasion in such a way that my previous occasions of personality turn out to be that part of its past which it values as the chief source of feelings relevant to its own aim. It becomes an occasion in my personality *because* it is provided with that past and the initial aim to appropriate feelings from that past.[180] In this way the past of an entity is always settled and definite, but the *way* it is settled depends on God, who may even eliminate certain aspects of the environment from effectiveness in a new occasion.[181]

We have discussed the significance of God's provision of initial

[174] PR 523–533.   [177] PR 104, 195.   [180] PR 420.
[175] PR 19.   [178] PR 104 f.   [181] AI 200 f.; PR 436.
[176] PR 18 f.   [179] PR 435 f.

aims, but now we must ask in addition: *how* do actual occasions derive their initial aims from God? This in turn raises the question of how entities prehend God, and Whitehead says the primary phase of each occasion is a hybrid feeling of God, i.e., a feeling of God's conceptual feelings.[182] Here we may pause to recall that a physical feeling is the general case of feeling another entity, while a hybrid feeling occurs when the entity felt is objectified not merely by its own physical feelings but by one of its own conceptual feelings.[183] In the case at hand, the conceptual feeling derived from God is God's feeling of value in that particular ideal possibility that he envisions for the becoming of the new occasion, and when this feeling is felt through a hybrid prehension of God it becomes the conceptual feeling of initial subjective aim for the new occasion.

The word " eternal " in the phrase " eternal objects " indicates Whitehead's belief that God does not *create* the realm of possibility.[184] But the ontological principle reminds us that nothing can be part of our philosophic scheme which is not discoverable somewhere in the subjective experience of some actual entity,[185] and this applies here to eternal objects. Therefore, their only reality is as ordered primordially in God's nature; [186] apart from this, their reality would be " indistinguishable from nonentity." [187] Eternal objects that have been realized previously in the world may be prehended by a hybrid prehension of the occasions in which they were realized, and, in this way, past novelty can be preserved. But if it were not for God's conceptual valuation of the whole realm of possibility, eternal objects still unrealized by entities in the world would be " relatively non-existent for the concrescence in question." [188] In the final analysis, then, we must trace to hybrid prehensions of God that novelty by which the world escapes from mere repetition, and which is the defining attribute of a living occasion.[189] Apart from God's desire to provide initial aims in which there is a lure toward relevant novelty, the world would be empty of all life.

[182] *PR* 342. [185] *PR* 253. [188] *PR* 46.
[183] *PR* 376. [186] *PR* 73. [189] *PR* 315.
[184] *PR* 392. [187] *PR* 392.

We have said that the initial aim of an occasion stems from its hybrid prehension of a conceptual feeling in God's primordial nature. Now, in the perfection of God's subjective aim each such conceptual feeling is held in perfect harmony with others, and we may, at this point, ask properly after the inclusive aim that is God's subjective aim for himself. Put concisely, God's aim is to elicit beauty in the world and, regardless of what happens, to receive the world into his consequent nature in such a way that every achievement in the world is conserved without loss. Whitehead suggests the image of God as urging the world toward creative advance with " a tender care that nothing be lost." [190] Therefore, God's purpose in the world is to evoke quality, not permanence,[191] since he is able to conserve every value consciously and everlastingly within his own consequent nature. His purpose for the entities in the world is quality of attainment,[192] depth of satisfaction,[193] intensity of feeling [194] — in short, it is for maximum beauty of experience, both for occasions in the world and for himself.

Just as the whole cosmological story revolves around the subjective immediacies of individual occasions,[195] so is God's aim for beauty in the world directed first of all toward individual entities, and he devotes his tenderness to each actual entity as it arises.[196] In this sense God does not aim primarily at the evolution of higher kinds of societies. Thus, it is not the mere existence of, say, a human personality that counts primarily for God, but the beauty of attainment which may be possible for individual occasions in that personality by reason of their participation in the society. Conversely, God's aim toward beauty in that larger society of human personalities is his aim toward a social background able to encourage the production of organisms harboring personalities in which increasingly beautiful experience may happen.

The relevant future for God's experience is infinitely long and infinitely inclusive, so that he can provide for individual occasions just those initial aims which are harmonious with movement

---

190 *PR* 525.   193 *PR* 161.   196 *Ibid.*
191 *PR* 160.   194 *Ibid.*
192 *RM* 152.   195 *PR* 254.

toward far-distant kinds of beauty as yet envisioned only by him. This is the reason that we have intuitions of a general providence, the reason that evolution appears as a movement toward higher kinds of societies, the reason that Le Conte felt something about human society which stemmed from " a drawing upward and onward from above and in front." [197] In this sense we may think of God brooding over the first primitive forms of marine life, conscious that from them could develop an infinite variety of more complex forms, one of which was man. But we must remember that in the infinite richness of his mentality God also was envisioning numberless other possibilities for high-grade beauty of creaturely experience on earth, occurring in kinds of creatures we cannot even imagine. It is reasonable to suppose that many of these possibilities have been excluded by the passage of history, but that others remain yet unjudged by time. In terms of human experience, we have intuitions of yet unrealized forms of beauty that God seeks to elicit in the world, but even our fairest glimpses of a harmonious world where God is " all in all " fail utterly to suggest the width of God's aims for all his creatures here and in the depths of starry space.

As we have seen, the flexibility of history can be traced to the fact that occasions in their freedom can deviate from the ideal aim proposed by God, but even this deviation is possible only within the realm of divine purpose. That is, God offers to each new occasion the entire realm of eternal objects in a graded way such that other possibilities than the ideal may be actualized, but always within the limits set by God for the general requirements of order. Thus I may well modify God's initial aim for me to be merciful into a final subjective aim to be callous, but not into an aim to appear suddenly as a tanager flitting through the woods. There is real freedom for the entities of the world, balanced by order in such a way that God's ideal aim toward higher forms of experience is expressed principally as a pervasive urge, always subject to frustration in individual cases. Thus we find in nature a general advance, coupled with unlimited variety and a share of regression. This balance is the reason that evil is possible, but

[197] See above, p. 105.

also it is the source of intuitions that evil will not be forever dominant over the divine purposes. It is in this sense that Whitehead writes: " The power by which God sustains the world is the power of himself as the ideal. . . . The world lives by its incarnation of God in itself." [198]

At this point we should pause to discuss what seems to be a problem within Whitehead's thought, a place where he does not quite succeed in reaching his goal of coherence in explanation. He intends that a generic description of an actual entity, i.e., the sort of description which we have ventured in Chapter IV, should apply to God as well as to any actual entity in the world.[199] But already our description of how occasions derive their initial aim from God seems to remove God from the genus of actual entities by suggesting that he is able to prehend other entities *during* his process of concrescence. If God is a single actual entity, as Whitehead proposes, and if one of the generic characteristics of actual entities is that they neither feel other entities nor are felt by them during the phase of subjectivity, how is it possible for God to feel and be felt in the way we have proposed? How is it possible for him to respond to each detail of history by providing initial aims that are directly relevant to situations which even he did not know until they happened? Putting the problem in a different way, if actual entities are able to prehend only already completed occasions, and if the consequent nature of God is never definite, but everlastingly enlarged by his prehension of entities in the world, how can there be any prehension of God? What does it mean when Whitehead speaks of God's " unity of satisfaction " [200] if there is never a completion of God's subjective actuality?

The question may be summarized by asking why Whitehead does not apply the notion of " transition " to God. We have seen that this notion is fundamental to his explanation of how other entities can affect each other, and it has been vitally important in our effort to illuminate evolutionary theory, often clarifying problems left unsolved by generations of reflection. In the face of this, it seems that Whitehead would have considered transition in God too; but of course it is impossible to know just why he held back

[198] *RM* 149.   [199] *PR* 168.   [200] *PR* 48.

from this step. Certainly he intended to describe God as the element in the world that "combines the actuality of what is temporal with the timelessness of what is potential." [201] But he did devote most of his attention to God's primordial nature, the aspect of God that accounts for the eternal valuation and ordering of the eternal objects and hence for the order of nature; [202] perhaps this was what led him, as it did philosophers before him, toward the notion of God as One, i.e., a single actual entity. Whatever Whitehead's reasons, to bring the description of God into line with the rest of his thought it seems that we need to introduce the notion of transition into our description of God. This we can do by conceiving of God as a society instead of a single actual entity. We should think of him as a personally ordered society, and specifically as a living person. Modifying Whitehead's own idea of God in this way makes the cosmological system more coherent, without introducing any serious new difficulties. [203]

In this case God may be understood as enjoying an infinite succession of divine moments of experience, each one complete and satisfied. Because of God's aim to perpetuate his personality, and his ability to do so by initiating new occasions, his existence will be without end; likewise, if we look backward, we discover that each divine occasion in turn has received its existence from earlier ones so that we fail completely in trying to imagine a beginning of the series. Thus we may say that God exists from everlasting to everlasting, as a historical personality. Now what about the intuitions of God's eternality that formed such a prominent part of Greek speculation? These notions seem to express the sense in which each occasion of God's personality prehends its past and envisions its future with perfect completeness. The fact of transition in God's personality does not entail the kind of loss that we know in our own lives, and each new divine occasion en-

[201] *PR* 64.

[202] See Cobb's detailed discussion in *A Christian Natural Theology,* p. 161.

[203] Hartshorne ("Whitehead's Novel Intuition," p. 23) and Cobb (*op. cit.,* pp. 188–192) both propose this solution to the problem, and Cobb shows in detail that this modification of Whitehead's doctrine introduces no serious problems.

joys fully the settled aims that we have attributed to God's primordial nature, as well as a perfect consciousness of everything that has happened in the past and which may happen in the future. In this way notions of God's eternality find their proper place within a vision of God as essentially historical. As Barth and others before him have maintained, the divine eternality *is* an immediate unity of past, present, and future, i.e., that hidden inwardness which is God's subjective immediacy apart from the world is the primordial example of what it means to be historical.

The notion of God as a living person also relieves us from the awkwardness of wondering how God's aim for beauty ever can be realized, if he is a single entity everlastingly in process. Likewise, we can avoid Schelling's notion of a God who is never fully himself until the whole evolutionary process of history has finished its course, since, as a living person, God's experience is repeatedly satisfied but everlastingly widened by his conscious prehension of events in the world. His identity as God is established with perfect definiteness in each occasion of his life, but in a way which allows him to surpass himself endlessly while carrying his primordial steadiness of purpose along with no loss at all.

Then too, if God's primordial and consequent natures are joined inseparably in each moment of God's experience and in their effect on the world, we are quite clearly justified in considering God's causal efficacy in the world as exactly analogous to and along with that of other entities. This means that we are free from having to speak of God's acts in symbolic or analogical language as Bultmann, Tillich, and Gilkey propose. Our problem in understanding and speaking of God's causal relation to the world turns out to reflect the puniness of our conscious grasp of things, not a radical ontological otherness of God himself. Further, if God really is a living person as we have suggested, then we are quite justified in speaking of him using personalistic words from our own experience as persons. Here we should note that although we have focused our attention mainly on the way actual entities prehend God's conceptual feeling of their initial aims, they may and do prehend other aspects of God's personality. Therefore, if we find ourselves " addressed by God . . . questioned, judged, and blessed by him," as Bultmann puts it, this discovery *may* be grounded in God's actual questioning, judging, and blessing of us, felt as we prehend occasions of God's personality along with other occasions in our past. The question — and it is vexing indeed — is whether in tracing the origin of our own conscious feelings we are correct in attributing feelings of judgment and blessing to God, or whether they, in fact, originate in some other actual entities — perhaps merely in our own personality! But that God addresses us, questions, judges, and blesses *may* be quite literally true, not an archaic expression in need of demythologization.

In line with this view of God as a living person, it seems simplest if we suppose that each occasion of God's experience has, like other entities, a spatial standpoint. Here we may conjecture that his region includes the regions of all other entities, just as the region of a molecule includes the regions of its electrons.[204] This is equivalent to saying that God " occupies " all space, but in making this statement we must bear in mind that we are not thinking of space as a great receptacle filled with things. On the contrary, we must think of God's existence as *defining* the space and time in which it occurs; they are aspects of his extension. In this we may see the truth of Newton's notions of absolute space, but with one important difference: using Whitehead's notion of space we need not think of the world as existing " inside " God, which is the usual problem faced by pantheism. The reason for this is that all occasions, in their subjectivity, exist in absolute spatial and temporal independence from their contemporaries and from God; only as they become objectified may we speak of one entity as " inside " another. Finally, we might conjecture, also, that God enjoys a succession of exceedingly brief moments of subjective immediacy, each briefer, perhaps, than the vibration of a single electronic occasion.[205]

---

[204] See Cobb, *op. cit.*, pp. 82–91, 192–196. William A. Christian, however, does not agree that the regions of two occasions can overlap in this sense. See *An Interpretation of Whitehead's Metaphysics* (Yale University Press, 1959), pp. 93–104.

[205] See Cobb, *op. cit.*, p. 192, and Charles Hartshorne, " Whitehead's Idea of God," in Paul Arthur Schilpp, ed., *The Philosophy of Alfred North Whitehead* (Tudor Publishing Company, 1941), pp. 535 f.

We have been discussing God's causal efficacy in the world as the source of initial aims, but we must turn now to a specific consideration of God as creator of the world. Whitehead says hesitantly that because God provides initial aims he can be called the creator of actual occasions,[206] and God's purpose is " in a sense " a creative purpose.[207] But he draws back from the notion of a God who creates by fiat, preferring Plato's notion of creation as the incoming of a certain type of social order as opposed to the beginning of matter of fact.[208] Whitehead would reject the idea of a Biblical God who could say, " Let there be light," as well as Calvin's statement that " the will of God is the necessity of things," [209] precisely because he objected so strongly to the notion that God imposes his will arbitrarily on the world. This image, thought Whitehead, must be purged of its origins in a Near Eastern world ruled by Oriental despots.[210] *That* God provides initial aims is, for Whitehead, grounded in God's nature; [211] God's decision is involved only in *what* the initial aims are.

Nevertheless, it is possible to say that God creates the world in a real sense which takes account of Whitehead's dislike of capricious divine power, by recognizing fully what is involved when God provides initial aims and then remembering that entities have their degree of freedom. As Cobb points out,[212] the initial aim of an occasion is far more than just one among several factors in its determination. It is *the* decisive factor in initiating the very existence of every new occasion, and we may well describe God's role in providing this initial aim as creation. However, though God's creative power is unrivaled, it is not absolute. We have seen that he is limited by the freedom of occasions as they modify their initial aims, and this means also that he is limited by what the

---

[206] *PR* 343.

[207] *RM* 100.

[208] *PR* 147. Birch's discussion of creation follows Whitehead accurately here, where he says, " The purposes of God in creation are . . . implemented . . . as a struggle between a disordered state and God's lure to completeness " (Birch, *op. cit.*, p. 99) and " Creation is the lifting of restraints on matter " (p. 102).

[209] Calvin, *Institutes* III. xxiii. 8.

[210] *PR* 520.

[211] *AI* 172.

[212] Cobb, *op. cit.*, p. 204.

already completed entities have made of themselves.[213]

In addition, our effort to view occasions in God's personality as being generically the same as occasions in the world suggests a further limitation to the effectiveness of God's initial aims for his creatures. To view occasions as generically the same means that they differ only in quality or degree, but not in terms of whether they exemplify the metaphysical categories. Therefore, if occasions in God's personality provide initial aims for new occasions, *in principle* it may be true that occasions in the world also can provide some initial aim for others. Whitehead does allude to this possibility by mentioning that transition to the future is essential to the existence of an occasion,[214] and that the subjective aim of an occasion can include the aim for future occasions to be derived from itself.[215] But even so, the *qualitative* difference between God and the world is so unimaginably great that his effectiveness in providing initial aims will always far outweigh that of any past occasion; and there is no reason to suppose that God's decisive role in determining the temporal and spatial standpoint of a new occasion is shared with other entities.[216]

At this point we may ask how our understanding of God as creator relates to the theological understandings with which we are familiar. First of all, how does this notion of a divine creator relate to the theological notion of *creatio ex nihilo?* Here let us recall some points made earlier in this chapter. We noted that the Greek thinkers who devised the notions of form and matter were not asking *why* things exist; they were merely trying to explain what already is, taking its existence for granted. Consequently, the notion of matter, while it might help explain *what* things are, did

---

[213] Some problems are felt by students of Whitehead's thought also at the point of understanding God's relation to " creativity," the general ongoingness of things. The important point here is that creativity is a metaphysical principle, not an actual entity; hence it has no purposes (*PR* 339) and cannot cause anything to happen. God is the reason for the existence of every particular thing, whereas " creativity " refers to the " becomingness " of those things which God causes to become.

[214] *AI* 195.

[215] *PR* 40.

[216] See Cobb, *op. cit.*, pp. 153, 183 for a discussion of this point, which is not considered by Whitehead himself. Cf. *PR* 434–436.

not serve them as a reason *that* things are. But men who knew the Biblical idea of divine creation could and did recognize also the possibility of asking philosophically why things exist in the first place, and to them it seemed important to show that the possible Greek answer of eternal matter was contained somehow within their view of creation. Thus they insisted on *creatio ex nihilo* to make it clear that only God was the reason *that* things exist, and they supposed that the coming-into-existence about which they wrote had happened once either in eternity or some thousands of years in the past. But according to our Whiteheadian view, the question must be put in a somewhat different way: why is it that new occasions keep happening? why are there repeatedly new events? Here the only possible answer within Whitehead's thought is God, for his provision of the initial aim is the only factor in the universe that can account for the start of a new process when old ones have been completed. Apart from God, past occasions by themselves would find their aims for a future completely thwarted,[217] and whatever effectiveness they may have in contributing toward initial aims depends upon God's infinitely greater role in achieving a harmony of initial aims. Therefore, we are justified in saying that the notion of God as providing initial aims serves the same function as the notion of *creatio ex nihilo* — both point to God as the reason *that* things are.

Now what about the notion of divine freedom in creation? This may mean either or both of two things: God decides *that* things shall exist, and God decides *what* shall exist. Let us begin with the second of these two meanings, returning later to the first. In spite of creaturely ability to shape the process of becoming, there is a quite definite sense in which God decides *what* each new occasion shall be, by determining which occasions shall compose its causal past. In this sense Barth is correct in intuiting that whatever God creates, he creates with a past: to be created *is* to be a historical creature. But God does not provide a past arbitrarily for each new occasion; he selects it from a perfectly definite inheritance left by the constantly growing number of completed occasions. That is, whatever God creates, he creates not only as a historical creature,

[217] *RM* 100.

but as part of *this* world, part of the historical process that is *this* universe of feeling. There is no such thing as creation of mere matter of fact, but only the creation of processes of value expressive of God's aim for beauty in the actual world.

Now, what about the notion that God decides *that* there shall be entities? As long as God was thought of as a single changeless being, it was necessary to suppose that God's creative decision was a single decision, somehow located in the unity of his eternal being. The meaning of " decision " in this case becomes very hazy, since ordinarily it seems to carry with it the sense of process or change that is inappropriate to eternality. Also in terms of Whitehead's view that God is one actual entity, there seems to be no intelligible meaning in saying that God " decides " to create, since it is of his nature to be related to a world; this polarity of God-world is what leads to Gilkey's suspicion of Whiteheadian dualism.

But if we view God as a living person, the question becomes slightly more complex, i.e., we may ask whether in particular occasions of his personality God decides that there shall be entities. In this case the answer clearly is that God *does* decide to create new entities by furnishing them with initial aims, for each occasion of God's personality enjoys a subjective aim that accounts for whatever harmony of conceptual feeling God achieves during that occasion. And since his initial aims for entities in the world fall among these conceptual feelings, we must conclude that it is his decision that just these new occasions originate by prehending him. All the divine purposiveness in the universe is caught up in each occasion of God's personality, so that whatever decision God makes is, in a real sense, the decision of *that* divine occasion. But we need not suppose that an aim to create some particular entity always or even frequently *originates* in the moment of divine experience where it is expressed through the provision of an initial aim, for the subjective aim of any divine occasion is in its turn a perfect expression of past divine aims. At this point we find ourselves in the same endless regress that faced our quest for a first occasion of God's personality, and we must say that God's basic decision to be creator has no beginning and no end. Again, notions of God as eternal (here eternally creative) find their place within the larger understanding of God as historical: it is within the subjective immediacy of each divine occasion, utterly beyond the world and its temporality, where God achieves harmony between his primordial aims and his aims for the details of history.

At this point we may remind ourselves that the primary intuition around which Jewish understandings of Creation arose was the sense of living in a constellation of events ordered basically in terms of divine purpose in history, and created by God, whose novel responses to the past were the chief expression of his creative and redemptive presence with Israel. Looking back over our Whiteheadian explanation of God's relationship to an evolving nature, it appears that by modifying Whitehead's idea of God in the direction of seeing God as a living person we are able to reconcile, in considerable detail, this Biblical sense of divinely ordered history and scientific knowledge about evolution. We have been discussing God's transcendence over the world and his immanence in the world, his creative power and his toleration for the freedom of his creatures, his role as sustainer of order and provider of novelty, his care for the individual creature and his hopes for whole societies. All these phrases are expressive of a vision of God and the world which is fundamentally Biblical, and to this extent our Whiteheadian interpretation of an evolving world is in harmony with Biblical understandings of Creation. Perhaps focusing on specific aspects of our interpretation will facilitate discussing the points which still need to be made.

a. *God creates a purposeful real world and sustains it from lapsing into chaos.* We have tried to show that God can be seen as the everlasting creator of real things whose reality is distinct from his, that the things in the world come into existence as historical in nature, embodying God's historical purposes, and that God's role as sustainer of the world is intimately associated with his role as creator. Tillich's proposal that God is the ground of being can be accepted, as can his ontological assumption that reality is basically an interplay of subjects and objects. But in thinking of God as a living person we can broaden Tillich's understanding so that the doctrine of creation becomes not only " the basic description of the relation between God and the world " but also " the story of an event which took place ' once upon a time,' " i.e., a description of past events in nature before the appearance of man. Furthermore, we have suggested that God is not opposed in creation by any polar entity, but that the collective deviations of creatures from his aims for them are responsible for our intuitions of some opposition to God's purposes in Creation. Any lapses into disorder that may occur in the world must occur secondary to creation, not " before " or " outside " the real world, for they have to do with failure to achieve that harmony of feeling which is within the limits of order set by God's initial aim for some entity or entities. So we may agree with Tillich that God holds back the threat of nonbeing, i.e., he orders the past of each new occasion in such a way that a final harmony of feelings and, therefore, concrete existence is possible.

But we are not compelled to link Creation and Fall so closely as Tillich does, for there is nothing in the metaphysical scheme which *requires* that occasions in the world will deviate from the divine aim for their becoming. So far as our powers of observation and introspection are concerned, departure from God's aims is prevalent, but it would be merely speculative to assert that *every* occasion deviates from God's aim. On the contrary, there are moments of human experience which seem to approach that beauty of feeling which is God's aim, and for all we know, there may be electrons whose placid obedience to the divine aims is complete. What Macquarrie calls the " inarticulate, unconscious ' travail ' of the lower levels of creation . . . striving toward a goal " may be crowned with a degree of success that brings joy to God. Finally, intuitions such as those of Origen, that creatures depart from God's purposes in a realm outside of history, find their place as an expression of that creaturely freedom to reject God's ideal aims in a process of becoming that is utterly beyond God's reach and outside of physical time.

b. *Creation and the realization of God's purposes in history are linked together.* We have seen that it is hard to distinguish between God's role as creator, his role as sustainer, and the ways in which his purposes become realized in evolutionary history. It is not possible for us to suppose that God creates the world without supposing that he sustains it, and it is not possible to suppose that his sustaining of the world at any given time in history takes place apart from his purposes to achieve higher forms of beauty. This situation seems to be in agreement with Biblical intuitions that creation and salvation are intimately related, for salvation is always understood in the Bible as an expression of God's best purposes for a particular situation. Also we seem to be in agreement with Biblical notions that God's continuing effects on history may be seen as creation, and that as the source of providence he foresees every best possibility and encourages its realization.

We may accept Zöckler's Lutheran proposal that *creatio, conservatio,* and *gubernatio* compose a togetherness of divine act,[218] in that each occasion of God's personality combines these aims harmoniously. Also we may see in a new light the point of Brunner's distinction between creation and preservation, for God ensures the preservation of enduring objects and personal societies by offering their cumulative history to a new occasion which he creates. But Macquarrie's notion of " letting-be-ness " as God's essence and the foundation of his goodness does not quite capture the sense in which to be created *is* to be placed in a divinely purposed historical universe. The notion of " letting-be " captures part of what we mean by God's provision of initial aims, but it lacks the note of divine responsiveness to the past in terms of hopes for the future, and this is essential to the original Biblical intuition of divine creativeness.

For the same reason we cannot agree completely with Macquarrie that the fullest imitation of God is creaturely " letting-be-ness," for this suggests that God's central aim is that his creatures express feelings which are conducive to harmony in their environment. This by itself is the image of near-perfect social order that we have attributed to a society of rock molecules, and we have said that God's aim is not for such social order but for beauty of individual experience, although higher forms of order encourage

[218] See the notion of Thomas Aquinas that divine conservation is a " continuation " of the timeless act of creation.

such beauty. Gilkey's proposal that the basic Christian intuitions are of a " dependent, contingent, and yet real finitude, and a transcended order " may be accepted with the same provision, that it be enlarged to include intuitions of purposeful divine response to history. In the same vein, we may agree with Altner that the notion of mere contingency cannot serve alone as the basis for a Christian doctrine of creation, since it fails to express the Biblical sense of historical purpose.[219]

Since God's purposes respond to what often must be felt by him as tragic departure from his aims, it seems appropriate to discuss a bit more explicitly at this point the limitations to divine aims in history. Our earlier discussion has made it clear that God is not absolutely sovereign over the world, for the final causation in creatures passes over into efficient causation that limits the effectiveness of God's aims, as occasions prehend him along with other entities in their past. Judging from their literature, however, the Jews erred in the direction of overestimating God's power. They were so impressed with the efficacy of divine purposes in history that they had very little sense of the other (natural) causes for events, and Reinhold Niebuhr says correctly that in Jewish thought " nature is subsumed under history." [220] For example, the Jewish story of the Fall is a story of conflicting aims, laid entirely within the subjective immediacy of human personalities, and it is really not until The Book of Job that we find Old Testament writers grappling to understand more widely the objective causes for events, allowing a proper place for the causal effects of nondivine agencies. The Greeks, by contrast, seem to have been equally overimpressed with the rational order of nature. For example, the myth of Prometheus expresses Greek awareness of the inexorable givenness of things, the ways in which nature rolls on ponder-

[219] Altner (*Schöpfungsglaube und Entwicklungsgedanke*, pp. 106–108) argues that the notion of contingency is not even peculiarly Biblical, being anticipated in Aristotle's notion of potentiality (*dynamis*). He presents an interesting summary of recent efforts in Germany to reconcile the Biblical sense of contingency with the notion of complementarity in modern physics. On this see above, Chapter III, note 37, and Chapter IV, note 183.
[220] Reinhold Niebuhr, *The Self and the Dramas of History* (London: Faber and Faber, 1955), p. 89.

ously, crushing ineffective flashes of conceptual novelty in the subjective immediacy of human beings.

In one sense, our problem has been to reconcile Jew and Greek, to see how the rational order of things can be apprehended and vividly expressed within the personal categories derived from the Biblical vision of reality. In this vein we may agree with Aristotle that there is a natural development in terms of final causation, with Newton that there is brute physical causation amenable to mathematical description, and with the Bible that the purposes of God are effective everywhere. But everything depends on finding the relevance of each factor in a particular event, and our powers of penetration are so puny that only rarely do we achieve any awareness of causal relationships exceeding that which we derive from sense perception.

Certainly we fail almost completely in explaining the causes for evil, beyond saying that, ultimately, evil is to be traced to creaturely aims and the failure to achieve some possible level of beauty. Evil is not ontologically real, in the sense of being an element traceable to actual entities, but it is incorrect to say with Gilkey that from a Whiteheadian perspective the world's evil is for God " not real, but only an error due to a finite point of view." [221] Nothing in our philosophic system implies that when actual occasions enjoy a wider viewpoint they adhere more closely to the divine aims; whether they do so must be settled empirically, and at this point there is at least introspective evidence that men often reject God's aims purposely. The course of evolution so far would seem to indicate that man's ability to rebel against God's wishes may increase if his mental capacity evolves further. Also, since recognition of evil depends upon knowledge of what *might* have been, we must assume that God feels all the evil in the universe, and intuitions of suffering and tragedy in God may well reflect the completeness of his sensitivity to pain and evil. For all we know, the extinction of Neanderthal man may have extinguished the chance for some form of human beauty that our present species cannot imagine. Perhaps we may place here Macquarrie's notion of divine " risk " in creation, for although we cannot agree

[221] See above, p. 265.

that God's personality ever is in danger of becoming " fragmented and torn within itself," God certainly does risk the frustration of his aims in every occasion which he creates.

c. *Human personality is the part of nature where God's aim for beauty in the world may be most fully realized.* So far as we can tell, occasions of human experience enjoy a capacity to synthesize contrasts of feeling that allows for kinds of beauty unknown elsewhere on our planet. This means that the society in which these occasions occur, the personality or soul of a man, is the particular historical strand in which occur God's highest earthly creations. Therefore, we may say that God creates the soul, even though we do not have to suppose that it is a " special creation " or agree with present Roman Catholic doctrine that creation of a human soul is just " one place where God has to step in." [222] We have already suggested that the appearance of soul in a creature is closely related to the development of a central nervous system and that other animals than humans have souls. For understanding the human situation the relevant approach is to ask when in the development of an individual human being there is first available the rich physical and mental environment that can be the past for occasions of soul. Here, although we probably would not attribute soul to a freshly fertilized ovum, we may suggest (admittedly on very flimsy grounds) that some kinds of feeling characteristic of human personality may be available in the fetal brain toward the end of the first trimester of pregnancy. But any such speculation must be tempered by recalling that God aims not at the mere existence of human souls but at the beauty of feeling that individual occasions may enjoy as members of that society. Fetal occasions of human soul may not enjoy experience so rich as that felt by a bird or a kitten; but in maturity the human soul is the place on our planet where divine aims are most intensely focused, and where frustration of divine aims is most diversely possible. This is the reason that human beings have intuitions of divine blessing and judgment, while we suppose that other animals do not. But perhaps animals are more sensitive to the

---

[222] J. Franklin Ewing, S.J., " Current Roman Catholic Thought on Evolution," in Tax and Callender, eds., *Evolution After Darwin*, III, p. 26.

divine aims than we imagine!

To regard human personality as part of a historically evolving nature means, as we have mentioned in the previous chapter, that the evolution of man was but one way in which the divine aim for beauty of creaturely experience might reach concrete expression. We are the unlikely outcome of an immensely long process, during which countless other possibilities have been excluded, and it may be that as God envisioned the future a billion years ago he was quite indifferent as to whether *Homo sapiens* would turn out to be the avenue through which his aims for beauty on earth are now mainly channeled. But as things have turned out, a particular spectrum of God's primordial aims does apply to us; for one thing, whatever forms of beauty we may achieve will be limited by a host of feelings (e.g., feelings of arms and legs) that would not enter the experience of creatures evolving on a planet completely covered with water.

The historical nature of our world must be remembered in any effort to understand the modes of feeling that become characteristic of a single personality or of the broader social background which comprises its chief environment so far as conceptual feelings are concerned. Empirically it appears that human societies develop or may develop defining mental characteristics, including modes of consciousness that may be socially transmitted in a way quite analogous to the transmission of other feelings. We have seen, for example, that Jewish society developed a sense for divine purposiveness in history, while Greek society was expressing its preoccupation with natural order. But we are now in a position to realize that, like other products of a historical nature, modes of consciousness depend for their continued existence on a linkage with those feelings in their history which have brought them to social expression.

Therefore, we must not assume with Asa Gray that a conscious sense of purposeful order in nature is " innate," only that it has developed in history and may persist if it is nourished. And we cannot agree fully with Reinhold Niebuhr's affirmation that Christian faith survives partly because " all the testimonies of philosophers and scientists against it cannot avail against the inner witness of the human self, that it is a real self, burdened with both responsibility and guilt." [223] This sense of responsibility and guilt, which has been so marvelously illuminated by existentialist thought, appears in the light of our evolutionary study as the product of a history, not as a " given " aspect of human existence; indeed, one has only to look around in modern society to discover human beings whose lives express only a fleeting awareness of such responsibility and guilt. Just as it was possible for Darwin to lose his sense that nature was purposeful, so it is possible for human beings to lapse into modes of existence in which the subjective aims typical of occasions of their personalities embody little more than the blind aim to reproduce patterns from the past, and in which the relevant future is blunted and impoverished both in extent and in width of compassion.

One way of denoting the upward course of evolution is by observing that the higher creatures increasingly are able to modify their inheritance, or to put it another way, they enjoy an ability to be selective about which elements in their past form present and future experience. This is of special significance in Biblical faith, which revolves around the persuasion that it is by affirming one's connection with a particular strand of human history in Palestine that human existence becomes informed by aims that lie at the center of God's intentions for man, aims around which every secular pursuit find their meaning. These divine aims, as reported in the Bible, have to do with man's possibility of recognizing consciously that he is God's historical creation and that his life is part of a history created by God and intended by God to move steadily toward increasing beauty.

The Christian doctrine of creation as it comes to us from the New Testament suggests that in Jesus of Nazareth, in his career, death, and resurrection, we can recognize the realization of God's best intention for *Homo sapiens,* that central organizing aim which God everlastingly has held for a world in which man might appear. To say that God's *central* aim for man was realized in Jesus implies that God is indifferent to many details of our experience, and we must suppose that the beauty of personality that God

[223] Niebuhr, *op. cit.,* p. 163.

desires for us may be expressed in countless ways — in the joyful games of our children, in our delight over clouds and sunshine, in the transformation of a slum by new vision, even (why not?) in our fascination with space rocketry. But God's central aim is for a kind of personal experience that is able to view every new situation in terms of God's own aim for beauty. This unifying divine aim for man which early Christians felt to be disclosed in Jesus produced among these people what Pannenberg calls the persuasion that " in the Christ-event the end of history happened in advance." [224]

It is, of course, the task of Christology to understand in detail what this New Testament claim means, but central to the original intuitions are a sense of God's unbounded willingness to forgive his creatures, his long-suffering patience in the face of evil and failure, and his ability to overcome even death by the novelty of the resurrection. Whether these intuitions really originate in God's personality, whether what God most yearns for in man is a kind of beauty in which these feelings are central, is known only by God. We struggle to clarify our fleeting glimpses of divine purpose, and in the end we confess that the source of our faith lies beyond the bounds of consciousness in that stream of history which has produced us.

It is in this sense that we may understand Brunner's affirmation that Christian faith in Creation arises by encountering the point in history where God's purposes are most fully disclosed, for it is also history which we encounter whenever we encounter God. He aims for us to enjoy each moment as the appropriation of a history, and if it be true that his aims for man are most fully realized in that strand of history culminating in Jesus, perhaps God holds that history out for us with particular concern as part of the lure for feeling with which we begin each moment of our lives. Whether we aim to make it part of ourselves seems to depend partly on our willingness to participate in a society of other people who seek to realize the divine aims — but here we move

---

[224] Wolfhart Pannenberg, " Dogmatische Thesen zur Lehre von der Offenbarung," in Pannenberg, ed., *Offenbarung als Geschichte* (Göttingen: Vandenhoeck & Ruprecht, 1963), p. 106.

toward the notion of the church as the body of Christ, which is the proper study of ecclesiology.

Teilhard de Chardin's evolutionary vision culminated with the image of human history converging to its fulfillment around Christ at the " Omega Point," [225] where mankind will be united in feeling God's aims in Jesus. For him Omega was the single point toward which all history moves, drawn on hesitatingly but certainly toward a state where all disharmony is overcome in a mankind that has become psychically indivisible.[226] However, we have commented that Teilhard regarded evolutionary history as though it were somehow a single concrescent occasion, and his notion of Omega is more likely an expression of the final harmony of feeling achieved in each moment of God's personality. But perhaps this is why his vision continues to be felt as an eloquent and moving testimony of faith, for there is at the center of the Christian doctrine of creation that surprising confidence in a divine harmony and beauty which may indeed appear in human lives as singleness of heart, that unity of feeling possible for occasions of personality in which Christ is all in all.

What shall we say in conclusion? Perhaps this: God is the Father of all these creatures rocks, sheep, and men — the reason for their existence and the One whose love defines their possibilities. And we continually find ourselves surrounded by novelty, so that the future for God's creatures both separately and together is laden with joyful surprise, but also with the possibility of great evil. The beauty in each present moment is enriched by the way God's purposes crowd into the aims of his creatures, but the " stone of stumbling " remains — God's love does not push rudely into the world. It acts not by suspending the effectiveness of other agencies, but by the steady urging of harmony, spreading through creation by " overcoming " the world.

The earth moves onward in its cycles around the sun, in a tiny corner of the universe. But the finger of God is now upon the history that springs from one tiny land near a sea whose waters sweep around the world, and that history reaches wherever there

---

[225] Teilhard de Chardin, *The Phenomenon of Man*, pp. 257–263.
[226] Teilhard de Chardin, *The Future of Man*, p. 280.

are men, urging earth on to its goal. One small part of God's Creation moves toward its end in Christ, and the agonies of the world are overcome with love from heaven.

" Behold, I make all things new."

" I am the way, and the truth, and the life."

" I am the Alpha and the Omega, the beginning and the end."

INDEX

NAMES